The **GLOBAL POLITICS** of **ENERGY**

FOREWORD BY
JOSEPH S. NYE & BRENT SCOWCROFT

EDITED BY
KURT M. CAMPBELL & JONATHON PRICE

The Aspen Institute
One Dupont Circle, NW
Suite 700
Washington, DC 20036

Published in the United States of America in 2008 by The Aspen Institute

Cover design by Billy Sountornsorn and Crabtree + Company
Cover photograph: © CORBIS
Interior design by Crabtree + Company

aspen strategy group

■ Acknowledgements

Kurt M. Campbell
Director, Aspen Strategy Group

Jonathon Price
Associate Director, Aspen Strategy Group

From August third through August eighth, 2007, the Aspen Strategy Group met in Aspen, Colorado to examine questions surrounding the global politics of energy. Representing diverse perspectives from multidisciplinary fields, Aspen Strategy Group members, invited guests, and energy experts examined the complexities and challenges for the United States within the global energy framework with an emphasis on national security. This publication presents the eleven papers that helped guide and illuminate our discussions over the week. It also includes the workshop scene setter and a set of concluding observations.

Our meeting was a result of the collaborative efforts of a number of organizations and individuals to which the Aspen Strategy Group is deeply grateful. In particular, we thank the Joy Foundation for its generous and essential support for the preparation and publication of this book. Other generous supporters of this year's workshop include the Feldman Family Foundation, the Harman Family Foundation, Robert and MeiLi Hefner, Hastings Johnson, McKinsey and Co., Thomas O'Gara, John Osborn, The Rockefeller Brothers Fund, Terrence Turkat, and Leah Zell Wanger.

We also thank our General Brent Scowcroft Award Fellows, Lacy Kilraine, Shannon Hiller, Rob Brown, Lauren Griffith, and Ben Andruss, for their important contribution to this initiative, and we wish them well in their future endeavors in the field of foreign and national security policy. Finally, our efforts would not have been possible without the support of our Co-Chairmen, Joseph Nye and Brent Scowcroft. Thank you both for your leadership, vision, and the invaluable contributions you make to the group.

Contents

Part 1

ENERGY: GLOBAL PERSPECTIVES, GLOBAL POLITICS,
GLOBAL CONCERNS

Part 2

FOCUSING THE ENERGY SCOPE: REGIONAL OUTLOOKS
AND A MULTITUDE OF THREATS

Part 3

THE GREAT ENERGY DEBATE: THE NATIONAL SECURITY IMPLICATIONS OF GLOBAL CLIMATE CHANGE AND IMPACT POTENTIAL OF ALTERNATIVES

Part 4

A GLOBAL ENERGY CONSENSUS: NEW POLICY DIRECTIONS AND THE WAY FORWARD

■ **Foreword** by ASG Co-Chairmen

Joseph S. Nye, Jr.
ASG Co-Chairman

Brent Scowcroft
ASG Co-Chairman

As the United States prepares for the November 2008 Presidential election, we face a diverse set of challenges to our national security. The ongoing war in Iraq, the struggle against terrorism and extremism, and the continued threats posed by the proliferation of nuclear weapons pose complex and difficult questions for the next occupant of the Oval Office. Nonetheless, the Aspen Strategy Group decided to dedicate its time this past summer to exploring a separate, yet related, challenge — the global politics of energy. This topic is connected to virtually every other challenge confronting the United States and is a natural area of focus for a group whose mandate is to develop new thinking on U.S. national security, cooperative measures to reduce conflict, and bipartisan policy solutions to current critical challenges.

The roots of the Aspen Strategy Group date back to the 1970s, when the Aspen Institute along with Harvard, MIT, Stanford, and Aspen Berlin organized semi-annual conferences for arms control researchers from various universities and think tanks. In the early 1980s, with the Ford and MacArthur foundations' backing, we, along with Bill Perry, reinvented the arms control conference series as a policy program of the Aspen Institute and began revitalizing its work, creating a diverse roster of "members" — regular attendees who included U.S. Senators and Representatives, current and former administration officials, relevant industry representatives, and journalists. Critically important was ensuring that both political parties, and the range of perspectives within them, were represented.

Today, our longstanding commitment towards identifying topics of national concern and providing appropriate assessments of American national interest, must take into account the way these interests have evolved in our pluralistic world. The ASG has covered issues spanning from the Cold War to the War on Terror, and the many issues in between — such as missile defense, the militarization of space, a multi-front Jihadist threat, East Asian crises, and the rise of China.

While our specific members have changed, in conjunction with new generations of rising policymakers, so have our topics, evolving along the trajectory of American foreign policy interests. However, our approach has remained constant: use a bipartisan lens to take on the most contentious foreign policy and national security concerns facing our nation.

This past summer the ASG tackled the global politics of energy, which we believe will dominate American politics for the foreseeable future. No longer on the periphery, energy security and climate change have moved to the forefront. Indeed, growing dependence on foreign energy has blurred our nation's borders. While in Aspen, we explored a broad range of issues surrounding energy, thanks to the presentations from a diverse array of experts. The commissioned papers herein are a lucid distillation of the policy themes.

It became clear that that there is no single "silver bullet" solution to these policy issues, which will require a comprehensive approach integrating alternative energy, better energy market mechanisms, investment in renewable energy, and establishing global institutions. It was also clear that the United States would need to exercise greater leadership and help align developed and developing countries to address this most significant threat. It is our hope that the workshop in Aspen will bring us one step closer to finding a comprehensive solution for one of the greatest challenges to this generation.

■ The Global Politics of Energy: An Aspen Strategy Group Workshop
Preface

Kurt M. Campbell
Director, Aspen Strategy Group

Jonathon Price
Associate Director, Aspen Strategy Group

Not since Jimmy Carter donned a cardigan in the White House in 1977 while turning down a thermostat have energy issues so dominated American politics. Not since the Suez crisis or the torched oil wells at the climax of the first Gulf War have energy imperatives and national security concerns so manifestly intersected. Due to the rise of instability throughout the Middle East; the increase of gas prices at the pump; assertive new players on the global energy scene (producers and consumers alike) represented by China, India, Russia, and Venezuela; and the increasing alarm associated with carbon-triggered global climate change, the global politics of energy now occupy center stage among a broader set of foreign policy and national security concerns. Indeed, every major issue confronting the United States today — including climate change, the rise of China and India, Jihadist financing, an increasingly bellicose Russia, worrisome trends in Latin America, and endemic hostilities in the Middle East — is either inextricably linked to or exacerbated by decisions associated with energy policy.

There is no question that the United States stands at the crossroads of an historic energy transition. Unlike the transition from wood to whale oil or coal to petroleum, however, we will only successfully move through this transition if the world moves with us, or, perhaps in some cases, even ahead of us. Moreover, this is a transition that cannot be allowed to plot its own course. This is an urgent matter: current U.S. energy consumption patterns constitute a clear and present danger to our national security. It is often said that the Stone Age ended before we exhausted our supply of stones and that the same will be true of oil; but it is probably more true to say that we will end up throwing some of these stones as we fight for control over the remaining oil. Not only is our economy unacceptably vulnerable to price shocks and supply disruptions, our dependency on oil is empowering hostile states, heightening regional instability (the consequences of environmental degradation), and undermining relations with other consumer nations. The United States needs an integrated agenda of short- and long-term policies to re-emerge beyond the oil age relatively intact.

Defining and implementing such policies will not be easy. According to recent polling, the American public understands the urgency of energy security but is unwilling to change personal behaviors to achieve it. Each energy "community," from the corn ethanol crowd to the high priests of Corporate Average Fuel Economy (CAFE) standards, has one small part of the solution; but if implemented alone and not in combination, the result will be insufficient to the challenge. In sum, the status quo will not give us the energy security we so urgently need. Despite useful steps to address energy-related concerns taken at the state and local level and among the more cosmopolitan business set, this Gordian knot can only be cut at the executive level. While Congress will play a secondary role, it must be a partner in order for U.S. energy policy to change. The next President of the United States will have to unite public opinion, political will, communities of interest, and global partners to achieve energy security, but it is yet unclear how our nation's leaders will accomplish this complex and challenging task.

Yet, despite these myriad dangers and the daunting nature of the task ahead, this is also a moment of extraordinary hope and possibility. Every major candidate for President in the United States has articulated a plan or national ambition — if incomplete — aimed at achieving "energy security" through a combination of innovation, more viable alternatives, increased domestic supply, conservation, and newfound efficiencies (some have gone even further, promising that an "energy independence" is somehow attainable, perhaps if only more people cycled to work more often). Senator Joe Biden has made energy security his "first priority;"[1] Governor Bill Richardson has called energy security "the most important issue facing the United States;"[2] and former Massachusetts Governor Mitt Romney has asserted that the United States should "end our strategic vulnerability to an oil shut-off by nations like Iran, Russia, and Venezuela."[3] As we approach the 2008 election, these issues are taking on a new political precedence, and the next President of the United States will surely be pressed to come into office prepared with an energy security plan of his or her own.

Indeed, there is a profound hope to transcend and broaden the possibilities of energy-related national legislation far beyond the parameters of the Energy Policy Act of 2005, a bill whose primary attributes could be summarized simply as: drill for more oil in more places. In response, a new energy bill is making its way through Congress that, over opposition from powerful figures in both parties, has at least made a small start in attempting to address this daunting set of challenges. Concepts such as: "renewable fuels," "Energy Star products," and "limits on greenhouse gas emissions" are sprinkled throughout various versions of the legislation and provide at least a glimmer of hope that Washington is primed to take small but concrete steps. There has also been a smattering of talk around the halls of the Capitol about increasing CAFE standards and even the possibility of enacting elements bordering on a carbon tax to spur innovation and conservation simultaneously.

There is a growing bipartisan awareness of and interest in global climate change — and, more importantly, debate over what needs to be done to arrest it — after years of political sidestepping and apparent apathy. There is also a greater awareness that our deep global reliance on Middle East crude fills the pockets and fuels the rages of the Jihadists in Saudi Arabia, Egypt, and elsewhere.[4] There are more discussions on energy related themes at the G-8 and in other global forums. So too, we are in the midst of an exhilarating era of scientific exploration and market innovation in search of cleaner, more reliable, and domestically available sources of energy — ranging from biofuels, to wind energy solutions, to photovoltaic cells. Consumers are in the market for more fuel-efficient vehicles and energy-saving appliances as concerns mount over gas and oil bills. Global corporations, often with little government prodding, are striving to become more environmentally responsible.

America's awareness and discussion of energy issues spans the country through ever-expanding media interest. One media analysis group estimates that the number of column inches and TV news segments devoted to energy-related subjects has increased nearly three-fold in the last four years. Indeed, the national media currently maintains a vigilant, watchful eye on the current state of all manner of energy concerns (a recent headline in the local Aspen paper screamed, "Big Differences in Gas Prices Across the Valley: County is Asked Why") — and the possible international factors that might affect them. On any given day, the major newspapers of the world provide an assortment of articles on the price of oil and natural gas, the next generation of emerging biofuels, reports on financing mechanisms to spur energy-related innovation, the possible nationalization of oil resources, and the implications of global warming. More telling than the number of stories is their placement. These issues are no longer relegated to a small paragraph on an inside page; instead, energy-themed articles are often found on the front page above the fold and leading the evening newscasts and cable talk shows.

The subject of global climate change, until recently a subject normally reserved for dry academic discourse and international scientific conferences, now has crossed over into popular culture. Some California hotels have replaced the standard Gideon Bible in their hotel rooms with a book on global warming. John Travolta's character in a recent Hollywood blockbuster made a show of eschewing a gas-guzzling Cadi in favor of a more responsible hybrid drive vehicle. The recent Live Earth concerts featuring such artists as Sting and Justin Timberlake were by some measure the largest international awareness campaign in history.

Finally, climate change has the potential to become a defining issue for the next generations of government practitioners, just as negotiating the contours of the Cold War was for the last. Former Vice President Al Gore has become an international celebrity for his documentary, *An Inconvenient Truth*, which explores the dire consequences to the planet from continued carbon loading. The film won two Oscars, received broad critical acclaim, and has become the third highest grossing documentary at the box office of all time. Its exposure of the coming crisis and encouragement to take individual actions to reverse global warming, received worldwide recognition when Al Gore and the U.N.'s Intergovernmental Panel on Climate Change shared the 2007 Nobel Peace Prize. Collectively, these transformations have fed a gnawing anxiety in Washington policy circles and in world capitals that we are moving inexorably towards the brink of an energy crisis involving either abrupt shortages or alarming warming trends (or both) should we fail to put forth concrete solutions and take action in the near term.

Amidst this backdrop of peril and possibility, the Aspen Strategy Group this past summer tackled the global politics of energy and how these complex and multifaceted issues of energy supply and demand have come to assume a role of central importance in national and global politics. Over the course of five days in Aspen, the group examined several facets of the global energy paradigm and, in the process, developed the elements of a national approach to these issues that can win support across the increasingly wide political divide in Washington. We assembled a stellar group of our regular ASG members, energy analysts, climate scientists, regional specialists, and financial players to help us in our exploration. These issues of energy security and supply could not be more relevant for our collective consideration.

The primary focus of the ASG in this overall context was to explore how energy issues, foreign policy, and national security pursuits are likely to intersect in the near future. We were ultimately concerned with understanding whether a kind of "energy security" is potentially attainable and within our grasp as a nation, with the clear caveat that defining energy security is an exceedingly difficult task. The term evokes very different meanings for different players in this ongoing global drama, depending chiefly upon whether a country has at its disposal an internal supply of energy or rather is reliant on imports to meet energy needs. Michael Klare defines energy security as: "The uninterrupted acquisition of adequate petroleum to satisfy national requirements."[5] Others, such as Daniel Yergin, argue that the definition needs to be expanded in our global age to cover electric power shortages, natural gas supplies, and the vulnerability of the energy infrastructure to terrorist attacks. Still others suggest a need for a much more holistic and encompassing definition that takes into account a range of factors, including financial and environmental considerations. The goal was to come away with a clear picture of the global energy paradigm and of the role that the United States plays in it as consumer, supplier, arbiter, and enforcer.

Like all stories of global politics, this one begins and ends with control and power. Perhaps the greatest shift in control and power for the United States in the context of energy derives from the change in the balance of its supply of oil sources. Ten short years ago, the United States met more than half of its oil needs from domestic sources. Today, imports account for approximately two-thirds of U.S. supplies — a portion that most experts contend will only continue to rise in the immediate future. In addition to the potential international vulnerabilities associated with these new realities of supply, our domestic system is also vulnerable. When Hurricanes Katrina and Rita hit the coast of the United States in 2005, oil production was initially down by 25% and natural gas production was down by 20%.[6] In addition to natural disasters, oil and gas pipelines have been targets for terrorists around the globe and could cause sudden and severe disruptions to energy flow.

Another important shift in this correlation of power over energy has occurred in the areas of oil exploration and development. Though the United States still imports the majority of its oil from Canada, today's major oil producers are a new breed on the global energy scene. They come from countries in Africa, the Persian Gulf, and South America — areas where the United States has not been historically active or generally welcomed. Moreover, state-owned giants are increasingly competing with the privately owned multinational corporations for primacy. The "New Seven Sisters" — Saudi Arabia's Aramco, Russia's Gazprom, China's CNCP, Iran's NIOC, Venezuela's PDVSA, Brazil's Petrobras, and Malaysia's Petronas — control nearly one-third of the world's oil and gas production, and they can be expected to flex their new muscle in the months and years ahead.[7] As consumption continues to increase, rising powers are crossing over their borders to seek new sources of oil. For the United States, oil fields of traditional allies are starting to run dry, paving the way for a new competition of energy resources and hard U.S. policy choices in these more challenging regions. All of this is transpiring at a moment when America's "soft power" and global reputation is at its lowest ebb.

The nature of the U.S. relationship with these players on the energy scene is not the only cause for concern. In several cases, these states must deal with potentially destabilizing internal conflicts or a contentious political climate, often making it complicated to secure and transport oil supplies or other forms of energy in a reliable fashion. Colombia is a prime example of these concerns. Once a leading supplier of oil to the United States, Colombia's internal armed conflict has disrupted the flow and lowered the country's oil output substantially in recent years.[8] In fact, oil pipelines have become strategic targets in the war, with armed groups frequently attacking them to disrupt supply. Further, the relentless global pursuit of oil has had the unintended consequence of strengthening some brutal and undemocratic regimes across the globe.

The Middle East is a diverse region marked by the twin realities of worrisome internal instability and its external supply of vast amounts of oil to world markets. This juxtaposition of profound insecurity and manifest reliance has long been a subject of concern for the United States. President George W. Bush highlighted this dangerous dichotomy during the 2006 State of the Union Address when he said, "America is addicted to oil, which is often imported from unstable parts of the world."[9] However, in contrast with the drug pusher parallel, the real culprit in the oil world is the user, i.e., the American consumer rather than the pusher, in this case, the governments and producer cartels of the Middle East.

In the Oscar-winning film, *Syriana*, we are shown a world of shadowy characters willing to commit any crime, including killing a prince of an oil kingdom, to secure the oil fields in the Middle East. Although the premise may seem far-fetched, it has long been the policy of the United States to take the necessary steps to secure our energy needs in this region, by force if necessary. President Carter in his 1980 State of the Union Address delineated this approach by declaring, "Let our position be absolutely clear: An attempt by any outside force to gain control of the Persian Gulf region will be regarded as an assault on the vital interests of the United States of America, and such an assault will be repelled by any means necessary, including military force."[10]

Since the enunciation of the so-called Carter Doctrine, a commitment to the security of the Persian Gulf has been a steady principle in the formulation and execution of American policy. President Reagan ordered the U.S. Central Command to develop detailed plans to ensure the protection of the flow of oil to the West from the Persian Gulf Region. President George H.W. Bush considered the Iraqi invasion of Kuwait as not only an act of aggression that "must not stand," but also as a dangerous move that would put a large share of global oil reserves into the hands of a despot. This state of affairs indeed did not endure after the United States, with a global coalition painstakingly constructed, restored the status quo antebellum by force of arms. President Bill Clinton practiced a policy of "dual containment" for Iran and Iraq in an attempt to maintain stability in the Persian Gulf. President George W. Bush went back into Iraq under force of arms, and only time will tell how the current American imbroglio in Iraq affects the security of oil supplies from the region. Just across the border, the combination of Iran's role as a key exporter and potential nuclear proliferator poses perhaps the most profound set of questions for contemporary policymakers.

Europe is facing challenges similar to America, including a population that has grown accustomed to importing its oil and gas needs while the European output of gas declines, resulting in a sharp surge of imports. In an attempt to manage these new realities for governments and consumers alike, the European Commission is drawing up a European Energy Consumers' Charter that will hopefully help outline a new energy compact across Europe. A principle concern for Europe as a whole is that their energy industry and supply is inextricably linked to Russia, and Moscow has found increased political influence and power in recent years because of its new clout in energy politics. According to the IMF and World Bank, the overall energy industry accounts for 20% of Russian GDP and 65% of Russian tax revenues.

Not only does Russia control one-fifth of global oil reserves, but the Kremlin seems intent on exercising this power to its advantage. Russia is Europe's largest supplier of natural gas, a relationship that has caused considerable strain in recent years. In 2006, GazProm, Russia's largest company, attempted to dramatically raise the prices of natural gas sold to Ukraine. Though this new pricing was more consistent with the prices faced by other European nations, it was viewed as a political move to punish the ascension to power of Victor Yushchenko's government. Russia further roiled energy markets in January 2007 by shutting down a pipeline that carried oil exports to Europe, following a dispute with Belarus. This pipeline supplies 15% of Europe's overall oil imports, and the shutdown was met with rapid condemnation by European nations and has left a lingering anxiety.

Any thorough discussion of energy in the modern world must consider Asia and two of the rising energy giants — China and India. While the region remains heavily reliant on coal, oil plays a large and growing role in meeting mounting energy needs. China is already the·third largest importer and the second largest consumer of oil in the world, and China's unquenchable thirst for oil has led Beijing to scour the globe in search of energy for its massive population. China currently receives 11% of its oil from Iran and another 5% from Sudan, raising difficult questions for American policymakers. Even if we assumed the United States could reduce its oil dependence from Middle East sources or other unstable areas or unpalatable regions, other states like China are more than willing to fill the U.S. void. China, along with India, increasingly holds the key to concerns associated with global climate change as carbon emissions from both continue to rise even beyond those of the traditional polluters in the industrialized north.

India shares many of the same population concerns and rising expectations with China. Likewise, India is exploring several approaches to alleviate its growing energy demand and domestic shortages. India is the world's third largest producer of coal after the United States and China, and the nation relies on electricity from coal burning plants to meet more than half of its energy consumption. Natural gas is the fastest growing energy source in India, but the politics of pipelines with neighboring countries have caused considerable tensions and raised uncertainty over the security of supplies. Over the past year, the potential for a massive new commitment to nuclear power has spurred considerable comment with the recent deal reached by the Bush administration and the Indian government. These rising powers are not the only nations in need of a steady energy supply. Japan is the second largest economy in the world and is nearly wholly reliant on external supplies of both petroleum and natural gas. These swirling energy ambitions in Asia take place against a backdrop of rising nationalism, growing suspicions, and deep distrust.

Finally, Latin America is playing out the intricate intersection of its politics and energy in a way that evokes the essence of our session on the global politics of energy, known also as "petropolitics." Venezuelan President Hugo Chávez has articulated a flagrantly anti-American foreign policy and staked his power to a newfound influence in energy markets, relying on the wealth his country is receiving from producing 7% of the world's oil supply. He has sought to nationalize the oil industry by mandating state control of Venezuelan oil companies and negotiating for higher royalties. This trend has spread throughout the region with both Bolivia and Ecuador now seeking to nationalize gas and oil companies and renegotiate contracts. The United States and Venezuela are already acting in ways to reduce their interaction with one another in the energy arena. In so doing, Venezuela has simply increased its exports to Iran and China. Nevertheless, there are some encouraging signs in the region. Brazil is the world's largest exporter of ethanol and has achieved the highest level of oil independence of any country, having replaced 40% of its gasoline consumption with ethanol. President Bush and President Luiz Inácio Lula da Silva of Brazil recently signed an agreement to further encourage the use of biofuels. There is hope that Latin America can one day become a top provider of ethanol as the United States and other industrialized nations seek to reduce their oil dependency.

Any earnest discussion on the global politics of energy must also include two intertwined topics: the perils of global climate change and possibilities associated with alternative sources of energy. These twin topics were considered in tandem as the second logically follows the first. We reviewed many of the most up-to-date assessments associated with climate change and presentations that provide a synthesis of the many "silver bullet" solutions currently being discussed that might simultaneously relieve our reliance on dangerous oil and dirty coal, and in so doing, also reduce the greenhouse gases that are spurring climate change.

Most of the scientific community stands now squarely behind the belief that global warming is both real and threatening to the planet, should current energy usage trends and patterns continue. The most recent reports of the Intergovernmental Panel on Climate Change (IPCC) paint a picture of planetary flux, with concerns mounting over increased flooding due to the melting of glaciers and ice sheets, more dangerous weather patterns, abrupt changes in ocean and atmospheric currents, dangerous new disease vectors, the collapse of ocean-wide fisheries, massive species extinctions, dislocations in agricultural output, and uncontrolled migration patterns triggered by losses of land in coastal areas. Respected experts, such as those associated with the National Academy of Sciences, estimate that global warming could cause sea levels to rise anywhere from 4 to 35 inches in the next century. Moreover, there is a growing group of outliers in the scientific community that believe such predictions are dangerously and tragically low, that the planet is approaching a "tipping point" in which global temperatures and sea levels might rise dramatically (think meters rather than inches), and that the very security of the human race and civilization is at risk. Suddenly, doomsday scenarios that are often dismissed as hyperbole must be taken seriously.

And lest we think that global warming is something that will only affect future generations, the truth is that the consequences of climate change are already being felt and have triggered security-related concerns across the globe. In the late 1980s, a rise in temperature of the surface layers above the thermocline in the Indian Ocean disrupted seasonal monsoons. One consequence of this disruption was a steep decline in the average precipitation in certain areas of Africa. The drought affected certain areas of Sudan, and one place of particular concern — Darfur. In part, it was this very drought that stirred existing tensions in the area. Suddenly, the Arab nomadic herders and African farmers were competing for an ever-shrinking precious resource: water. Farmers responded to the loss of rain by fencing in their land, causing the nomadic herders to resort to violence to find the water they desperately needed. The rest of the tragic story is still unfolding in the desert sands of Sudan.

When we agree that we are facing an energy crisis, that global temperatures are rising — and that humans have played a key role in this process — we arrive at the inescapable conclusion that the hydra-headed problem of energy security/insecurity cannot be ignored. It is a curious feature of the current state of energy politics in the United States that many have grown tired of waiting for Washington to take steps and have already begun to act without political top cover, inspiration or prodding. Nearly 280 colleges and universities have signed the American College & University Presidents Climate Commitment to bring about environmental change through research, education, and reduced emissions. Innovative ideas are being developed by students and faculty alike on how to reduce an institution's carbon footprint, or measure the impact of human activities on the environment in units of carbon dioxide. Everything from replacing old AC units to strategically placing bicycles around campus for transportation is being considered.

Similarly, 532 mayors from all fifty states, including such major metropolitan areas as Atlanta, New York, Seattle, and Philadelphia, have signed on to the U.S. Mayors Climate Protection Agreement. The agreement strives to meet the goals of the Kyoto Protocol and urges the federal government to meet or beat the greenhouse gas emission reduction target suggested for the United States in the Kyoto Protocol.

Individual states also are taking matters into their own hands. California Governor Arnold Schwarzenegger, for instance, signed a bill requiring the

California Air Resources Board (CARB) to develop the means to drop California's greenhouse gas emissions by 25 percent by the year 2020. Even major corporations are addressing the energy security predicament. One hundred major companies (including GE, Volvo, and KLM) are standing behind a specific program that takes steps to fight climate change. The CEO of coffee giant Starbucks has led an environmental footprint team that has looked at how to minimize the company's negative effect on the environment from the time the coffee bean is picked until the steaming juice of the java is poured into your cup.

The wide-ranging discussion of alternatives to the current energy course must include an examination of renewable sources, natural gas, and nuclear energy. Despite wide agreement that no silver bullet exists or is likely to appear, a collection of alternative sources and solutions might combine to make a difference in the overall energy picture. Scientific innovation and creative financing mechanisms are also of manifest importance to spur new possibilities. Such steps by definition must extend beyond national borders. Even the most positive steps and solutions enacted in one country will be undermined by dangerous, dirty, and wasteful energy practices in another. While it is tempting to be buoyed by new and exciting trends in the realm of renewable energy sources, it bears repeating that viable alternatives to the major fuels of today — coal, oil, and gas — remain over the horizon. A Center for Strategic and International Studies (CSIS) energy report released in 2001 concluded that: "One of the ironies of the turn of the century is that, in an age when the pace of technological change is almost overwhelming, the world will remain dependent, out to the year 2020 at least, essentially on the same sources of energy — oil, natural gas, and coal — that prevailed in the twentieth century." [11]

The chapters that follow are devoted to a deep examination of what is both necessary and possible within the context of American politics in the complex realm of energy policy. We asked eleven distinguished experts, who each operate at the intersection of energy policy and national politics, to provide us with a thorough assessment and recommended courses of action when it comes to energy policy. We sought a review that bridges both domestic policy and foreign policy — and hoped for recommendations that span both worlds. The goal of our session was to carefully review our list of national options for how best to provide for "energy security" in the time ahead. Are market forces enough in terms of providing incentives for innovation in energy technologies? Is there a need for new U.S. government instruments or organizations to help manage or deal with the complexities of energy policy? What new aspects of international architecture might be necessary to cope with the new global politics of energy? Is some form of carbon tax all but essential to address the overarching challenge? Is such a step even feasible in American politics today? What might be necessary to trigger a broader realignment inside American politics to make such a move (or other politically difficult positions) more palatable? These are the questions and issues with which we ended our time in Aspen as we considered the increasingly complex global politics of energy. It is our hope that this will enable us to frame a set of constructive plans for national leaders and policy planners in the period ahead.

■ ■ ■ ───

Kurt Campbell is CEO and Co-Founder of the Center for a New American Security. He is concurrently Director of the Aspen Strategy Group, founder and Principal of StratAsia, and Chairman of the Editorial Board of the *Washington Quarterly*. Prior to co-founding CNAS, he was the Senior Vice President, Henry A. Kissinger Chair in National Security, and Director of the International Security Program at the Center for Strategic and International Studies. He has also been a contributing writer to *The New York Times* and a consultant to ABC News. Dr. Campbell has served in several capacities in government, including Deputy Assistant Secretary of Defense for Asia and the Pacific in the Pentagon, Director on the National Security Council Staff, Deputy Special Counselor to the President for NAFTA in the White House, and as a White House Fellow at the Department of the Treasury. Dr. Campbell was Associate Professor of Public Policy and International Relations at the John F. Kennedy School of Government and Assistant Director of the Center for Science and International Affairs at Harvard University. He served as an officer in the U.S. Navy on the Joint Chiefs of Staff and in the Chief of Naval Operations Special Intelligence Unit. He serves on several boards, including the Woods Hole Oceanographic Institution, the U.S.-Australian Leadership Dialogue, the Reves Center at the College of William and Mary, STS Technologies, the 9-11 Pentagon Memorial Fund, and New Media Strategies. Dr. Campbell is also a member of the Trilateral Commission, the International Institute for Strategic Studies, and the Wasatch Group. He is the co-author of *Hard Power: The New Politics of National Security* (Basic Books, 2006), the co-author of *To Prevail: An American Strategy for the Campaign Against Terrorism* (CSIS Press, 2001), and the editor of *The Nuclear Tipping Point* (Brookings Press, 2004). Dr. Campbell received a B.A. from the University of California, San Diego, a certificate in music and politics from the University of Erevan in the Soviet Union, and doctorate in international relations from Oxford University as a Marshall Scholar.

Jonathon Price is the Associate Director of the Aspen Strategy Group, a program of the Aspen Institute that seeks to promote high level bipartisan dialogue on critical foreign policy issues facing America today. He is also responsible for an ongoing track II initiative between the United States and India along with the transatlantic dialogue project, the Aspen Atlantic Group, which is headed by Madeleine Albright. Before joining the Aspen Institute, he served as Deputy Assistant for the Korean Ambassador to the United States, H.E. Lee Tae-sik. Prior to his work with Ambassador Lee, he was the Special Assistant to the Consul General with the Korean Consulate in Atlanta and interned with The Carter Center, an NGO run by former U.S. President Jimmy Carter, focusing on the conflicts in Sudan and the Democratic Republic of Congo. Mr. Price received a bachelor's degree from Emory University and a master's degree in government from Johns Hopkins University.

[1] Klonsky, Joanna, "The Candidates on Energy Policy," *Council on Foreign Relations*, 17 July 2007. *Council on Foreign Relations*, 29 July 2007, <http://www.cfr.org/publication/13409/candidates_on_energy_policy.html>.

[2] *Ibid.*

[3] *Ibid.*

[4] Friedman, Thomas, "The First Law of Petropolitics," *Foreign Policy*, May 2006.

[5] Klare, Michael, "The Futile Pursuit of 'Energy Security' by Military Force," *The Brown Journal Of World Affairs*, 13 (2007): 139.

[6] Bamberger, Robert, "Energy Policy: Conceptual Framework and Continuing Issues," CRS Report for Congress (2007): 1.

[7] Hoyos, Carola, "A new era of nationalism," *Financial Times*, [London], 19 June 2007: Energy, p. 2.

[8] Klare, Michael, "The Futile Pursuit of 'Energy Security' by Military Force." *The Brown Journal Of World Affairs*, 13, (2007): 147.

[9] Bush, George, "State of the Union Address," United States Capitol, Washington, D.C., 31 January 2006.

[10] Carter, Jimmy, "State of the Union Address," United States Capitol, Washington, D.C., 23 January 1980.

[11] Caruso, Guy, "The Geopolitics of Energy Into the 21st Century," Testimony before the Senate Energy and Natural Resources Committee, Washington, D.C., 21 March 2001.

Part 1

ENERGY: GLOBAL PERSPECTIVES,
GLOBAL POLITICS, GLOBAL CONCERNS

"Today, the concept of energy security needs to be expanded to include the protection of the entire energy supply chain and infrastructure — an awesome task."

— DANIEL YERGIN

■ Energy Under Stress

Daniel Yergin
Chairman, Cambridge Energy Research Associates (CERA)
Executive Vice President, Information Handling Services, Inc.

D uring the years of the "new economy" around the beginning of this decade, nothing seemed more "old economy" and destined to be left behind than the energy industry (notwithstanding the fact that it is a high-tech business). Yet it is ironic to find that in this Internet age, almost a decade later, energy and resource nationalism have moved to the forefront in national politics and international affairs.

How did this happen? How might the energy picture develop in the future? What are the elements of energy security? Also, what are the implications for national policies and international relations? These are the questions that this chapter explores.

How Did It Happen?

Oil prices collapsed in 1998 primarily as a consequence of the fall in demand that came with the downturn of the Asian financial crisis, combined with a decision by OPEC to increase oil production. Prices fell to as low as $10 a barrel. Yet in recent months, oil prices have exceeded $110 a barrel. They have also surpassed the previous record in real prices ever reached — in April 1980. The consequences can be observed in major shifts in the world economy, the build-up of financial surpluses in exporting countries, widespread anxiety about energy availability, and rebirth of resource nationalism.

The reasons for the multi-fold increase in prices are to be found in supply and demand.

The fundamental driver of demand is income, and significant increases in incomes are driving prices today. As incomes rise around the world, so does demand for energy. The last several years have seen the best global economic performance in a generation. Over the previous half decade, world economic growth has averaged 4.9%, and oil demand growth has averaged 1.7% (see Figure 1). The biggest impetus for growth is coming from what used to be called "developing countries," and then became known as "emerging markets." At the top of the list are what are now known as the BRICs (Brazil, Russia, India, and China). Although China and India are often lumped together, it is China — with oil demand almost three times that of India — that is particularly significant. Economic growth of 10 to 11 percent a year has meant oil demand growth averaging 8 to 9 percent. A decade and a half ago, China was self-sufficient in oil; it now imports over half of its oil. In 2004, China overtook Japan as the second largest consumer of oil in the world, after the United States.

A slowing U.S. economy, and certainly a recession, would reduce demand pressures. Recently, however, the credit crisis, rate cuts, and a weakening dollar have combined to fuel further increases in oil prices (and other commodities). But a deeper and more geographically-widespread economic slowdown would lead to lower oil prices.

One consequence of the increasing oil demand from the rapidly-growing countries is stronger trade, and economic and political links between them and the oil exporters. It is likely that over half of total oil demand over the next 25 years will be in Asia. The global industry is recalibrating towards this new more Asia-focused nexus. This should be recognized as a given.

The supply system was caught unprepared for this surge in demand. For in the aftermath of the 1998 collapse, companies had downsized, reduced expenditures, and cut investment programs. The economics of new projects had to work at $20 per barrel. The workforce in the industry shrank. "Caution" was the watchword when it came to making new investments. That attitude was strongly reinforced by the financial markets — sell-side analysts and institutional investors — who insisted

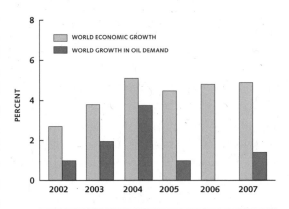

Figure 1

WORLD ECONOMIC GROWTH VERSUS **WORLD OIL DEMAND**

Source: Cambridge Energy Research Associates.
Note: The 4.9% growth forecast for 2007 is taken from the IMF. Other numbers are from CERA database.
70716-1

on "discipline" and criticized companies that were more aggressive in their investment programs.

This contraction has left the oil and gas industry — along with other energy industries — very short of people. The U. S. Department of Labor describes the oil and gas industry as facing a "demographic cliff." Some 55 percent of industry professionals are less than ten years away from eligibility of retirement.[1] The global industry is showing a similar shortage of people and skills as found in the United States.

In 2004 and 2005, the level of OPEC crude oil "spare capacity," the extra oil production capacity above actual production deliberately held in reserve, was tighter than it had ever been in anyone's memory — tighter even than on the eve of the 1973 crisis. A tight market is one, of course, in which prices go up. It is also a market that is vulnerable to "accidents," disruptions, and crises.

There have been no single massive disruptions of the kind that occurred with the 1973 embargo and the 1979 Iranian revolution. But there have been a series of shortfalls that add up to an "aggregate disruption" that has further accentuated the tightness in the market and pushed prices higher: Iraq, at around 2 million barrels per day (and recently rising), is struggling to regain its prewar production level (and is many years away from the target production level of 6 million barrels per day described on the eve of the 2003 war).[2] Violence in Nigeria's Delta region has shut-in 20 percent or more of Nigeria's output — this from the country that has sometimes in recent years been the third largest exporter to the United States. Capacity continues to decline in Venezuela because of lack of investment and loss of capability in the country's state oil company, owing to a large-scale firing of employees, intense politicization, and diversion of investment. In 2005, Hurricanes Katrina and Rita damaged the vast U.S. Gulf of Mexico energy complex — knocking out about 20 percent of domestic oil and natural gas — although most of that has since returned. Growth in Russian output has slowed in the face of very high taxes, rising costs, and increasing government control over the energy sector. At various times, smaller disruptions add to these losses, whether they be a pipeline accident in the North Sea, the closure of a Japanese nuclear reactor, or attacks on pipelines in Latin America.

In addition, a hard-to-measure "security premium" is built into the price of oil. This principally reflects anxiety about instability and unrest in the Middle East, and what is seen as the possibility of a clash involving the second largest producer in OPEC, Iran, owing to the conflict with the international community over its nuclear program. Iraq is a continuing source of anxiety. Fear of an additional disruption in Nigeria also figures large in the security premium today. Tight markets lead to more futures buying, which propels prices higher.

Four Observations On the High-Price Oil World

I The economic impact of higher prices has been smaller than anticipated. Prices recently have, in real terms, been even higher than in the period from 1980 to 1981, which helped precipitate the deep recession of the early 1980s (see Figure 2). Today's prices are a big burden for consumers, especially lower-income, in the United States, and for non-oil developing countries. (This is not the case in Europe, where most of the price at the gasoline pump remains sales tax.) High prices are also changing the "correlation of forces" among global automobile makers, adding to the woes for Detroit. However, the current episode of high oil prices has been accompanied by the best global economic performance of a generation — at least until recently. Why the difference from the 1970 and the 1980s (see Figure 2)?

These price levels are mainly (though not exclusively) the consequence of a "demand shock" — not a "supply shock" as in the 1970s. They are the result of "good news," not "bad news," and reflect the same forces that are driving the worldwide commodity boom. (The "aggregate disruption" is on top of the basic forces of demand growth.)

While oil remains the world's most important commodity, its relative role in the global economy is smaller than during previous periods. Today the United States is twice as efficient in its use of oil as in the 1970s. In the United States, gasoline consumption as a share of household

Figure 2

NOMINAL VERSUS **REAL OIL PRICES, 1969 – 2007**

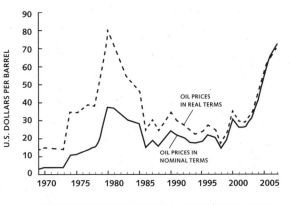

Source: Cambridge Energy Research Associates. 70716-2_0312

income is not out of line with the general trend—at least until very recently.[3] Although China's demand is increasing rapidly, as is its oil bill, its massive financial reserves are growing. To put it simply, it can more than pay for the oil.

Central banks have assimilated lessons of the oil shocks, and government policies have not inadvertently accentuated negative impacts.

With all this said, there is some level at which surging oil prices would have far more negative impacts on the world economy, especially if accompanied by some upheaval or disruption that shakes confidence and shocks global financial markets. The chief economist of the International Monetary Fund has recently suggested that oil prices in the range of $100 or above would constitute a "serious inflationary shock" and bears more resemblance to a "supply shock."[4] In addition, the credit crisis has the potential to be that additional factor that shakes global confidence.

II High prices have, as might be expected, revived resource nationalism, which in certain key cases is changing the political balance. Countries earning large revenues, far more than they had anticipated, or budgeted, a few years earlier are more confident and assertive (see Figure 3).

Less than a decade ago, Russia was essentially bankrupt. Today it is sitting on the third largest foreign reserves of any country in the world—behind only Japan and China—and its holdings, on a per capita basis, are three times that of China. Although Vladimir Putin has said that he does not like the term "energy superpower," energy certainly powers Russia's international position today.[5]

High oil prices and high revenues are fueling Venezuela's Hugo Chávez in his pursuit of a "Bolivarian Revolution" and his program for "socialism in the twenty-first century." It is striking how relatively little attention

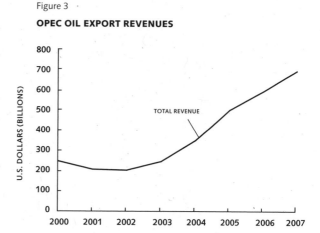

Figure 3

OPEC OIL EXPORT REVENUES

Source: Cambridge Energy Associates. 70716-3_0312

is being given to his oil-fueled drive to expand his influence across Latin America and into the other parts of the world.

The Iranian economy is under pressure from external formal and informal sanctions and domestic economic mismanagement.[6] Still, high oil prices have been providing a foundation for Iran's wider programs and its relative imperviousness to outside pressure. In 2002, Iran earned $19 billion from oil exports; in 2007, it earned close to $70 billion. Verbal ripostes from Tehran that drive up the oil price by $5, for example, translate into an additional $85 million a week of extra oil earnings for Iran.

This resource nationalism is amplified by a shift away from international oil companies (IOCs) to state-owned national oil companies (NOCs). The range of NOCs is wide. It includes companies partly owned in the capital markets that are at the forefront of technology, such as Brazil's Petrobras. Some are wholly-owned, such as Saudi Aramco, also a technology leader; Angola's Sonangol; and Venezuela's Petróleos de Venezuela. (PDVSA).

It extends to national oil companies like China's Sinopec and Russia's Rosneft that also have international listings. While headline writers are partial to the term "Big Oil," in fact the five supermajors (Exxon Mobil, Chevron, BP, Shell, and Total) are responsible for less than 15 percent of total world oil production.

III A time of high prices and tight supplies stokes fears that the world is running out of oil. This time, the fear has a name —"peak oil." As in the past, such fears underestimate the impact of technology and new regions and horizons. Also, "peakists" overestimate the significance of "discoveries" and disregard the much larger impact of "additions and discoveries," which is where most new reserves come from.[7] The current system mandated by the U.S. Securities and Exchange Commission for "reserves disclosure" itself is in need of overhaul, for it is based on the technology of the 1970s when the "deep water frontier" was 600 feet, not, as it is today, 12,000 feet.[8] Recently, the SEC has begun a review process to update its definitions, which will bring greater clarity to the concept of "proven reserves."

IV Markets do respond, but with a lag. This time the lag is being extended for both political and economic reasons. Companies need "access" to new prospects. But with high prices and high revenues, the perceived need on the part of governments to encourage investment goes down, and decision-making takes far longer. Governments are also inclined to change the rules and increase their share of the "take"— from what had been the typical 80 to 85 percent to 90 to 95 percent — changing the economics of projects.[9]

Moreover, while the public and markets are focused on price, the energy industry is reeling from rapidly-escalating costs. The IHS/CERA Upstream Capital Cost index shows that the cost of developing a new oil and gas project has doubled in just three years.[10] This reflects shortages of trained personnel, services, drilling rigs and other equipment, as well as the overall commodity boom, which has driven up the cost of steel and other inputs. The consequences include postponements and delays for projects. All this is adding to the growing concern about capacity constraints and pressures on supply, as reflected in the new National Petroleum Council study, Facing the Hard Truths.[11]

This cost escalation is not limited to upstream oil and gas. It is having similar effects on the construction of refineries, pipelines, electric generating plants, and infrastructure of all kinds — with similar results. Projects are much more expensive, and they end up being delayed, postponed, or put off.

Yet, notwithstanding delays, the prospects favor significant growth in production capacity. CERA, drawing on its own analysis and data bases, along with those of its parent, IHS, has recently completed its latest outlook for oil production capacity to the year 2017. (These data bases include several tens of thousands of oil fields.) This analysis included not only existing fields, but also 350 projects that might reasonably be sanctioned by 2010. The conclusion is that world production capacity will likely increase by more than 20 percent over the decade ahead. It may be a rocky road. Shortfalls would likely be the result of political factors, including conflict and decision-making, and constraints in the supply chain.[12] And indeed more delays and postponements are becoming evident because of the rapid increase in costs and supply bottlenecks.

Yet after 2010, one does start to see the growth in capacity concentrated in a relatively-limited number of countries — what we call the "O-15" for the "Oil-15." Brazil and Canada are on the list. But most of the countries are in the former Soviet Union, the Middle East, and West Africa. This reconcentration is likely to further accentuate current concerns about energy security.

The Growth of the Global Gas Trade

So far we have been talking about oil. The other notable growth is in terms of natural gas. Natural gas is an attractive fuel for electric generation. Its emissions are low, and generating plants using natural gas can be built more quickly than either coal or nuclear plants. Long-distance pipelines are tying producers and consumers together. Liquefied natural gas (LNG) was once thought to be a constrained business, with the market centered in Asia. No longer. An LNG business that took 40 years to reach its current size will double over the next six years (although delays are here too becoming more evident). Technological advances that have brought greater efficiency and scale are facilitating this growth.

Asia, Europe, and North America will be drawn towards a common global gas market. In recent years, the United States has had a tremendous build-up of natural gas-fired electric capacity, but North American natural gas supplies — at least with the restrictions that now exist — cannot keep up with the demand. This means that — discussions of "energy independence" notwithstanding — the United States could well go from importing about 3 percent of its gas in the form of LNG to more than 20 percent by 2020. The growth of this business, and the interdependence and political issues that come with it, will add further to the need to think through energy security in the 21st century.

A Perplexing Question

But we now come to a perplexing question. Most forecasts of future energy demand show substantial growth. Yet policies, driven by climate-change concerns, will increasingly be aimed at curbing that growth. Today, the consensus for global carbon management is increasingly strong. The new European Union energy policy calls for 20 percent of total energy in the EU to be supplied by renewable energy by 2020. That is to be achieved by what EU Energy Commissioner Andris Piebalgs calls a "new industrial revolution."[13] Many U.S. states have imposed renewable energy mandates on the electric power sector, and auto and truck fuel efficiency standards are in the process of being raised.

Moreover, we are seeing a "great bubbling" in terms of spending on energy research and technology, not only in the conventional sectors, but also in terms of renewables and alternatives.[14] Venture capital has now made an entrance into the energy sector. Last year, North American venture capital spending on "clean energy" was $2 billion — four times what it was just two years earlier. Many of these investors are looking for returns — and impacts — comparable to those they found in information technology and biotech.

Dawn of a New Age: Three Scenarios to the Year 2030

In an effort to make sense of this complexity, CERA undertook its "Dawn of a New Age" scenarios project.[15] A great deal of analysis and quantification underpinned the various scenarios, including examination of geopolitical, economic, health, demographic, and other key drivers of global energy consumption. Each scenario sought to answer a specific question.

The three scenarios are laid out below.

Strategic Questions to Scenario Themes CERA's *Dawn of a New Age* **Scenarios**

Strategic Questions	CERA Scenarios
How will the rise of Asia affect the global balance of power and world order? How will geopolitical changes affect energy markets and the competitive landscape for access to resources?	**Asian Phoenix** Examines a future in which the center of global economic and political gravity shifts to Asia, challenging the United States and Europe for global economic preeminence and changing the global strategic and business environment.
Less than eight years ago, energy prices were very low. Recently, they have been setting record highs. What conditions could keep energy prices at high levels for an extended period? What would be the long-term impact of even higher energy prices? At what point do changes in demand and technological advances trigger lower prices — and could oil lose its premier position?	**Break Point** Explores a future of sustained high oil prices and intensified climate change policies in which substitutes to conventional oil supply gain traction, oil loses its near monopoly over transportation, and prices come down again.
Many take for granted the continued expansion of cross-border flows of people, goods, and services. But can global economic integration continue indefinitely, or are there political limits to globalization? How would a sustained global economic slowdown and rising trade protectionism affect global energy markets?	**Global Fissures** Considers a world with widespread political backlash against trade and globalization, combined with growing political tensions and security concerns, leading to long-term weak economic growth and falling energy prices.

Currently, Asia represents about 40 percent of world GDP; by 2030, in *Asian Phoenix*, it reaches 54 percent. *Asian Phoenix* is not a world without crises. The scenario includes a "blue water crisis" involving China, Taiwan and the United States, and a renewal of tensions with North Korea that triggers reunification on an unexpected timetable. But these crises are managed, and the world remains on a strong track. It is also the scenario with the biggest requirements for energy. World oil demand grows by 45 percent. Over half of the demand growth is in Asia, as is two-thirds of both the growth in demand for electric power and the construction of new power plants.

In *Break Point*, oil loses its traction and its virtual monopoly position in transportation. This shift is driven by a strong policy and popular drive to reduce dependence on oil. The drivers could be fueled by political turbulence and prices that catapult as high as $150 a barrel. The reaction could be symbolized by what we imagined for the purposes of the scenario, perhaps prematurely, as "the Aspen Declaration of National Energy Independence." [16] But perhaps an even greater driver could be climate change concerns. "By 2015 the break point is materializing — the world's energy system has evolved in ways that make it very different from the one that existed in 2005."

In *Global Fissures*, the limits of globalization are reached and world economic growth is lower than in recent experience. Large parts of the world turn against liberalization and towards protectionism, and the result is lower economic growth. Security concerns increase, and nationalism looms larger in domestic and international politics. Moreover, social pressures increase within and among nations about gaps in wealth and opportunity. Lower growth means slower growth in energy demand.

In all three scenarios, energy demand does grow. Oil consumption grows in absolute terms, but loses market share. Both natural gas and coal gain market share. The likely growth of coal puts a particular premium on finding a route to "clean coal." Sequestration of carbon underground now receives much attention, but still awaits demonstration that it can be accomplished on a large scale. Moreover, a regulatory system will have to be created for sequestration. [17]

What could change these results? It could be much more intensive improvements in energy efficiency. Today, one sees stronger and broader advocacy for energy efficiency — conservation — than ever before. It has the great virtue of not only meeting energy security needs but also having the biggest near-term energy impact for meeting carbon-reduction objectives. The second would be substantial improvements in technology — particularly in batteries and in solar energy. A third would be advances in "second generation" biofuels.

But, in all of this, it is important not to lose sight of the sheer scale of the system that supplies world energy. The world consumes about 87 million barrels of oil per day, and, in total energy, well over 200 million barrels per day of oil equivalent. Renewables can turn into a very big business yet constitute only a small fraction of the total energy supply. Moreover, one is talking about capital stock that does not turn over quickly. Only about 8 percent of the U.S. auto fleet is replaced each year.[18] Power plants are in service for decades, and buildings — one of the biggest users of energy — are often around much longer.

Energy Independence or Energy Security

How to assure energy security in the face of these trends? The first step is to consider what it means. One often hears it conjoined with "energy independence." The latter is a very popular and appealing term, with deep popular resonance. Yet, if it is taken literally, it is a less useful guide. The nation is really seeking an energy security system that is robust and resilient and less vulnerable.

To elaborate, if energy independence is taken in a literal sense, it runs the risk of disappointment and cynicism and loss of focus. Today about 70 percent of our total energy is produced within the United States. But, in terms of oil, the reality is that, in the last 30 years, the United States has gone from importing a third of our oil to importing 60 percent. Moreover, the U.S. is on track, as already noted, for LNG imports to meet a much larger portion of gas demand. Large amounts of new natural gas-fired electric generation have been added over the last few years. To the degree that coal's market share is reduced, the United States will import more natural gas. The growth of ethanol is creating a new market for natural gas, used in its production, which will require additional imports of LNG.[19]

A literal "energy independence" mindset can also obscure the realities of world energy — the interdependence and reliance on global markets and on other countries. The United States needs to maintain policies that encourage investment and openness to investment in exporting countries. It is not constructive to pursue policies that cause countries to think twice about exporting oil to the United States, and instead encourage them to strengthen their trade (and political ties) with Asian countries. Moreover, it does not seem wise, given global capital flows, to promote policies that inadvertently push countries to steer their investment out of U.S. markets. These kind of initiatives would likely lead to lower investment in developing new supplies on the part of these countries at a time when the United States should, as policy, be encouraging them to maintain and step up such investment — especially at a time when the need for alternatives to Iran could take on a new urgency.

In the face of U.S. engagement with global markets for energy, as with so many other global markets, thought needs to be given to what the message of "energy autarchy" sends to the countries with which we wish to collaborate or want to encourage to maintain or increase the levels of investment. As the table indicates, the two largest sources of oil imports are Canada and Mexico. In 2006, Middle East imports comprised 19 percent of our total imports, and 11 percent of consumption. Yet, at the end of the day, there is only one world oil market, and upheavals in one part affect all participants. This reality is one of the imperatives that make energy security so important a consideration (see Table 1).

The Energy Security System

The current energy security system was created in response to the 1973 Arab oil embargo to ensure coordination among the industrialized countries in the event of a disruption in supply, encourage collaboration on energy policies, avoid bruising scrambles for supplies, and deter any future use of an "oil weapon"

Table 1

"THE TOP FIVE" U.S. IMPORTS OF **PETROLEUM 2007**
(Million Barrels Per Day, First Ten Months)

Country	
Canada	2.4
Mexico	1.6
Saudi Arabia	1.4
Venezuela	1.4
Nigeria	1.1

Source: Energy Information Administration.

by exporters. Its key elements are the Paris-based International Energy Agency (IEA), whose members are the industrialized countries; strategic stockpiles of oil, including the U.S. Strategic Petroleum Reserve; continued monitoring and analysis of energy markets and policies; and energy conservation and coordinated emergency sharing of supplies in the event of a disruption. The emergency system was set up to offset major disruptions that threatened the global economy and stability. It was not established to manage prices and the commodity cycle, although that temptation occurs and reoccurs.

Several principles underpin energy security. They are indicated in Table 2. As important as the current principles are, recent years have highlighted the need to expand the concept of energy security in two critical dimensions:

- The recognition of the globalization of the energy security system, which can be accommodated especially by engaging China, India, and Brazil, and
- The acknowledgment of the fact that the entire energy supply chain needs to be protected.

A New Element of Energy Security: Bringing China and India "In"

Despite all the attention being paid to China's efforts to secure international petroleum reserves, the entire amount that China currently produces per day outside of its own borders is equivalent to a fraction of the daily production of one of the supermajor oil companies. If there were a serious controversy between the United States and China involving oil or gas, it would likely arise not because of a general competition for the resources themselves, but rather because they had become part of

Table 2

FUNDAMENTALS OF **ENERGY SECURITY**

Diversification
Resilience: a "security margin"
High-quality and timely information
Collaboration among consumers and between consumers and producers
Expansion of "IEA System" to include China and India
Inclusion of infrastructure and supply chain
Robust markets and flexibility
Renewed emphasis on efficiency for both energy and climate reasons
Investment flows
R&D, technological advance, and new technologies

Source: "The Fundamentals of Energy Security" Testimony by Daniel Yergin, before the U.S. House of Representatives Committee on Foreign Affairs of March 22, 2007.

larger foreign policy issues (e.g., Sudan, or over how to respond to Iran's nuclear program). Indeed, from the viewpoint of consumers in North America, Europe, and Japan, Chinese and Indian investment in the development of new energy supplies around the world is not a threat but something to be encouraged because it means there will be more energy available for everyone in the years ahead as India's and China's demand grows.

It would be wiser — and indeed it is urgent — to engage these two giants in the global network of trade and investment rather than see them tilt toward more mercantilist, state-to-state approaches. But, for that to happen, both countries need to be encouraged to see that their interests can be met in global markets and that they will not be disadvantaged compared to other consumers. Thus India and China, and other key countries such as Brazil, should be brought into coordination with the existing IEA energy security system to assure them that their interests will be protected in the event of turbulence and to ensure that the system works more effectively. There is much talk of a clash between the United States and China over oil, but there is nothing inevitable about it. Commercial competition need not turn into national rivalry.

Another New Element: Securing Infrastructure and the Supply Chain

The current model of energy security, which was born of the 1973 crisis, focuses primarily on how to handle any disruption of oil supplies from producing countries. Today, the concept of energy security needs to be expanded to include the protection of the entire energy supply chain and infrastructure — an awesome task. None of the world's complex, integrated supply chains were built with security, defined in this broad way, in mind. Hurricanes Katrina and Rita — which disrupted more energy supply to the United States than any previous supply crisis — brought a new perspective to the security question by demonstrating how fundamental the electric grid is to everything else. After the storms, the Gulf Coast refineries and the big U.S. pipelines were unable to operate — not just because some were flooded and damaged, but also because they could not get electric power.

Energy interdependence, the growing scale of energy trade, the lengthening supply chains, the shift towards more offshore oil production — all these require continuing collaboration among both producers and consumers to ensure the security of the entire supply chain.

The challenge of energy security will grow more urgent in the years ahead, because the scale of the global trade in energy will grow substantially as world markets become larger and more integrated. Assuring the security of global energy markets will require coordination on both an international and a national basis among companies and governments, including energy, environmental, military, law enforcement, and intelligence agencies. But in the United States, as in other countries, the lines of responsibility — and the sources of funding — for protecting critical infrastructures, such as energy, are far from clear. The private sector, the federal government, and state and local agencies need to take steps to better coordinate their activities. Maintaining the commitment to do so during future periods of moderate or low prices will require discipline as well as vigilance. Both the public and private sectors need to invest in building a higher degree of security into the energy system — which inevitability, one way or the other, would need to be reflected in the cost of energy.

The Important Role of Markets as a Source of Security

Markets *themselves* need to be recognized as a source of security. The energy security system was created when energy prices were regulated in the United States, energy trading was only just beginning, and futures markets were several years away. Today, large, flexible, and well-functioning energy markets provide security by absorbing shocks and allowing supply and demand to respond more quickly and with greater ingenuity than a controlled system could. Thus, governments do well to resist the temptation to respond to short-term political pressure and micromanage markets. Intervention and controls, however well meaning, can backfire, slowing and even preventing the movement of supplies to respond to disruptions. At least in the United States, any price spike or disruption evokes the images of the infamous gas lines of the 1970s. Yet those lines were to a considerable degree self-inflicted — the consequence of price controls and a heavy-handed allocation system that sent gasoline where it was not needed and denied its being sent where it was.

Contrast that to what happened immediately after Hurricane Katrina. A major disruption to the U.S. oil supply was compounded by reports of price gouging and of stations running out of gasoline, which together could have created new gas lines in the Southeast and along the East Coast. Yet the markets were back in balance much sooner, and prices came down more quickly, than had generally been expected. Emergency supplies from the U.S. Strategic Petroleum Reserve and other IEA reserves were released. At the same time, two critical regulatory restrictions were eased. One was the Jones Act (which bars non-U.S.-flagged ships from carrying cargo between U.S. ports), which was waived to allow non-U.S. tankers to ship supplies bottlenecked on the Gulf Coast around Florida to the East Coast, where they were needed. The other was that "boutique gasoline" regulations, which require different qualities of gasoline for different cities, were temporarily lifted to permit supplies from other parts of the country to flow into the areas running short.

This experience highlights the need to incorporate regulatory and environmental flexibility — and a clear understanding of the impediments to adjustment — into the energy security machinery in order to cope as effectively as possible with disruptions and emergencies. Markets can often more efficiently and effectively, and more quickly, resolve shortfalls and disruptions than controls can.

This is not a theoretical discussion about the value of markets. Proposals for direct or indirect systems of price controls aimed at the gasoline market — could well, if in place in 2005, have blocked the kind of swift adjustment that occurred after Hurricanes Katrina and Rita. Indeed, controls could end up creating the kind of shortfalls that led to the famous gas lines. What would be the message to a station owner? Would it be safer for that station owner to risk running out of gasoline than take on the very real risk of extended investigation and litigation, with all the accompanying costs?

Energy and Foreign Relations

Energy and energy security cannot and should not be compartmentalized. For energy security inevitably exists in a larger context of overall security and international relationships. In a world of increasing interdependence, energy security will depend much on the overall relationships among countries. That is why energy security will be one of the main challenges for U.S. foreign policy in the years ahead. Energy has to be seen in terms of larger relationships. At the same time, the energy dimension of the overall relationships also needs to be recognized — and taken with the seriousness it deserves.

■ ■ ■

Daniel Yergin is Co-Founder and Chairman of Cambridge Energy Research Associates (CERA). He is also Executive Vice President of IHS, the parent company of CERA and serves as CNBC's Global Energy Expert. Dr. Yergin's most recent book is *Commanding Heights: The Battle for the World Economy*, now a three-part PBS documentary. He authored the Pulitzer Prize-winning *The Prize: The Epic Quest for Oil, Money and Power*, which was made into an eight-hour PBS/BBC series. Dr. Yergin chaired the U.S. Department of Energy's Task Force on Strategic Energy Research and Development. Dr. Yergin is a member of the Board of the United States Energy Association, and a member of the National Petroleum Council and in 2006 became the only foreign member of the Russian Academy of Oil and Gas. He is a Trustee of The Brookings Institution, on the Board of the New America Foundation, a Director of the U.S.-Russia Business Council, and on the Advisory Boards of the Peterson Institute for International Economics and the MIT Energy Initiative. Dr. Yergin received a B.A. from Yale University and a Ph.D. from Cambridge University.

[1] U.S. National Petroleum Council, *Facing the Hard Truths about Energy — a Comprehensive View to 2030 of Global Oil and Natural Gas: Report to the U.S. Secretary of Energy*, (2007), p.177.

[2] Remarks by Thamir Ghadbahm, one of the main figures in the Iraq oil industry, at CERA's *East Meets West* Conference, Istanbul, June 27, 2007.

[3] *Gasoline and the American People 2007*, Cambridge Energy Research Associates, 2007.

[4] Simon Johnson quoted in *Financial Times*, November 22, 2007.

[5] See Angela Stent, "Russia and Europe," paper for Aspen Strategy Group, August 2007.

[6] "Iran Economists Criticize Gov't Economic Management," *Turkish Daily News*, June 14, 2007.

[7] *Why the Peak Oil Theory Falls Down*, Cambridge Energy Research Associates, 2006.

[8] On the issues involving reserve disclosures, see *Modernizing Oil and Gas Reserves Disclosures*, Cambridge Energy Research Associates, 2006, and *In Search of Reasonable Certainty: Oil and Gas Reserves Disclosure*, Cambridge Energy Research Associates, 2005.

[9] *E&P Fiscal Terms: Larger Pies but Smaller Portions*, Cambridge Energy Research Associates, November 2007.

[10] *World Oil Watch*, Cambridge Energy Research Associates, 2007.

[11] *Facing the Hard Truths about Energy*, U.S. National Petroleum Council.

[12] *Bumpy Road Ahead: Global Liquids Capacity to 2017*, Cambridge Energy Research Associates, 2007.

[13] Andris Piebalgs, speech to CERA's *East Meets West* Conference, Istanbul, June 26, 2007.

[14] Daniel Yergin, "A Great Bubbling," *Newsweek*, December 18, 2006.

[15] *Dawn of a New Age: Global Energy Scenarios for Strategic Decision Making — The Energy Future to 2030 (A CERA Multiclient Study)*, Cambridge Energy Research Associates, 2006.

[16] From the scenarios: "A manifestation of evolving U.S. opinion is embodied in the Aspen Declaration of (National) Energy Independence … The declaration warns that continuing growth in U.S. oil imports increases the country's vulnerability and imperils its security, and calls for the United States to make a forced march to more diversification and new technologies. The declaration also emphasizes the benefits in terms of climate change."

[17] See *The Future of Coal: Options for a Carbon-Constrained World, (An Interdisciplinary MIT Study)*, Massachusetts Institute of Technology, 2007.

[18] See *Gasoline and the American People 2007*, Cambridge Energy Research Associates, 2007.

[19] *The Ethanol Boom: Creating a New Market for Natural Gas*, Cambridge Energy Research Associates, 2007.

"Energy productivity is not about placing huge bets on spectacular, hard-to-attain breakthroughs — it is about a focused drive to make hundreds of incremental improvements that add up to a huge cumulative impact on reducing energy consumption."

— DIANA FARRELL, IVO BOZON

■ Demand-Side Economics: The Case for a New U.S. Energy Policy Direction

Diana Farrell
Director, McKinsey Global Institute

Ivo Bozon
Director, McKinsey & Co.

G lobal energy markets have entered a period of renewed uncertainty. After two decades of relatively low prices — that typically lead to complacency and policy stagnation — energy anxiety has returned with a vengeance. Prices are higher and likely to stay that way. Geopolitics is once again a key factor encompassing everything, from the vigorous use of energy as a foreign-policy tool by countries such as Russia and Venezuela, to persistent strikes and unrest in Nigeria, to rising instability in the Middle East. Alongside growing concern about the security of supplies are two new phenomena: an unprecedented surge in demand, spurred by the rising economic might of China and other populous emerging markets, and increasing public anxiety about the environmental consequences of energy consumption, in particular climate change. Deep change, growing uncertainty, and high anxiety add up to a perfect time to rethink creatively the U.S. approach to energy policy.

Any revision to our approach to the energy challenge must start by acknowledging that the often overlooked demand side of the energy equation is just as important as the supply side. We believe that amid the current deep uncertainties, two aspects of the 2020 energy outlook are not in doubt. First, without significant change to policy and behavior, the world will see an unprecedented surge in energy demand. Second, there is no conceivable breakthrough on the supply side that would allow the United States or any other country to achieve anything close to energy independence.

With these two certainties in mind, the goal of national policy should be to enhance energy resilience — a broader definition of security than the chimera of self-sufficiency that emphasizes an economy's ability to adapt to a range of possible futures through more flexible sources of supply and greater control over demand. In our view, the most effective and politically viable way to reach the goal of energy resilience is a national effort to boost U.S. energy productivity, or the level of output we achieve from the energy we consume, which addresses both sides of the supply-demand equation. We believe that the results of such an effort could be nothing short of spectacular.

McKinsey & Company is the leading management consultancy on energy, working with companies and governments around the world in this area. In recent years the firm has conducted significant proprietary research into aspects of energy — and on energy productivity in particular — through the McKinsey Global Institute (MGI) and McKinsey's Global Energy practice.

In this chapter we will:

- Give a broad overview of the likely supply-demand outlook to 2020;
- Tie that outlook to a framework for setting energy policy;
- Make the case for how a concerted push towards raising energy productivity could deliver a surprisingly large pay-off.

What is Driving the Global Energy Outlook to 2020?

Too many forecasters focus primarily on the supply side of the energy market. We believe it is critical to have a clear perspective on *both* supply and demand. In our base case scenario, we assume an oil price averaging $50-a-barrel through 2020 and an average annual rise in global GDP of 3.2 percent. The energy demand produced in our base case would change somewhat if either growth or oil prices were significantly higher or lower. However, we believe that under all plausible business-as-usual scenarios, the world between now and 2020 will see a marked acceleration in energy demand growth.

GLOBAL ENERGY DEMAND WILL ACCELERATE TO 2020

The MGI's base case scenario, which assumes no change in policy, sees global energy demand accelerating dramatically from the trend rate of 1.7 percent annual growth, in place since the mid-1990s, to 2.2 percent a year to 2020. This sharp rise will occur despite our assumption of continued modest improvements (1 percent a year) in energy efficiency and energy productivity. Developing nations rather than advanced economies have been driving energy demand growth for some years now, but emerging-economy dominance of energy demand growth is set to be overwhelming. Fast-growing emerging markets will account for 85 percent of the global increase in energy demand to 2020 (Figure 1).

China alone represents one-third of total energy demand growth to 2020, due both to the sustained strength of the country's industrial demand and to an explosion of buildings, the penetration of appliances, and car sales, as rising incomes vault millions of citizens into a bracket that is recognizably middle class. By 2020, China's total energy demand will outstrip that of the United States (although the United States will remain by far the biggest consumer per capita).

More unexpectedly perhaps, energy demand in the Middle East will be rising rapidly as oil revenues boost GDP growth at

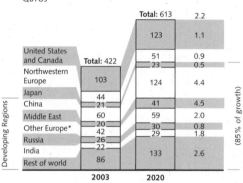

Figure 1

MOST **ENERGY DEMAND GROWTH** WILL COME FROM **DEVELOPING ECONOMIES**

End-use energy demand* by region
QBTUs

Compound annual growth rate 2003–2020, %

* Transformation losses (power generation, refining) allocated to end-use segments.

** Includes Baltic/Eastern and Mediterranean Europe and North Africa.

Source: MGI Global Energy Demand

the same time energy subsidies continue to encourage energy-intensive use. By 2020, Middle-Eastern energy demand, already rising quickly, will approach the level that currently prevails in Northwestern Europe.[1]

Another surprise, perhaps, is that India will not be a key contributor to global energy demand growth to 2020 partly because the country is still in the early stages of its development — income levels per capita are still below the $5,000 threshold at which the penetration of many energy-consuming products takes off. Another reason for India taking a back seat in global energy demand growth is that the country will see a significant, positive shift in its fuel mix as the economy moves from its heavy reliance on traditional biomass fuels, such as wood and charcoal, to more efficient, modern energy sources such as natural gas.

The other significant global trend that we observe is that consumers rather than producers will drive energy demand growth as the world economy continues to shift away from heavy industry and toward less energy-intensive services. Sectors that have the characteristics of consumer goods, such as residential and commercial buildings and road transportation, will account for 70 percent of energy demand growth in developed regions and 55 percent in developing regions (Figure 2). As well as recalibrating policy in response to the shifting weight of energy demand growth to emerging economies, policy makers hoping to curb this growth will need to reexamine their approach in light of the increasing role that consumers are playing in the energy demand picture.

Figure 2

CONSUMER-DRIVEN SECTORS WILL ACCOUNT FOR **57 PERCENT** OF **GLOBAL ENERGY DEMAND GROWTH**

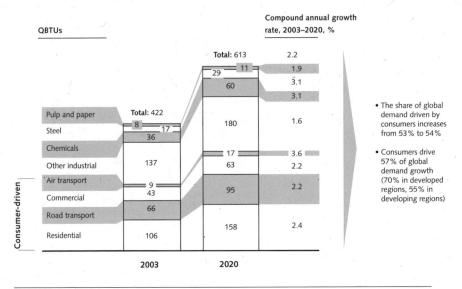

Note: Transformation losses (power generation and refining) allocated to end-use segments.

Source: MGI Global

Nowhere is the impact of this shift to consumer-led growth more apparent than in the United States. In MGI's base case scenario, U.S. energy demand growth to 2020 will increase slightly from the annual rate of 1.0 percent that prevailed over the past two decades to some 1.1 percent a year. This occurs despite the fact that industrial energy usage will grow by only 0.8 percent a year (and actually falls in certain heavy-use sectors such as steel). By contrast, energy demand growth in consumer-driven sectors such as transportation will continue to climb. Air transportation energy demand will grow the quickest at 2.7 percent a year while road transportation energy demand will increase by 1.5 percent annually, thereby contributing one-third of overall U.S. energy demand growth.

In short, unless policy and behavior changes, the United States will retain, and even build upon, its historic role as the most energy-intensive developed nation with the highest energy consumption per capita (Figure 3). Consider road transportation. Driving one mile in the United States currently requires 37 percent more fuel on average than in Europe — the result of both larger average vehicle size and less efficient engine technology. Under existing policies this gap widens to 42 percent by 2020. If business continues as usual, the United States will also fall further behind other countries in terms of energy efficiency across all main end-use segments — commercial, residential, and transportation (Figure 4).

The result of all this is that the United States will also remain the nation with the highest energy-related CO_2 emissions per capita and the highest CO_2 intensity of any developed country (Figure 5). Happily, as we will explain, it does not have to be this way.

Figure 3

THE UNITED STATES REMAINS THE **MOST ENERGY-INTENSIVE DEVELOPED REGION**

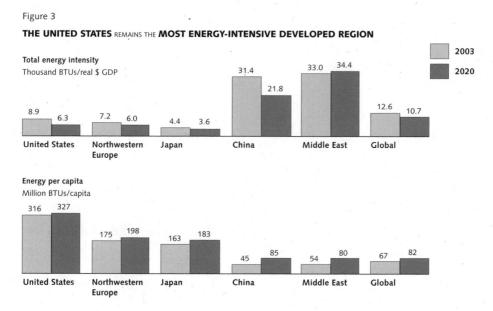

Source: MGI Global Energy Demand Model

Figure 4

UNITED STATES WILL SEE THE **LOWEST ENERGY-EFFICIENCY IMPROVEMENTS ACROSS ALL SECTORS**

Annual improvement of Energy-Efficiency indicators, 2003–2020

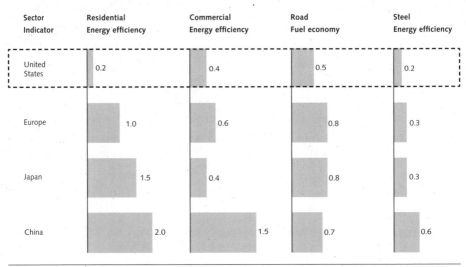

Sector Indicator	Residential Energy efficiency	Commercial Energy efficiency	Road Fuel economy	Steel Energy efficiency
United States	0.2	0.4	0.5	0.2
Europe	1.0	0.6	0.8	0.3
Japan	1.5	0.4	0.8	0.3
China	2.0	1.5	0.7	0.6

Source: EIA; Lawrence Berkeley National Lab China Energy Group; McKinsey Global Institute analysis

Figure 5

UNITED STATES WILL CONTINUE TO PRODUCE **THE HIGHEST CO_2 EMISSIONS PER CAPITA TO 2020**

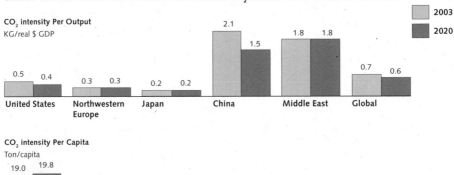

CO_2 intensity Per Output
KG/real $ GDP

	2003	2020
United States	0.5	0.4
Northwestern Europe	0.3	0.3
Japan	0.2	0.2
China	2.1	1.5
Middle East	1.8	1.8
Global	0.7	0.6

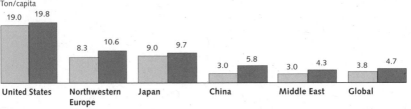

CO_2 intensity Per Capita
Ton/capita

	2003	2020
United States	19.0	19.8
Northwestern Europe	8.3	10.6
Japan	9.0	9.7
China	3.0	5.8
Middle East	3.0	4.3
Global	3.8	4.7

Source: MGI Global Energy Demand Model

OIL WILL CONTINUE TO DOMINATE GLOBAL ENERGY SUPPLY TO 2020

Any forecast of global energy supply is inevitably affected by critical variables ranging from terrorism to technology breakthroughs, from acts of governments (another oil embargo, war, domestic unrest in key supplier countries, radical new policy initiatives), to acts of God (hurricanes and other natural disasters). However, we have opted to stick to the assumptions made in our base case scenario for energy demand, including a $50-a-barrel oil price and no radical change in the overall geopolitical outlook, and examine in this chapter a few reasonable near-term certainties.

First, oil will remain the most important energy source globally for the foreseeable future. Today, petroleum products account for 34 percent of world energy consumption. Demand for such products grows at 2.1 percent per year in our base case scenario driven mostly by the transportation and chemicals segments and by developing regions, especially China and the Middle East. Global crude oil consumption rises from its current level of 85 million barrels per day to 102 million barrels per day by 2020.

Despite the growing belief in some quarters that global supplies have peaked, as they did in the United States in the early 1970s, we do not subscribe to the notion that the world is approaching the point of "peak oil." There is no shortage of oil resources in the world. To date cumulative global production represents only 20 percent of remaining resources, including both very substantial unconventional resources such as heavy oil and oil shale as well as large conventional oil reserves.

In the long term, global oil markets should, in theory, return to some form of supply and demand price equilibrium. However, three factors conspire to ensure oil prices are not likely to return to the extraordinary lows the world enjoyed between 1986 and 2003. First of all, new supply sources are increasingly remote, difficult to access, and host governments from Russia to Venezuela are demanding a larger share of potential returns, which is driving up costs more steeply. These potential supplies also tend not to be in territories under the jurisdiction of relatively stable developed economies. By 2020, non-OECD (Organisation for Economic Co-operation and Development) oil production will represent more than 80 percent of global production, up from 75 percent today, while exports to OECD nations will climb by more than one-third. We therefore have the prospect of longer, more complex supply chains and greater potential for geopolitical events that might curtail supply. Finally, oil-exporting countries, most notably in OPEC, have seen the world adjust successfully to higher prices and have substantial internal incentives to maintain prices above the true costs of supply and demand. These nations have little reason to allow pure market forces to prevail — although the fact remains that they may not be able to control prices in the short term. In combination these factors are likely to ensure structurally higher prices as well as greater volatility, justifying the $50-a-barrel oil price we use in our base case scenario.

Second, while gas will also remain plentiful — the world currently has well over 70 years' of supply, with Russia and the Middle East alone claiming 70 percent of that amount — the supply landscape is changing fundamentally. In the primary consuming regions of Europe and North America, reserves continue to dwindle, long-distance pipelines must stretch even longer to meet gaps in demand, and reliance on liquid natural gas (LNG) is rising. Global gas supply chains, which today account for 13 percent of the total market, will increase their market share to 24 percent by 2020. The LNG production should soar by 150 percent to 2020, from 200 billion cubic meters (bcm) today to around 500 bcm by 2020. The result will be a shift from a market structure with a range of locally set gas prices to one in which regional prices are increasingly linked to, or at least influenced by, LNG flows. Such a structure will likely endure greater price volatility and be more vulnerable to geopolitical and other disruptions. Countries that fail to anticipate this trend — by not creating a better pipeline infrastructure, building more LNG terminals, and the like — risk a less secure supply future while those that do will prove more resilient.

Third, renewable energy and biofuels will shift from being niche products to the mainstream in our base case scenario. Today, renewables (our definition excludes hydro-power and biomass) represent less than 0.5 percent of global primary energy supply. However, in power generation, wind and, to a lesser extent, solar are growing rapidly. Moreover, based on capital flows — renewables accounted for 35 percent of global power-industry investment in 2005 — the future footprint of such energy sources is sure to be far larger, at perhaps as much as 13 percent of global power production by 2020. This growing scale is rapidly lowering previously steep learning curves. Every doubling of capacity in renewables cuts costs by 15 percent. As a result, several technologies that have historically required government subsidies to compete could well be able to stand independently in the marketplace by 2015 – 2020. Higher fossil fuel prices or policy changes such as a government decision to start charging for the hidden costs of CO_2 emissions — could give renewables an even larger role.

Biofuels will play a more important role as a blending product in transportation fuels. Recent McKinsey modeling suggests that, with oil at $40-a-barrel, biofuels could account for 10 percent of total global transportation fuel by 2020, or eight times current production. Three factors will determine biofuels' rate of growth — feedstock costs, government support (either through cash subsidies or "hard" mandates that require levels of blended use), and technology development. For instance, the U.S. biofuels initiative currently relies almost entirely on corn, a situation that has already begun to drive up food prices. By 2012 however, the United States should have developed the capacity to produce bio-ethanol from cellulosic matter (the main bulk of plants), a breakthrough that will open up access to a range of much cheaper, non-edible feedstock.

Fourth, coal and nuclear energy remain two big question marks but also two major potential long-range game changers. Access to supply is not an issue here. The world has ample reserves of cheap coal. The United States alone has more than 200 years of reserves at current production levels. Increasing the role of nuclear power is limited largely by the speed at which new plants can be built. The most substantial hurdle for coal and nuclear power is that both industries are political pariahs. Over the past decade, coal has remained dominant in several regions, most notably China and India, but in the United States, where there has been rising concern about coal's outsized CO_2 emissions, coal plants have accounted for only 2 percent of new generating capacity. In the case of nuclear power, the aftermath of high-profile accidents at nuclear plants, at Three Mile Island and Chernobyl, combined with low energy prices and relative energy stability put a virtual stop to the growth of nuclear power by the 1990s.

Despite their unpopularity, coal and nuclear power both offer some clear advantages in a world characterized by more expensive energy and rising anxiety about the security of supply. With nuclear energy back on the agenda in Europe, and never off the agenda in China, we believe it is time to reopen an honest dialogue about the role of nuclear energy in the U.S. energy mix. We also believe that while carbon capture and storage technologies are currently uneconomic and yet to be proven at scale, it would be short-sighted not to launch a more vigorous national effort to find ways to make coal CO_2 neutral, given the fuel's obvious advantages in terms of low cost and secure supply. Such an effort barely makes an appearance on today's policy radar.

While we do not advocate governments picking winners and losers, we simply point out that current "supply-side" policies supporting wind and biofuels do exactly that — at the expense of both coal and nuclear power, which offer far greater potential to "move the dial" on longer-term energy resilience and environmental goals. Given the long lead times required to figure out how to make coal cleaner and to overcome political objections to restart the nuclear engine — lead times that mean that neither is likely to play a significant role in changing the U.S. energy mix to 2020 — we strongly urge that those debates begin now.

II The Energy Policy Framework: Balancing Security, Politics, and Economics Through Resilience

McKinsey emphasizes fact based analysis and we therefore do not intend to take a stand on various policy choices and trade-offs (say between higher taxes and mandates). However, we do believe that it is important to provide a clear framework for the energy discussion. Too much of today's debate centers on the false promise of "energy independence" — a goal that we believe is not only unrealistic but inadequate. It fails to address what we identify as the three current, overriding goals of U.S. energy policy: the national security imperative to ensure that U.S. energy demands can be met; the emerging political imperative to address rising public concern about climate change and global warming; and

Figure 6

THROUGH HIGHER ENERGY PRODUCTIVITY, THE UNITED STATES COULD CAP GROWTH IN

ENERGY DEMAND AND **CO$_2$ EMISSIONS**

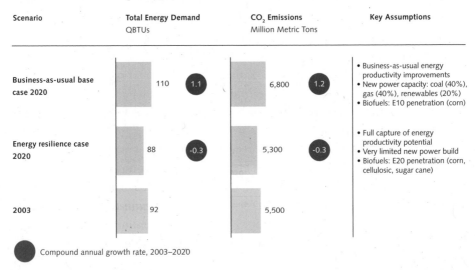

Scenario	Total Energy Demand QBTUs		CO$_2$ Emissions Million Metric Tons		Key Assumptions
Business-as-usual base case 2020	110	1.1	6,800	1.2	• Business-as-usual energy productivity improvements • New power capacity: coal (40%), gas (40%), renewables (20%) • Biofuels: E10 penetration (corn)
Energy resilience case 2020	88	-0.3	5,300	-0.3	• Full capture of energy productivity potential • Very limited new power build • Biofuels: E20 penetration (corn, cellulosic, sugar cane)
2003	92		5,500		

⬤ Compound annual growth rate, 2003–2020

Source: McKinsey Global Institute analysis; McKinsey Integrated Power Perspective 2007; McKinsey GEM practice

the economic imperative not to damage, and if possible to enhance, the country's competitive position and growth prospects. To connect those policy goals to the broad outlook for energy supply and demand, we consider two possible futures for the U.S. energy landscape in 2020 (Figure 6).

"BUSINESS-AS-USUAL"

Our first scenario is our base case. The U.S. economy will continue to advance despite a large increase in energy demand, but doing nothing — beyond allowing the current shift to renewables to build modest momentum and extending the life of existing nuclear capacity — will not ensure an optimal future. In fact, the contrary is the case. On the security front, with an energy mix still dominated by growing imports of oil and gas, the United States will find itself even more vulnerable to price volatility and supply interruptions. The only partial short term supply-side fix — accelerating the use of coal without achieving a breakthrough in carbon sequestration technology — will guarantee a substantial, and probably politically intolerable, worsening of the U.S. CO_2 footprint. Even if the role of coal were to remain the same, as we project in our base case, CO_2 emissions would rise. In short, failing to take any serious action to change the country's current role as the world's largest carbon emitter and least energy-efficient developed nation utterly fails to address the realities of domestic and international politics.

Even in pure economics terms, doing nothing is a poor choice based on the false notion that there is an inevitable conflict between economic growth and raising energy efficiency or environmental standards. The fact is that policies that promote innovation in energy technology can promote broader economic growth. On the supply side, much of the new energy investment over the next 15 years will be made in emerging markets, and companies that want to lead in nuclear and coal technology will need to participate in these markets. On the demand side, continued progress in Japan and the European Union toward tighter efficiency and environmental standards is encouraging companies in these regions to drive much of the current innovation. With its highly developed venture capital and private equity markets and a dynamic business environment that enables rapid diffusion of new, more productive technologies and processes, the United States and U.S. companies should be well-positioned to help shape the future of energy markets. They will be less so if policy makers cling to the phony security of the status quo.

"ENERGY RESILIENCE"

Our alternative scenario paints a brighter future in which, instead of accelerating, U.S. energy demand actually declines by 0.3 percent a year to 2020, in the process significantly lowering U.S. demand for crude imports and capping U.S. greenhouse gas emissions at today's levels.

The key to achieving this highly positive outcome is a sustained and concerted national effort to boost U.S. energy productivity. To achieve success in this regard, there will need to be more targeted government intervention to overcome market barriers that stand in the way of greater energy productivity, as well as more effective federal standards-setting. (Currently, the United States has seen only sporadic action at the state level on issues such as limiting CO_2 emissions.) However, the good news is that such interventions can take place without damaging critical market signals and U.S. business. Indeed, we believe that U.S. businesses are likely to welcome better federal-state coordination instead of the current bewildering array of mandates that makes national and international investment decisions difficult. In fact, a well-designed national effort to boost energy productivity would not only do little damage to the U.S. economy but has every potential to enhance national competitiveness.

A campaign to boost energy productivity goes well beyond simply securing more energy supply and artificially suppressing demand. What we are calling for is nothing less than an effort to achieve at the national level what any good business strives for at the microlevel every day — to get more out of the resources that are available. We believe that increasing energy productivity is a true "no-regrets" solution for U.S. policy makers around which they can build political consensus.

III Tackling the Demand Side: A Winning Solution

Pushing to raise U.S. energy productivity positively addresses the three overriding national energy goals that we have described — greater energy supply security, progress on CO_2 emissions, and enhanced competitiveness — and, above all, promises stunning results.[2]

We calculate that simply by pursuing investments with an internal rate of return (IRR) of 10 percent or more — using *available* technologies and without impacting negatively on economic growth — the United States could achieve annual declines in its energy demand of 0.3 percent a year to 2020 instead of energy demand growth of 1.1 percent annually, with large opportunities across energy-using segments (Figure 7). U.S. emissions of CO_2 would decrease by 0.2

percent per annum instead of growing by 1.1 percent. Overall, the United States would be able to cap its annual energy consumption and CO_2 emissions at their current levels by 2020.

We should note that although the focus of this chapter is the United States, the global opportunities afforded by a drive to boost energy productivity are even greater since so much future energy demand growth is in emerging markets. Using that same 10 percent IRR hurdle as a benchmark, we find that the world could reduce overall energy demand growth from a projected 2.2 percent a year to a mere 0.7 percent annually — a huge improvement. Capturing the full opportunity to improve energy productivity that we identify would reduce the world's energy use by 135 quadrillion British thermal units, 150 percent of current U.S. annual energy consumption.

Figure 7

LARGE OPPORTUNITIES FOR IMPROVING **ENERGY PRODUCTIVITY** ARE AVAILABLE **ACROSS SECTORS** IN **THE UNITED STATES**

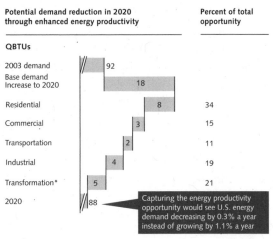

Potential demand reduction in 2020 through enhanced energy productivity

Percent of total opportunity

QBTUs

		Percent of total opportunity
2003 demand	92	
Base demand Increase to 2020	18	
Residential	8	34
Commercial	3	15
Transportation	2	11
Industrial	4	19
Transformation*	5	21
2020	88	

Capturing the energy productivity opportunity would see U.S. energy demand decreasing by 0.3% a year instead of growing by 1.1% a year

* Power generation and refining sectors.

Source: McKinsey Global Institute analysis

Market forces and market price signals alone will not capture this substantial potential — even a sustained oil price of $70 a barrel, which is higher than our base case forecast, would not be sufficient to incentivize higher energy productivity. The reason why even high oil prices cannot deliver the full potential for higher energy productivity that is available is partly because consumer-driven sectors will be increasingly important contributors to energy demand growth. Consumers often lack the information and capital they need to become more energy productive and tend to make comfort, safety, and convenience priorities over energy productivity. Moreover, agency issues, such as landlord versus tenant incentives, abound. Businesses also often leave available opportunities for improving energy productivity on the table because of the small and fragmented nature of energy costs. In response to such hurdles and disincentives to energy productivity, U.S. policy makers need to think constructively about addressing market inefficiencies, not by picking winners or setting prices but by creating standards and incentives that facilitate private sector investment and innovation. In our view, key policy areas could include:

RESIDENTIAL

The largest energy productivity opportunities, some 34 percent of the overall U.S. potential to increase energy productivity, lie in the residential sector. This sector's energy demand could be almost 30 percent lower than today's level if there were to be a concerted effort to improve energy productivity. High-efficiency heating and cooling systems and better insulation in new houses could deliver 25 percent of the U.S. residential opportunity; replacing incandescent light bulbs with compact fluorescent lighting another 17 percent; high-efficiency water heating (solar and demand-instantaneous) 20 percent; and higher-efficiency appliances the remaining 38 percent. However, achieving this opportunity will require policy and regulatory interventions that pull on four levers:

1. Changing the incentives of energy intermediaries.
Many utilities are today encouraged by regulatory structures to maximize the amount of electricity they generate — in other words to focus on expanding supply-side investment rather than improving demand management. To change this, regulators can set rates in ways that decouple utility revenue from sales growth and encourage utility companies to focus on higher productivity. Evidence from states that have introduced this type of energy efficiency program indicates that they can lead to annual savings of close to 1 percent of annual energy consumption.

2. Increasing information flows.
Consumers currently have insufficient understanding of the energy consequences of their purchases. In a promising innovation, power suppliers PG&E, Centerpoint, and Entergy have recently begun delivering automated meter information over power lines to help residential customers understand the electricity consumption of individual appliances and thereby make informed appliance choices.

3. Setting tighter standards.
Many higher-efficiency appliances currently carry premium prices that discourage purchases and slow the ability to use demand to drive down costs. For example, a room air conditioner that is 35 percent more efficient than the current standard

costs 260 percent more, an obvious disincentive even for consumers who may not understand the concept of "negative IRR." However, when new standards are implemented, economies of scale in manufacturing lead relatively quickly to the decline of high-efficiency appliance prices to levels similar to the previous prices of less efficient equipment. Tighter standards have proven to be an effective forcing mechanism towards higher efficiency. For example, beginning in the 1970s and spearheaded by tougher regulations in California, refrigerator efficiency improved in the United States by 4.4 percent per year in 1970–1985 and at a slightly slower rate of 3.4 percent annually in 1985–2000. Similar improvements occurred in insulation and there is still more potential available.

Another area in which new standards could have a major impact is in standby power consumption. This currently ranges from 20 to 60 watts, equivalent to 4 percent to 10 percent of total residential energy consumption. However, the technology is already available to reduce standby power to 1 watt. Another tool to reduce peak energy demand would be the automated turn-off of power at peak prices, which would simply require ensuring that consumers retain the capacity to overrule the turn-off if they so desire.

4. Providing financing and other incentives to energy-efficient builders.
An additional set of opportunities includes helping builders of new housing developments to finance positive return investments in energy-efficient homes or providing lower financing costs to upgrade existing stock when these assets change hands. The energy savings over time can be captured to offset the costs of providing the financing.

Transportation.
The single largest policy lever in U.S. transportation is the tightening of fuel economy standards, which would accelerate the introduction of fuel-saving technologies. Europe and Japan already plan a progressive increase in standards in 2012 and 2010 respectively. If the United States were to match these efforts, the average fuel economy of the national vehicle stock would improve by up to 5 miles per gallon by 2020, which is the equivalent of cutting U.S. demand for crude oil by up to 4 million barrels per day — i.e. a 20 percent reduction of projected oil imports in 2020. At the same time, increased standards would align the fuel economy requirements of the U.S. market closer to those prevailing in the rest of the world, so helping to level the playing field for struggling U.S. carmakers.

Industrial.

Two of the largest energy-saving opportunities are the recovery of the heat generated in the production of mechanical or electrical power and the optimization of motor-driven systems such as pumps and compressors. To encourage industrial companies to capture such opportunities, the government could undertake demonstration projects and energy audits. For example, the U.S. Department of Energy (DOE) has helped perform energy assessments in order to identify savings opportunities in specific plants. The Martinez refinery project, an energy audit performed by the DOE, showed a potential to improve energy efficiency by 12 percent with a payback in two years or less. Following Hurricane Katrina in 2005, the DOE sent teams of experts to 200 industrial plants in the United States. The teams found that 40 percent of these opportunities would recoup the initial investment within nine months and 75 percent of them within two years. Washington could also consider offering subsidies or tax credits to companies that adopt energy conservation technologies, a policy overwhelmingly supported by U.S. public opinion. Government might also opt to finance new energy conservation projects at low rates.

There are many more steps than the ones we have outlined that the United States needs to take if it is to embrace the opportunity that is available to improve the country's energy productivity. However, the building blocks that we have described at least give a sense of our preferred approach. None are particularly dramatic — and that is part of the appeal. Energy productivity is not about placing huge bets on spectacular, hard-to-attain breakthroughs — it is about a focused drive to make hundreds of incremental improvements that add up to a huge cumulative impact on reducing energy consumption.

A pragmatic demand-side program to tackle the U.S. energy challenge has too long been missing from a national debate that has been obsessed simply with securing new sources of supply. A national effort to lift U.S. energy productivity makes economic sense, enhances energy resilience, and reduces carbon emissions — all in a politically achievable way. A chance to achieve such major goals simultaneously with no downside is rare indeed. The only regret will be if the United States fails to seize the opportunity.

■-■-■————————————————————————————————————

Diana Farrell is Director of the McKinsey Global Institute (MGI), McKinsey & Company's economics research arm. MGI research priorities include sector-based productivity studies, global economic integration, the ascendance of China and India, labor markets and off shoring, capital markets, health care, global energy demand, consumer demand, and demographic shifts. Ms. Farrell was previously a McKinsey partner in the Washington, D.C. office and a leader of McKinsey's Global Financial Institutions and Global Strategy practices. Her work has appeared in academic journals, books, and on the op-ed pages of leading international publications. A frequent speaker at major U.S. and global conferences, she is the editor of an anthology series based on MGI research (Harvard Business School Press), and is the co-author of Market Unbound (Wiley & Sons, 1996). She is a member of the Bretton Woods Committee and the Pacific Council on International Policy; a trustee for the Committee for Economic Development; a board advisor to the Bay Area Economic Pulse; a member of the Bay Area Economic Forum's Research Council; and Senior Advisor to the American Assembly's Next Generation Project. Ms. Farrell has a B.A. from Wesleyan University in Economics and an M.B.A. from Harvard Business School.

Ivo Bozon is a Director in McKinsey & Company's Amsterdam office. He is the global leader of oil and gas practice of McKinsey and has been working with clients in Asia, Russia, Africa, Europe, and the U.S. He has extensive experience in working with International Majors, National Oil Companies, and host governments, as well as selected independents and oil field services providers. He has significant expertise in driving transformational change programs on a global basis in upstream and downstream as well as in selected markets in the Middle-East, Asia, and Russia. His major research interest lies in the future evolution of the oil industry in the next decade and he has been leading several knowledge investments in this arena. He is a frequent speaker and participant in the key "podia" in the oil and gas industry across the globe. Within the Firm, he is a member of a number of the core governance committees, including the shareholders committee. Before joining McKinsey, Mr. Bozon worked with Royal Dutch Shell, both in the Netherlands and in Singapore. He holds master's degrees in econometrics and economics and studied at the Indiana Business School and London Business School.

[1] Northwestern Europe includes: Belgium, France, Germany, Iceland, Ireland, Luxembourg, the Netherlands, Norway, Switzerland, and the United Kingdom.

[2] Our year-long research project examined the underlying microeconomic drivers of energy demand in each end-use segment in the United States, China, and other major demand regions; how company and consumer behavior affect energy demand; and the impact of energy policies. We then built a model of global energy demand and productivity evolution to 2020.

Part 2

FOCUSING THE ENERGY SCOPE: REGIONAL
OUTLOOKS AND A MULTITUDE OF THREATS

CHAPTER 3

Arab and Gulf Perspectives on Energy

Dennis Ross
Counselor and Distinguished Fellow,
The Washington Institute for Near East Policy

CHAPTER 4

An Energy Superpower?
Russia and Europe

Angela Stent
Director, Center for Eurasian, Russian & East European Studies,
Georgetown University

CHAPTER 5

Rising China and Rising Oil Demand:
Real and Imagined Problems
for the International System

Jeffrey A. Bader
Director, John L Thornton China Center,
The Brookings Institution

"One should not expect the Middle East to take the lead in looking for energy alternatives. The oil-rich countries of the region have little stake in creating alternatives to their main source of revenue."

— DENNIS ROSS

◼ Arab and Gulf Perspectives On Energy

Dennis Ross
Counselor and Distinguished Fellow, The Washington Institute for Near East Policy

The oil-producing countries of the Middle East know something about global markets, but have been slow to react to the challenges of global climate change. They have failed to practice conservation in any meaningful way and generally have tended to view the development of alternative energy sources as a potential threat to their economic well-being. Saudi Arabia and the smaller oil-rich Gulf states have been actively seeking to diversify their economies. Nonetheless, they remain heavily dependent on revenues from the export of oil, or in some cases natural gas, and this reality will not change any time soon. Consequently, they seek to preserve the status of oil as the most cost effective of energy sources. Will they act to make its production more environmentally friendly? There are some signs of this, but in the case of the Saudis, the most dominant of the oil-producing states in the Middle East, it seems clear that their most important preoccupation in the energy domain is to preserve the international stake in oil and not in alternatives to it.

Background
Oil-rich countries in the Middle East have understood they were part of a global oil market for the last several decades. Fluctuations in the price of oil, particularly during periods of soft demand, made them only too aware of the global nature of the market.

The attitudes toward that market and trying to affect it were heavily shaped by the circumstances of the different countries. Those who were constantly in need of revenues and felt domestic economic pressures were price hawks, pressing for higher oil prices. The irony is that these countries — mainly Iran, Libya, and Algeria — were also the ones most likely to violate their oil production quotas set by OPEC. Ironic not because they wanted to generate more revenue, but because by violating the production ceilings they often flooded soft markets with supply that drove the price of oil down.

Countries like Saudi Arabia and Kuwait, with relatively small populations and vast oil and financial reserves, historically have sought to preserve balance in the market. They have taken the long view toward the market, seeking balance in price — never going too high or too low. In other words, they want a price that would not create boom and bust cycles in demand and yet would yield enough revenue and predictability to meet their longer term needs for economic well-being and to maintain the primacy of oil as an energy resource.

Historically, Saudi Arabia and Kuwait have sacrificed their own production to prevent the price of oil from going too low. In this era of high oil prices and tight markets, we tend to forget earlier eras in which economic recessions depressed the demand for oil and produced a glut in the market. Consider Saudi and Kuwaiti behavior during the economic slowdowns of 1975 and 1981.

In 1975, the world demand for oil dropped to 41.5 million barrels a day (million b/d) from the 45 mbd it had been in 1974. To prevent a complete collapse in prices both Saudi Arabia and Kuwait voluntarily cut their production to 60 percent of their capacity. Similarly, in 1981, when demand had dropped from a peak of 52 mbd in 1979 to 47 mbd in 1981, the Saudis and Kuwaitis again cut their production to try to preserve some semblance of stability in the price. In the latter case, however, their production cuts were not sufficient to keep the price from continuing to decline. At that time, Iran, Libya, and Venezuela flouted their OPEC production quotas and actually boosted their exports. Their need for additional revenues, particularly in the case of Iran which was fighting a very costly war with Iraq, actually drove their decisions to offer discounts on sales from their surplus capacity.[1]

In this case, the Saudis were less prepared to cut their production dramatically and, at one point, their oil minister at the time, Sheikh Yamani, even threatened to retaliate by increasing Saudi production and sales to force others to observe their OPEC quotas. Two factors probably drove the Saudis to be less willing to accommodate the violation of the production quotas during this period. First, the Saudis, in effect, were subsidizing the Iranian war effort against Iraq by permitting them to sell beyond their quotas. Since the Saudis viewed Iraq as providing a Sunni bulwark against the revolutionary Shia regime in Tehran, this was not tenable. Second, to preserve oil prices, the Saudis would have had to cut their own production to below 4 mbd. Even for the Saudis this was too low and not only for budgetary reasons. For the Saudis, and others, natural gas is produced as a natural by-product of oil and is used to generate electricity for power stations, water distillation plants, and refineries. A cut in oil output that is too steep risks the sufficient availability of natural gas to meet the requirements of the national grid system.[2]

The Saudis have typically been very mindful of trying to avoid price wars in OPEC, but they have also exerted their weight when they considered it necessary to affect the behavior of the cartel. The Saudis see themselves as the swing producer and have tried to shape the market in a way that serves their long-term interests. The chart below shows why the Saudis, both in terms of production and proven reserves, are the dominant producer in the Persian Gulf area. Given their dominant role in the region as a whole, it is worth taking a closer look at the Saudi approach to energy, its development, the market, conservation, and alternative energy sources.

PERSIAN GULF COUNTRIES **PETROLEUM STATISTICS (2006)**

Country	Reserves Total Liquids Billion bbl	Capacity Total Liquids Million bbl/d	Production Total Liquids Million bbl/d	Consumption Total Liquids Million bbl/d	Net Exports Total Liquids Million bbl/d
Saudi Arabia	262.3	12.1	10.7	2.1	8.7
Iran	136.3	4.3	4.1	1.6	2.5
Iraq	115.0	2.0	2.0	0.6	1.4
Qatar	15.2	1.2	1.1	0.1	1.0
UAE	97.8	3.1	2.9	0.4	2.5
Kuwait	101.5	2.8	2.7	0.5	2.2
Bahrain	0.1	0.1	0.05	0.03	0.02
Total	**728.0**	**23.6**	**23.6**	**5.3**	**18.2**

Source: EIA Short Term Energy Outlook
Available at: http://www.eia.doe.gov/emeu/cabs/Persian_Gulf/Oil.html
Data published June, 2007

The Saudi Approach to Energy and Development

The place to start in any such discussion is to note how central oil is to the Saudi economy. Notwithstanding all their efforts over the last several decades to diversify the economy (and these efforts remain massive and ongoing), the IMF reported in 2005 that oil export revenues accounted for roughly 90 percent of total Saudi export earnings, 70 – 80 percent of state revenues, and 44 percent of the country's GDP.[3]

For the Saudis, it all starts with oil. Their oil reserves are about 262 billion barrels, or one quarter of the world's proven oil reserves. According to their Minister of Petroleum and Mineral Resources, Ali al-Naimi, there is a good possibility of "increasing these reserves by almost 200 billion barrels. In other words, the Kingdom will continue to be the largest and the most important oil producer and exporter during the 21st century, just as it has been over the past half century."[4]

For the last half century, the Saudis were leaders in trying to forge a managed approach to the global market. In a speech to the fourth annual conference of Cambridge Energy Research Associates, al-Naimi described how OPEC assumed the "stewardship" of petroleum resources in the 1960s and 1970s, and that this was necessary because it had become apparent that the low price environment of the 1950s and 1960s "was no longer sustainable." Low prices were depleting the resource base, encouraging neither conservation nor efficiency, and providing no incentive to spur development of new supply. In al-Naimi's words, things could not continue as they were because "the oil market was headed toward a so-called 'train wreck'."[5]

Higher prices, managed by OPEC, wrung "waste … out of the system" and also "encouraged the industry to bring to market previously undeveloped crude oil reserves." But those higher prices, according to al-Naimi, were not precise enough and swung back to oversupply as they helped to depress demand and economic growth internationally.[6]

Here we see the essence of the Saudi perspective: keep the oil market in balance. The prices have to be high enough to provide a sufficient return to producers but "not so high that they harm economic growth."[7] The Saudis basically have sought to preserve a balance in the market between supply and demand, with a sufficient spare capacity to ensure that the market can handle unexpected disruptions. They literally have seen themselves as the key to providing that spare capacity so they could respond and limit sharp spikes in prices.

That is the Saudi logic, and one could argue it serves the interests of all those producers who have significant oil reserves, small populations, and a strong reason to take the longer-term view of the market. The smaller states of the Arabian Peninsula that fit this category — Kuwait and Abu Dhabi of the UAE — together have close to 20 percent of the world's known oil reserves and they typically follow the Saudi lead on oil policy. In truth, the Gulf Cooperation Council (GCC) states tend to take their lead from the Saudis on oil and national security policy. (The only possible exception is Qatar. While a member of the

GCC and rich in natural gas, Qatar has only limited oil reserves and often acts independently from Saudi Arabia on its foreign policies. Nevertheless, it has not been a maverick on energy-related issues.)

Over the last several years, the Saudis have maintained their mantra of wanting to preserve a balanced pricing approach to the oil market. Interestingly, however, prices that would have once been considered likely to depress demand and the global economy have not done so. Compare the price of a barrel of crude oil at roughly $27 a barrel in March 2003 with its benchmark price of roughly $70 a barrel in the summer of 2007. The standard of what might be disruptive prices economically has changed even for the Saudis, particularly as the global economy continues to grow and has demonstrated the ability to absorb high oil prices without dampening consequences.

Does that mean the Saudis are losing their interest in price balancing that meets the needs of consumers and producers? Hardly; it means only that they have redefined their standard on pricing and what produces equilibrium. As long as the global economy and demand are growing, the Saudis will consider the market to be relatively stable at much higher prices.

That does not mean the Saudis are necessarily comfortable with the current realities. For the last several years, the Saudis increasingly have been focused on the deliverability, not availability, of oil as well as the predictability of prices over time, especially given the burgeoning interest in creating energy alternatives to oil.

Saudi Concerns

The Saudis and others in the Gulf point out that there is no shortage of available petrochemicals to be developed and produced. While they note that there was once talk of oil scarcity, particularly in the 1970s, the facts show that the world's oil reserves more than doubled from estimates of 550 billion barrels in 1970 to 1.2 trillion barrels as of 2005. That the world consumed over 800 billion barrels of oil during the intervening period shows that with new technologies for discovery and extraction — and prices that make it profitable to discover and extract — there will be no shortage of oil.[8]

So what is the problem? Deliverability — or what makes up the entire petroleum supply system, including the capacity to develop, produce, transport, refine, and deliver to consumers — is the problem. The Saudis emphasize the need for stability and predictability in pricing for reasons related to the massive capital investments that are needed with very long lead times along the whole supply chain. Should one make the decisions now for such investments in producing spare capacity and for refineries? Only if one knows with some certainty what prices are going to be. Environmental regulations and standards tend to raise the time and the cost of building refineries, and one basic bottleneck in the supply chain today is refining capacity. Here again, knowing with certainty what prices will be is essential from the standpoint of the Saudis and others. The Saudis, in particular, have argued for greater transparency on reliable oil supply and demand data. They have called for and worked with the International Energy Forum, an organization formed to improve the dialogue between producers and consumers, to improve the available data on the oil market. Oil Minister al-Naimi has gone further and said he favors efforts by consuming countries to develop energy demand roadmaps.

As important as improved data is for enhancing the predictability in the oil market, there is another factor that is clearly impinging on Saudi decision making on investments and production. The more there is talk of investing in alternatives to oil (e.g., wind, solar, sugar or switch-grass-based ethanol, clean coal, and nuclear power), the more the Saudis have indicated hesitancy to make some of the necessary investments. Note, for example, that in 2005 the Saudis were talking not only of expanding their production capacity to 12.5 million barrels a day of oil, but had also prepared a production capacity scenario that would be expanded up to 15 mbd. In the last two years, with increasing calls for alternatives to oil, the Saudis are no longer speaking about such an expansion — even though they remain committed to preserving a spare production capacity of 1.5 mbd to deal with unexpected contingencies.

Recently, the Saudis appear to have become more explicit in explaining why they are reducing their investment rate in expanding productive capacity. In May, an article in the pan-Arab newspaper, *Al-Hayat*, reported that Saudi Arabia had no intention of increasing its productive capacity beyond that which is currently planned and the reason given was "energy conservation and the expansion of alternative energy projects at the global level." [9]

The Saudis may not be fighting the issue of conservation but they certainly want to guard against massive investments in alternative energy sources that may devalue their prime resource. Their position is probably best explained again by Oil Minister Ali al Naimi when he says that, "We need to provide products to consumers at reasonable costs so that they are both economically and environmentally friendly ... more broadly speaking, I believe that we should not impoverish people in the name of a cleaner environment." [10]

It is hard to argue with that position, provided that environmental needs and the demands of climate change are taken seriously. And, it is fair to say that the Saudis, at least publicly, now appear to be more committed to doing something about reducing CO_2 emissions. Though interestingly, Saudi officials tend to favor research into carbon sequestration in no small part because they want to make the oil sector both more productive and cleaner. One Saudi official, Mohammad al-Sabban, has spoken of the investment opportunities that are being created for the private sector by the clean development mechanism (CDM) of the Kyoto Protocol. Article 12 of the protocol is designed to promote foreign investment in emissions reductions. As al-Sabban put it, "This is an additional investment channel that could be utilized in the oil sector where we have a new technology that removes carbon dioxide from petroleum and injects it into empty oil fields to enhance oil recovery."[11]

The Saudis are not alone in seeing the benefits of carbon capture storage for the oil industry. Last year Riyadh hosted an EU-OPEC roundtable on carbon dioxide capture and storage. Since then, Abu Dhabi has established a company, The Abu Dhabi Future Energy Company, which is planning a feasibility study to evaluate options for the capture of carbon dioxide emissions.

Conservation and Climate Change

Conservation has not been a hallmark of any of the states in the Middle East. On the contrary, when it comes to efficient use of energy, no region in the world ranks lower than the Middle East.[12] Electricity demand is growing everywhere, but is especially strong among all the Gulf states. Qatar, as an example, is the norm, not the exception, with its consumption of electricity projected to grow by at least 200 percent by the year 2015. Notwithstanding what appears to be runaway demand in all of the GCC states, none of these states presently has a credible policy for restraining electricity; in many of these states the consumers simply do not pay their bills.

The governments typically subsidize the electricity rates by about 90 percent, but the provision of water and electricity tend to be seen as a "central plank of the welfare service of the government;" raise the rates or actually collect on the bills and there is the risk of a political explosion. So, at this point, no one is making much of an effort to change consumption patterns. Even on those practical steps that would not risk a political backlash, such as having building codes that promote insulation or constructing buildings to reduce the impact of intense sunlight, little is being done.[13]

It should be noted that the Saudis have launched an energy conservation program, but it has largely been limited to flame discharges at refineries. According to Al-Naimi, Saudi Arabia made major investments in its Master Gas System, which is designed to prevent the release of natural gas into the atmosphere.[14] But like the other GCC states, the Saudis have done little by way of trying to alter consumption habits.

While none of the GCC states have acted seriously to change habits or behaviors on conservation, there is one country, Abu Dhabi in the UAE, that is now launching serious initiatives on climate change. As noted above, the Abu Dhabi Future Energy Company (ADFEC) is financing a feasibility study on carbon capture. But much more is being done in Abu Dhabi at least on promoting energy alternatives. The ADFEC has been mandated to manage the Masdar Initiative in Abu Dhabi, an initiative designed to "drive Abu Dhabi's ... financial resources into global solutions for cleaner, more sustainable energy."[15] Not only is the Masdar Initiative planning its own carbon-neutral city, but it is also now organizing a summit for January 2008 in which it aims to bring together the world's leading experts, innovators, scientists, and venture capitalists in the field of future energy. Among other things, the summit will focus on solar energy, carbon dioxide capture and storage, sustainable desalination, and energy efficiency in buildings and industry.

Perhaps, it should not come as a surprise that Abu Dhabi and the UAE may be more open to innovation in the area of climate change. They have been much more open to economic change internally and to reducing their dependence on oil and natural gas. The non-oil sectors of the UAE's economy now contribute roughly 70 percent of the UAE's total GDP. Dubai in the UAE has sought to become the financial hub of the Persian Gulf and now accounts for 85 percent of the Emirates' re-export trade. If conservation still lags, the openness to innovation and economic reform has made Abu Dhabi and the UAE much more willing to embrace alternative energy programs than anyone else in the region.

No one should expect the pace to be quick. With the Masdar Initiative, Abu Dhabi has ambitious plans but few alternative energy projects have yet been built. As Mario Seneviratne, the founder and secretary to the Emirates Green Building Council, says, "These technologies are not available in vast scales so we have to look at natural gas as an alternative to reduce emissions and generate electricity."[16] To his credit, Seneviratne is also pushing the Council to encourage behavioral change as well. He knows it is hard to reduce energy costs and cut emissions if you do not change the behavior of people in the buildings: "In

Dubai and the Middle East, we are trying to make people understand that their [air conditioning] thermostats should stay at 76 degrees and not 74. To go from one of the highest consumers of energy to the other extreme will require massive behavioral change." [17]

Conclusion

One should not expect the Middle East to take the lead in looking for energy alternatives. The oil-rich countries of the region have little stake in creating alternatives to their main source of revenue. The oil-poor countries like Egypt and Morocco have more of a stake but lack the resources to do much; though with the help of the World Bank, both Egypt and Morocco now have developed small power stations with solar thermal elements.

Nonetheless, there are at least two areas in which the interests of the oil-rich countries and those interested in combating global climate change converge. First, when it comes to the reduction of CO_2 emissions, it is clear that investing in carbon sequestration technologies can be a strong common interest. The oil-rich states understand very well that carbon capture storage is bound to be a part of any likely climate change treaty that emerges in 2012. From this standpoint, the oil states see carbon capture representing a way to be both good global citizens and to invest in the longer term life of the petroleum resource.

Second, both those seeking massive investments in clean energy alternatives and the oil industry need predictability of price. Given the scale of the investments and the lead times involved, no one is going to take big risks if they do not have a clear idea on price. It is hard to commit to the non-oil based alternatives if it appears that the price of oil might go down dramatically. Those who favor a gas tax do not do so only because they see it as a source of revenue for investment in alternatives; they do so to hedge against the drop in the price that consumers will pay for oil. Ironically, the oil-rich states also want to know what the price is going to be. It is no accident that the Saudi oil minister wants an energy demand roadmap — the Saudis need to know where they should be making their investments.

The key to good statecraft is marrying objectives and means and knowing how to identify common interests in a way that maximizes the means available to fulfill even ambitious goals. If we are to tackle the climate change challenge, we certainly have a stake in getting the oil-rich states to play a role. At least in the carbon capture technologies, we may well be able to generate significant investment from the oil-rich states — and that's not a bad starting point.

■-■-■——

Dennis Ross is Counselor and Ziegler Distinguished Fellow at the Washington Institute for Near East Policy. An experienced diplomat, Ambassador Ross was the United States "point man" on the Middle East peace process in both the George H. W. Bush and Clinton administrations. He was instrumental in assisting Israelis and Palestinians in reaching the 1995 Interim Agreement. He also brokered the Hebron Accord in 1997, facilitated the Israel-Jordan peace treaty, and intensively worked to bring Israel and Syria together. Prior to his service as Special Middle East Coordinator under President Clinton, Ambassador Ross served as Director of the State Department's Policy Planning Office in the first Bush administration. In that position, he played a prominent role in developing U.S. policy toward the former Soviet Union, the unification of Germany and its integration into NATO, arms control negotiations, and the development of the Gulf War coalition. President Clinton awarded him the Presidential Medal for Distinguished Federal Civilian Service, and Secretaries Baker and Albright presented him with the State Department's highest award. He is the author of *The Missing Peace: The Inside Story of the Fight for Middle East Peace* and the recently published *Statecraft and How to Restore America's Standing in the World*. Ambassador Ross graduated from UCLA in 1970. He is a member of the Aspen Strategy Group.

[1] Raino Malnes, "OPEC and the Problem of Collective Action." *Journal of Peace Research*, Vol. 20, No. 4, (December 1983), p.347.

[2] Malnes, p. 351.

[3] "Saudi Arabia," *Country Analysis Briefs*, Department of Energy, February 2007, p.1.

[4] Ali Al-Naimi Address to Arab Economic Forum, Beirut, Lebanon, May 4, 2007.

[5] Ali Al-Naimi, "A Roadmap to the Energy Future: Saudi Arabia's Perspective," Address to Cambridge Energy Research Associates (CERA), February 7, 2006.

[6] *Ibid.*

[7] *Ibid.*

[8] Ali Al-Naimi, "Shaping the Energy Future: The Role of Saudi Arabia," Address to the 18th World Petroleum Congress, September 27, 2005, printed in *Middle East Economic Survey*, Vol. XLVIII, No. 40, (October 3, 2005).

[9] Walid Khadduri, "Economic Constraints and Variables in Saudi Oil Policy," *Al-Hayat*, May 13, 2007. Even before this report appeared in which al Naimi was cited, he was hinting at this in his speeches. When one compares his speeches from 2005 to 2007, one sees that all such references to the 15 mbd figure began to be dropped in 2006.

[10] Ali Al-Naimi Address to Cambridge Energy Research Associates.

[11] Javid Hassan and Rodolfo C. Estimo, Jr., "Kingdom Supports Kyoto, but 'Green Power' Can't Meet Demand: Al-Naimi," *Arab News*, September 20, 2006.

[12] "Energy Productivity," *The Economist*, May 31, 2007. Available at: <http://www.economist.com/markets/indicators/PrinterFriendly.cfm?story_id=9261785>.

[13] For a discussion of the lack of conservation in the GCC states and the difficulty of changing attitudes and forging a policy, see: "The Strange Case of the Missing Gulf Energy Strategy," *MEED, The Middle East Business Weekly*, March 30, 2007, and "Utilities: Energy Matters," *MEED*, December 8, 2006.

[14] Hassan and Estimo, Jr.

[15] "Masdar launches the first World Future Energy Summit in Abu Dhabi," *Middle East Company News Wire*, June 3, 2007.

[16] "UAE Plans First Green City," *MEED*, May 4, 2007.

[17] *Ibid.*

"For some in the West, Russia now seeks to achieve with oil and gas what it once sought to achieve with nuclear weapons during the Cold War, namely increased political influence over Europe and over its neighbors — as well as greater profits ... traditionally, experts have referred to energy as 'soft' power, but Europeans are increasingly referring to Russia's use of energy as 'hard soft power'."

— ANGELA STENT

■ An Energy Superpower?
Russia and Europe

Angela Stent
Director, Center for Eurasian, Russian & East European Studies,
Georgetown University

O ver the past four years a new geopolitical reality has emerged: Russia's impressive economic growth, fueled by high energy prices, has enabled it to re-emerge on the world stage as a country that promotes its interests through the use of "soft" energy power, as opposed to "hard" military power. Energy has become the dominant issue in Russia's relations with Europe since January 2006, when Russia briefly interrupted gas supplies to Ukraine — through which 80% of Russian gas exports to Europe flow — because of a pricing dispute. Although gas supplies resumed almost immediately, the Ukraine cutoff became a powerful symbol of Russia's new hydrocarbon clout that has created fresh anxieties about security of supply. Europeans remain wary of the motivations of Russia's state-owned oil and gas companies. Yet, a mere six years ago, in the wake of the 9/11 attacks, Russia was viewed as a promising alternative to Middle Eastern oil and gas. President Vladimir Putin's support for the U.S. campaign to rout the Taliban in Afghanistan, the promotion of a U.S.-Russian Energy dialogue, and the Russian president's landmark speech in the German Bundestag in September 2001 where he pledged his support for western values — all these appeared to signal the beginning of a promising new age of East-West energy cooperation. What accounts for the change in Western perceptions of Russian energy policies? And is the West exaggerating the potential dangers of dependence on Russian energy, confusing actions motivated largely by commercial considerations with larger geopolitical designs?

Much of the Western disquiet over Russian energy is related to Russia's more assertive foreign policy after more than a decade of weakness and disorganization. Vladimir Putin's Russia, benefiting from record energy prices, with annual GDP growth rates of 8%, currency reserves upwards of $470 billion and a $150 billion Stabilization Fund, seeks to renegotiate what it perceives as the unequal post-Cold

War agreements of the 1990's. It believes it was forced to accept a Western agenda that ignored its interests, and oil and gas (especially gas) are its main bargaining chips. The enlarged European Union, conscious of its dependence on Russian energy that will increase over the next decade, is simultaneously trying to bind Russia more closely to a European view of energy security and also to diversify its imports away from Russia, while increasingly preoccupied with the impact of climate change — an issue which does not have a high priority for Russia. Moreover, the EU has yet to develop a unified energy policy, and Russia meanwhile enjoys the benefits of competitive energy bilateralism in its relations with Europe.

Russia's global importance as an energy provider is undisputed. It is the world's number one producer of oil and has the world's largest natural gas reserves. In 2006, it supplied 21% of the world's gas and 12% of the world's oil. It possesses up to 13% of global oil reserves, 26% of global natural gas reserves and about 20% of known coal reserves. It is the world's leading pipeline gas supplier and its number one oil exporter. More than 90% of its energy exports go to Europe.[1] As President Putin has said, "If you put together Russia's energy potential in all areas, oil, gas, and nuclear, our country is unquestionably the world's leader." Although he has denied that Russia is an energy superpower, he has repeatedly emphasized that Russia's definition of energy security differs from that of Europe.[2] While Europe focuses on security of supply, Russia emphasizes the need for security of demand via long-term contracts and also for control of transit routes and the purchase of Eurasian and European downstream assets. In this sense, gas is the real issue between Russia and Europe. For some in the West, Russia now seeks to achieve with oil and gas what it once sought to achieve with nuclear weapons during the Cold War, namely increased political influence over Europe and over its neighbors — as well as greater profits. It rejects participation in structures that it cannot control and will not become dependent on third parties for transit. Traditionally, experts have referred to energy as "soft" power, but increasingly Europeans are referring to Russia's use of energy as "hard soft power."

Moscow's energy policies toward EU-Europe and toward its neighbors should be understood in the Russian context in which political, market and economic drivers coexist and often reinforce each other. Russia is increasingly seeking to buy into the downstream sector in Europe and to perpetuate its role as the main transit route for Central Asian gas, while greatly restricting the ability of European companies to buy into its upstream. Energy relations with Europe, therefore, involve Russia's ties to a number of Eurasian states — the Central Asian states whose gas Russia purchases and re-exports to Europe, and Ukraine and Belarus, through which most of the oil and gas are transported. Issues that on the face of it are economic — particularly gas prices and transit arrangements — are often hard to distinguish from the complex political relations between Russia and the post-Soviet states. Moreover, the new EU members, who are the most dependent on Russian energy and also the most wary of the Kremlin's policies, have clashed with the "old" EU members over how to deal with Russia on energy questions.

In examining Russia's energy relations with Europe, therefore, the commercial and political are intertwined — as indeed they are in the Kremlin, where the chairmen of the major energy companies are key members of the presidential administration. In today's Russia, the office of the President combines management of the state with the custody and management of the most important state assets. Under Putin, the state has recaptured the commanding heights of the economy — symbolized by the 2003 arrest and imprisonment of Yukos CEO Mikhail Khodorkovsky and the subsequent destruction of the company and takeover of most Yukos assets by Rosneft whose Chairman, Igor Sechin, is a key Kremlin advisor. Foreign energy companies — such as Shell and TNK-BP (a 50-50 British-Russian enterprise) have been forced to sell some of their assets to Gazprom and other state-dominated companies. The Russian state has reasserted control not only over energy companies but over other raw materials and strategic industries, most of whose chairmen also have Kremlin links (see Table 1). Thus, the symbiotic relationship between political and business elites makes it difficult to determine where politics ends and commerce begins. This is especially true of the giant behemoth Gazprom, which controls 80% of Russia's gas supplies and whose chairman, Dimitri Medvedev, was elected President in March 2008. It is sometimes difficult to determine whether Gazprom's policies are those of the Kremlin or the company. The opacity of the decision-making process both within Rosneft and Gazprom and within the Kremlin has enhanced Western concerns about Russian energy policies and their implications for Europe's security because of the challenge of discerning the motivation behind Russian actions and predicting what future actions might be taken.

Russia's Energy Supplies — The Historical Record

Ironically, there is more concern in the West about the political use of energy in capitalist Russia than there was in Soviet Russia. Although the United States twice (in 1962 and 1982) imposed sanctions on its allies to prevent them from exporting the materials that helped build Soviet oil and gas pipelines during the

Cold War because it feared the political consequences of European dependence on Russian energy, the USSR enjoyed the reputation as a reliable supplier to Western Europe. It was accepted that occasional supply interruptions were related to the weather, not politics (the same was not true, however, of supplies to its Eastern Europe allies, where the USSR on multiple occasions used the energy lever for political purposes). Indeed, the first major natural gas contract that was signed between the USSR and West Germany in 1970 was an integral part of Willy Brandt's new Ostpolitik that paved the way to improved Soviet-German relations.[3] For thirty years, Soviet gas exports to Western Europe were viewed as one of the more positive aspects of the East-West relationship.

After the collapse of the USSR, energy became a major aspect of the complex relationship between Moscow and its former republics, most of which were heavily dependent on Russian energy, for which they had hitherto paid bargain prices. As Moscow adjusted to the shock of losing its empire, energy was a powerful lever both to punish countries and to move toward market prices and increase Russia's earnings. There were numerous instances of Russia cutting off energy supplies to the Baltic and CIS countries. According to one estimate, gas and oil cutoffs were more frequent under Yeltsin than under Putin, but the reasons behind these supply interruptions are often ambiguous, enabling the affected country to claim political pressure when indeed the reasons may have been largely commercial or weather-related.[4] For instance, after the Baltic states demanded that Russia withdraw its troops still stationed there, Russia instituted a four-fold increase in energy prices. When Latvia, Lithuania, and Estonia failed to pay, Russia demanded that all debts be paid off in hard currency if supplies were to continue. Similarly, Russia cut 25% of Ukraine's gas supplies in 1993, one week before the conclusion of negotiations on the Black Sea Fleet and it threatened a complete gas cutoff to Moldova in 1998 just prior to negotiations about the future of Russian troops in the breakaway region of Transnistria.

During the Yeltsin era, there was limited concern in EU-Europe about these energy supply interruptions — they were viewed as part of a difficult post-Soviet adjustment period for Russia and its neighbors. Since 2004, however, the Baltic states are now part of EU-Europe, and Ukraine and Moldova are part of the EU's Neighborhood Policy. This, combined with Russia's more assertive policies, has infused the issue of energy supplies with a new political salience. And yet both the Ukraine gas cutoff in 2006 and the oil cutoff to Belarus in 2007 can be partly explained by economics. In 2005, Ukraine dragged out negotiations on completing a new gas contract; it was paying much less than Western Europe for

Russian gas and it has historically siphoned off Russian gas when needed. The fact that Moscow was furious about Ukraine's Orange Revolution and seeking to influence the upcoming March Rada elections and that it publicly announced the gas cutoff on a cold new year's morning in 2006 without informing its customers in Western Europe created the impression of political bullying, when there was commercial justification for what it did. Similarly, Chancellor Merkel criticized Russia's oil cutoff to Belarus in January 2007 because Putin failed to inform her about it, although it was recognized that Belarus was paying much less for oil than other Russian customers. In January 2007, Russia doubled the price of gas to Azerbaijan — which announced that it would no longer purchase Russian gas. Thus, the way that Russia handles energy supplies to Europe — not its right to charge commercial market prices — has reinforced the belief that Russia views energy exports as a political lever.

For some in the West, the main issue is whether Russia will use its energy supplies in the future as a form of political pressure and whether consciousness of increasing dependence of Russian energy will affect political decision-making in European capitals and possibly prevent European governments from adopting tougher policies toward Russia, should the need arise. The debate — including some of the rhetoric emanating from the U.S. Congress — is reminiscent of that during the Cold War. An examination of Russia's current and future ability to supply Europe — and of the nature of Russian-European energy interdependence — reminds us that both energy producers and consumers have leverage — especially when it comes to natural gas.

Russian energy policies are influenced by several key factors:
- Domestic politics surrounding the Putin succession;
- Moves to buy up energy assets in the CIS countries;
- Encouraging the construction of new pipelines to Western Europe that bypass Central Europe and the Baltic states;
- Discouraging the construction of U.S.-backed pipelines from the Caspian basin to Europe that bypass Russia and pre-empting the United States or Europe from purchasing gas from Turkmenistan or Kazakhstan to fill alternative pipelines;
- Buying into as many downstream European assets as possible, while restricting European participation in Russia's upstream.

The Oil Sector

Although Russia has an official energy policy ("Russia's Energy Strategy for the Period Up to 2020"), many experts believe that there is no overall strategy and that energy policy is subordinate to broader economic goals.[5] State control over energy resources and pipelines — a theme elaborated on by Putin in his 1999 doctoral dissertation — is the centerpiece of current policies. The state-controlled energy sector is largely non-transparent, and the rules of the game change and are often only evident post-facto. Transneft holds a monopoly over oil pipelines — since Khodorkovsky's arrest, it has become clear that private oil pipelines are not permissible. From 1999 – 2004, there was an "oil miracle," largely driven by private companies developing new fields, that raised oil production by impressive rates. However, crude oil production growth declined in 2005 and 2006, and the decline will only be reversed if there is significant ($13 – 14 billion) investment in western Siberian fields over the next 7 – 10 years. It is uncertain whether these West Siberian investments will be forthcoming.[6] Since figures for oil and gas reserves are state secrets, one can only guess at what these might be. Many of these reserves are located in remote regions, far from the existing transit infrastructure, in harsh climates and terrains that would require continuing high oil prices to makes their extraction profitable and would necessitate significant foreign participation with the latest technologies — something that runs against the Kremlin's current policies.

While Europe will remain in the next decade the main market for Russian hydrocarbons, Russia's capacity for oil shipments to Europe is limited. The main pipeline — Druzhba — is in need of renovation, the Baltic pipeline has almost reached capacity, and until the Burgas-Alexandropulos oil pipeline bypassing the Turkish Straits is built, there will be no new southern transportation routes because of congestion in the Bosphorous. Thus, the main impediments to oil production growth rates in Russia are: the critical condition of existing export pipeline infrastructure; low investments in new oil fields and political restrictions on private pipelines and foreign companies' access to the Russian market. Moreover, many of Russia's oil refineries are in need of modernization and refurbishing. This illustrates a broader problem in Russia today — behind impressive growth rates and high-performing stock market lies a decaying infrastructure.[7]

The Gas Sector

Russia's gas sector remains one of the least liberalized among the larger sectors of the economy. Whereas there are a dozen private and state-owned oil companies in Russia, one giant company — Gazprom — dominates the gas sector, has a monopoly on gas exports, and remains non-transparent. It is more interested in asset acquisition — especially in Europe — than in new investment in Russian fields, and it has underinvested in upstream gas production. In the past 15 years, Gazprom has expanded its control over the supply, sale, and distribution of natural gas throughout Europe by means of joint ventures with European firms. The first major deal was a joint venture with the German firm Wintershall, which established the firm Wingas to sell Russian gas throughout Europe. In 2006, Gazprom concluded agreements to sell gas directly to end users in the U.K., France, Austria, and Italy. Asset acquisition in Europe remains a core component of Gazprom's drive for vertical integration into the European market, as does the acquisition of gas storage facilities.[8] EU regulators and the EC's Competition Directorate are increasingly scrutinizing Gazprom's growing role in European markets. The Commission, as part of its antitrust plans to "unbundle" or separate transmission system operators from competitive electricity and gas businesses, seeks to limit non-EU companies from owning controlling stakes in European energy networks. Its proposed legislation which would limit Gazprom's access to European transmission networks, has been criticized by Gazprom, and this will become a more contentious issue in the future.[9]

Export pipelines have become the focus of much of the controversy over Russia's energy relations with Europe. One Soviet legacy that continues to affect Russia's gas exports is that the system was designed to transport huge Russian volumes from East to West, but there were no pipelines for North-South transportation. At the moment, 80% of "Russian" gas — a significant amount of which comes from Turkmenistan — is exported to Europe through Ukraine. Given the political tensions with Ukraine and Central Europe, Gazprom has sought to construct pipelines that circumvent Eastern and Central Europe. Nordstream, the $ 12 billion German-Russian pipeline project chaired by former Chancellor Gerhard Schroeder, is being constructed under the Baltic Sea and will deliver gas from Russia directly to Germany, bypassing Poland and the Baltic states, much to the latters' distaste. Sweden and other affected countries have raised environmental objections to the pipeline, but its construction is underway. In June 2007, Gazprom and ENI initialed the South Stream deal which will deliver Russian gas from the Black Sea to Bulgaria and then to Italy. In January 2008, Bulgarian and Serbian companies joined the project, further consolidating Gazprom's control of the southern export corridor. In order to pre-empt Western attempts to secure Central Asian gas for pipelines that circumvent Russia, President Putin made a three-day trip to Turkmenistan in May 2007 and secured an agreement in principle between Russia, Turkmenistan, Kazakhstan, and Uzbekistan for Central Asian gas to be sold exclusively to Russia. The agreement was confirmed in December 2007. However, Turkmenistan's President Berdimukhamedov has also signed an agreement to export gas to China and is also negotiating with the United States. Without Central Asian gas imports, Russia cannot continue to meet both domestic demand and its export obligations. Both South Stream and the Central Asian deal have yet to be implemented, but they underscore that Russia, China, and the West have become rivals for Caspian gas.

While Gazprom continues to promote new export pipelines, a major question remains: will Russia be able to produce enough gas to meet both growing domestic consumption and to fill the export pipelines? Gazprom's production has only increased by 2% per year in the past four years and has so far failed to make the necessary investments in upstream gas production to meet growing domestic and foreign demand.[10] As Europe turns from oil to natural gas, its demand for gas will grow — by 2020, imported gas as a percentage of EU consumption could rise from 40% to 70% — but so far, Gazprom has delayed developing its massive but untapped Yamal and Shtockman fields. It recently signed agreements with France's Total and Norway's StatoilHydro to participate in the fields' development. The main impediments to natural gas production growth in Russia are: Gazprom's reluctance to develop new supplies for the domestic market; the need to invest substantial resources in development of new deposits; the preference given to purchasing Central Asian gas over investment in Russian production projects; the Kremlin's policy of barring foreign companies from development of the most promising fields as project operators; and the poor state of the gas infrastructure.[11] There are those in Russia who argue that, with record high energy prices, there is no rush to develop more gas fields.

Russia is pursuing a dual strategy toward the CIS transit states — build pipelines that bypass countries deemed unreliable but also seek to bind those states closer to Russia. After the destruction of Yukos, the Kremlin restored formal government control over Gazprom and has transformed it into a key political and energy-market lever of Russian foreign policy in Eurasia.[12] While supply interruptions may have received more media attention, Russia's more successful tactic in gaining influence in its neighborhood over the past 15 years has been utilizing states' debts to acquire domestic energy assets. The policy of acquiring controlling stakes in key energy companies in the CIS predates the Putin era and has strengthened Russia's hand in dealing with Europe by increasing its control over transit routes to Europe. The two companies most involved in these deals are Gazprom and RAO-UES, the electricity monopoly run by Anatoly Chubais, 13% of which is owned by Gazprom. The usual practice has been for these companies to continue to provide energy to customers despite their non-payment and eventually accept assets in state-owned energy companies as payment when the debt becomes too large.

Several of the key transit countries have sold energy assets to Gazprom. In 1998, Moldova was forced to give up significant parts of its gas supply system to Gazprom. By 2003, its debt to Gazprom topped $1.137 million. In Armenia, Russia traded $150 million of debt for a thermal and a nuclear power plant. Gazprom owns shares in gas distribution companies in all three Baltic states and controlling shares in gas pipeline operators and gas extraction companies throughout the CIS. In May 2007, after tough negotiations, Belarus bowed to Russian pressure and sold 50% of its stake in Beltransgaz, the Belarusian pipeline operator, to Russia.[13] Gazprom is currently negotiating to take greater control over Ukrainian energy assets — indeed President Yushchenko's supporters have claimed that Gazprom seeks a monopoly on the use of Ukrainian gas transport until 2030.[14] The Ukrainian case illustrates the complexity of Russia's energy relations with the post-Soviet states. Much of the gas trade with Ukraine is controlled by an opaque Ukrainian-Russian intermediary company, RosUkEnergo, whose ownership structure is not transparent, but is partly owned by Gazprom.[15] Gazprom's ownership of energy assets in the CIS and its key role in transit states, therefore, give it a major lever in dealing with the EU, as the Ukraine and Belarus cutoffs revealed.

Can the EU develop a unified energy strategy?
The EU will remain the largest market for Russian hydrocarbon exports for the foreseeable future, but so far, it lacks a unified energy policy and a consensus on ways of improving energy security. Growing concern about climate change and the need to cut back on hydrocarbon use have also complicated the debate on future energy strategies. After the Ukraine and Belarus cutoffs, Europe has focused on diversifying its energy suppliers, but Algeria and Norway are the only alternatives to Russia, and, once Nordstream is completed, dependence on Russian gas will increase. Under the German EU presidency in 2007, Foreign Minister Steinmeyer promoted closer EU links to Central Asia, and Azeri gas from the Shah Deniz field is also a possibility for Europe, but so far, these alternatives remain in the future. Increasing reliance on nuclear power is also an

alternative for some European countries, but the subject remains largely taboo in Germany. Thus Russian gas will, for the foreseeable future, remain a mainstay of European energy security.

Andris Piebalgs, the EU Energy Commissioner, has identified three major issues for the EU: sustainability, security of supply, and competition. The sustainability issue focuses on the environment and climate change, and the EU has published a common strategy to deal with this — the March 2006 Green Paper.[16] (President Putin has joked that climate change would be good for Russia, since Siberia would be a little warmer — Federation Council head Sergei Mironov has said that climate change is a non-issue.) Security of supply means focusing on new sources of energy, such as renewables, and reducing dependence on imports. In terms of competitiveness, the EU will table a strategic plan for research into new energy technologies. Piebalgs has admitted that the EU, so far, does not speak with one voice and needs to strengthen its solidarity mechanisms.[17] These have not been on display in dealing with Russia.

The EU has found it increasingly challenging to deal with Russia on energy issues. Although Russia originally signed the EU Energy Charter, it has refused to ratify it because the Charter would permit European companies to participate in Russia's upstream and in the ownership of Russia's energy transit infrastructure, both of which run counter to current Kremlin policies. Indeed, as Russia seeks to revise the post-Cold War era arrangements in Europe, it wants to change the rules of the game in its energy ties to Europe. In 2000, the EU and Russia established an Energy Dialogue, designed to integrate the Russian and European energy systems, but that dialogue has not progressed, largely because Russia has realized that individual European countries prefer to deal with Russia bilaterally — as the Nordstream and South Stream projects testify — so there is little impetus for a common EU policy. The new EU states — former members of the Warsaw Pact — have pushed for a more unified EU policy, but so far to no avail. Moreover, although Russia has signed the Kyoto Protocol, it has been unwilling to incorporate environmental issues into its dialogue with the EU. The absence of a European will to deal with Russia with one voice has enabled the Kremlin and Gazprom to pursue policies of competitive bilateralism successfully and to disregard the new EU members who favor a much tougher policy toward Russia than do the old members.

The United States and Europe have, in recent years, sought to secure oil and gas pipelines for export to Europe that bypass Russia, thereby lessening Russia's control over Europe's energy supplies. Only one of these — BP's Baku-Tibilisi-

Ceyhan — has so far come to fruition after a long and expensive construction process. Four projects are still being pursued, although it is unclear whether any of them will ever be completed: the Nabucco gas pipeline, projected to run from the Caspian to Austria; a trans-Caspian gas pipeline from Kazakhstan to Europe; a trans-Caspian oil pipeline from Kazakhstan to Europe and the Odessa-Brody-Plock oil pipeline which has been built but has no oil because Russia is blocking deliveries to Odessa from Kazakhstan. With the exception of BTC, Russia has so far outmaneuvered the West in the great pipeline game.

Kremlin officials have also warned Europe that Russia has alternatives to exporting hydrocarbons to Europe, namely the Asian market. Chinese and Indian energy demand will increase dramatically over the next decades, and Russia has begun the construction of an oil pipeline to China with a possible spur to Japan. However, the Asian alternative — while theoretically plausible — is not on the near-term horizon, given the lack of investment in developing new oil and gas resources in Russia's Far East. Europe will, therefore, remain the prime destination for Russian oil and gas for the next decade and beyond.

Growing concerns about Europe's energy dependence on a Russia that might use energy supplies for political leverage are only partly justified, however. They neglect the fact that the Russian-European energy relationship is one of interdependence, albeit an asymmetrical interdependence, where Europe is arguably more vulnerable to Russian supply disruptions than Russia is to loss of European revenues. Russia depends on its European customers for energy revenues and on the CIS transit states for their continued cooperation in the transport of Central Asian and Russian gas. Russia and Europe are dependent on each other and will remain so for the foreseeable future. The difference is that Europe appears to have few energy levers to use with Russia. After all, the government of a democratic Germany could not credibly threaten Russia to stop importing its gas if that would leave Bavarians — who receive nearly all of their energy from Russia — freezing and in the dark. In theory, Russia's leverage should also be minimal — after all, Russia needs those energy revenues — but the perception of late is that a prosperous and assertive Russia enjoying $100 (a barrel) oil could credibly interrupt supplies to Europe for a time without suffering economically. Germany's response has been to focus on creating credible alternatives such as increased gas storage should Russia try to use the energy lever; but European unease about Russian intentions persists. Thus, there is a risk of the degradation of the basic energy business relationship between Russia and Europe that can only be addressed through the introduction of bilateral confidence building measures that address the key issues of competition, security, and environmental sustainability.[18]

What Is To be Done?

Russia's attitude toward the use of energy leverage is unlikely to change in the near future. The opaque succession maneuvering has reinforced the perception that the Kremlin will continue to project the image of a strong, successful power, back after more than a decade of humiliation. In 2007, President Putin and Gazprom have successfully negotiated three new agreements which, if completed, will strengthen Russia's role as a gas exporter to Europe and make it increasingly unlikely that alternative pipelines favored by the United States and some EU members that bypass Russia will ever be constructed. Since Putin's successor appears to share his world view, one can expect Russia's current energy strategy to continue. Were energy prices to fall significantly over a sustained period, the situation might change; but with $430 billion in currency reserves, Russia has a considerable cushion.

Table 1

DEPENDENCE ON **RUSSIAN NATURAL GAS, 2004**

Former Soviet Union		
Country	Quantity Billion cubic feet	% of Domestic Consumption
Ukraine	850	35%
Belarus	698	99%
Moldova	77	100%
Georgia*	39	100%

European Union and Turkey		
Country	Quantity Billion cubic feet	% of Domestic Consumption
Germany	1,290	39%
Italy	855	31%
Turkey	506	65%
France	406	24%
Hungary	318	64%
Czech Republic	253	77%
Slovakia	226	99%
Poland	212	43%
Austria	212	69%
Finland	163	98%
Romania	138	22%
Lithuania	103	100%
Bulgaria	99	99%
Netherlands	94	6%
Greece	78	82%
Latvia	62	100%
Sweden	39	Less than 0.5%
Estonia	34	100%
Slovenia	20	52%
Belgium	7	1%

Denmark, Ireland, Portugal, Spain, and the United Kingdom import less than 500 million cubic feet of Russian natural gas annually, and this represents less than 0.5% of gas domestically consumed.

*Georgia began importing Azeri and Iranian natural gas in 2007, but this does not significantly influence its reliance on Russian natural gas.

Europe will continue to have to deal with the new Russian reality and to try and minimize the potential for Russia's energy leverage while seeking to speak with one voice. Differences between "old" and "new" Europe could also hinder the emergence of a united European energy policy. A more difficult question, however, is whether Gazprom will do what it needs to do to invest in new oil and gas fields to produce enough to meet both future European and domestic Russian demand. The current Russian system has few incentives for that, and foreign participation will be needed.

Russia has so far proved to be a reliable supplier to EU-Europe, although its behavior in the last two years has raised concerns about its longer-term intentions. It remains to be seen whether, after the 2008 succession, Russia decides to revisit its relationship to Europe and resume the drive for closer ties that Putin adopted early on, but then abandoned as Russia became disillusioned with the EU and began to reap the benefits of high energy prices. Otherwise, bilateralism will continue to predominate in Russian-European energy relations to the detriment of Europe's energy security.

The author thanks Jonathan Leif Hayes for his research assistance.

Table 2

KREMLIN AND **RUSSIAN GOVERNMENTAL OFFICIALS SERVING** IN THE **ENERGY SECTOR**

Gazprom: Board of Directors	
Dmitri Medvedev (Chairman)	President-Elect
Alexei Miller (Chairman of Management Committee)	Deputy Energy Minister
Viktor Borisovich Khristenko	Minister for Industry and Energy
Igor Khanukovich Yusufov	Ambassador at Large for the Ministry of Foreign Affairs

Table 2 (continued)

KREMLIN AND **RUSSIAN GOVERNMENTAL OFFICIALS SERVING** IN THE **ENERGY SECTOR**

Transneft: Board of Directors	
Arkady Dvorkovich	Head of President Putin's Expert Department
Viktor Borisovich Khristenko	Minister for Industry and Energy
Andrey V. Dementiev	Deputy Minister for Industry and Energy
Yuri M. Medvedev	Deputy Head of Federal Property Management Agency
Dmitriy Yu. Petrov	Advisor of President Putin's Expert Department
Denis A. Askinadze	Head of Department of the Ministry for Trade and Economic Development
Vladislav Yuryevich Surkov (formerly served as President of the Board of Directors of Transneftprodukt, a subsidiary of Transneft)	Deputy Chief of Staff of the Presidential Executive Office, Aide to the President

Rosneft: Board of Directors	
Igor Sechin (Chairman)	Chief of Staff of the Presidential Executive Office, Aide to President Putin
Kirill Androsov	Deputy Minister of Economic Development and Trade
Sergey Naryshkin	Deputy Prime Minister
Andrei Reus	Deputy Minister of Industry and Energy
Gleb Nikitin	Deputy Head of the Russian Federal Property Agency

RAO UES: Board of Directors

Alexander Voloshin (Chairman)	Former Kremlin Chief of Staff, Putin Loyalist
Anatoly Borisovich Chubais (Chairman of the Board of Management)	Former Chief of Presidential Administration, Putin Loyalist
Viktor Borisovich Khristenko	Minister for Industry and Energy
Kirill Androsov	Deputy Minister of Economic Development and Trade
Andrey V. Dementiev	Deputy Minister for Industry and Energy
Gleb Nikitin	Head of Federal Energy Agency

Zarubezhneft: Board of Directors

Andrei Reus (Chairman)	Deputy Minister of Industry and Energy
Dmitry Pamkin	Head of the Department of Foreign Financial Relations, State Debt and State Financial Assets of the Ministry of Finance
Vladimir Salamatov	Head of the Department of State Industrial Policy of the Ministry of Industry and Energy
Gleb Nikitin	Deputy Head of the Russian Agency for the Management of Federal Property
Kirill Androsov	Deputy Minister for Economic Development and Trade
Igor A. Nagorniy	Deputy Head of the Presidential Foreign Policy Directorate

Table 3

RECENTLY COMPLETED AND **PROPOSED OIL** AND **NATURAL GAS PIPELINES**
ORIGINATING IN THE **FORMER SOVIET UNION**

Oil Pipelines

COMPLETED

- *Baku-Tbilisi-Ceyhan:* The BTC connects the Azerbaijan's oil fields in the Caspian Sea with the market in Southeastern Europe. The pipeline has a capacity to deliver 1 million barrels per day, but Azerbaijan does not have the reserves to sustain such deliveries.

- *Odessa-Brody:* This pipeline was constructed to deliver Caspian oil to Central Europe. The project was finished in 2001, but due to the non-delivery of Caspian oil, the pipeline remained unused for three years until 2004. The Ukrainian government reached an agreement with the Russian government to send oil in the reverse direction, from the Druzhba pipeline to the Black Sea, where the oil was then to be shipped to other markets by tanker. The future of this pipeline remains unclear, but the current Ukrainian government has expressed its interest to utilize the pipeline for its original purpose.

PROPOSED

- *Burgas-Alexandropoulis:* This will transport Russian oil through Bulgaria to the Greek port of Alexandropoulis. Russia, Bulgaria, and Greece will participate in its construction, and Kazakhstan recently expressed its interest in joining the project. Construction on the pipeline will begin in 2008 and will be completed by 2011.

Natural Gas

COMPLETED

- *South Caucasus Pipeline (Baku-Tbilisi-Erzurum):* This pipeline connects the Shah-Deniz natural gas field in Azerbaijan with the Georgian and Turkish energy markets. This pipeline runs 692 kilometers and is parallel to the Baku-Tbilisi-Ceyhan oil pipeline. Investors anticipated extending this pipeline with the Nabucco pipeline project, which would supply markets in south-east and central Europe. However, without additional Kazakh and Turkmen gas production, the Nabucco project may not be viable.

- *Blue Stream:* This pipeline a joint ENI/Gazprom project that delivers Russian natural gas to the Turkish market. The 1213-kilometer pipeline delivers 16 billion cubic meters of natural gas annually to Ankara. Due to a pricing dispute, Russia now sees Turkey as an unreliable energy partner and the proposed South Stream gas pipeline will be a competitor to Blue Stream.

PROPOSED

- *South Stream:* ENI and Gazprom signed a Memorandum of Understanding in 2007 to construct this pipeline. In 2008, Serbia, Bulgaria, Hungary, and Austria joined the project. The pipeline will begin at the same point as Blue Stream pipeline in Beregovaya and will travel 900 kilometers, at a depth of up to 2000 meters, to the Bulgarian coast; the destination for the gas is Italy. Construction on the Russian portion of the pipeline is expected to begin over the next several months.

- *Caspian Sea Pipeline:* The Presidents of Turkmenistan, Kazakhstan, and Russia, Berdymukhammedov, Nazarbayev, and Putin, signed a provisional agreement in May, finalized in December 2007, that would deliver Turkmen gas to Europe through Kazakhstan and Russia. Planning is still in the preliminary stages, but Russian Energy Minister Viktor Khristenko claimed that it would deliver 10 billion cubic meters of gas annually by 2009–2010.

- *Nabucco:* This pipeline would connect the Erzurum gas with the markets in Bulgaria, Romania, Hungary, and Austria. Nabucco will run 3300 kilometers and will cost $5.8 billion. The pipeline's capacity would start around 4.5–9 billion cubic meters annually and could reach 30 billion cubic meters by 2020. However, the combination of the proposed Caspian Sea pipeline and South Stream may render Nabucco non-viable.

- *Trans-Caspian:* This pipeline would connect Turkmenistan's vast natural gas reserves with the South Caucasus Pipeline with the prospect of linking Kazakhstan at a future date. Iran and Russia stand strongly opposed to this project, and the legal status of the Caspian Sea pose significant obstacles in obtaining country agreements. Moreover, the recent agreement between Turkmenistan, Kazakhstan, and Russia may render this pipeline non-viable.

- *Nord Stream:* This pipeline would connect Vyborg, Russia with Griefswald, Germany directly by crossing the Baltic Sea. This project would circumvent the Baltic states and Poland who stand in strong opposition to this project citing political and environmental concerns. Russia has begun construction on its portion of the pipeline, and the project is projected to be commissioned in 2010.

■ ■ ■ ───

Angela Stent is Professor of Government and Foreign Service and Director of the Center for Eurasian, Russian, and East European Studies in the Georgetown School of Foreign Service. Prior to her current position, she served as the National Intelligence Officer for Russia and Eurasia at the National Intelligence Council. From 1999 to 2001, she served on the Policy Planning Staff of the U. S. Department of State, where she dealt with Russian and Central European affairs. She has taught at Holy Cross College, M.I.T., and the State Department's Foreign Service Institute. Dr. Stent has served as a consultant to the State Department, to the Congressional Office of Technology Assessment, to Shell Oil, and was a senior associate of Cambridge Energy Research Associates (and contributed to their publication *Russia 2010*). She is on the editorial boards of World Policy Journal, The Journal of Cold War Studies, and Internationale Politik. Dr. Stent received a Ph.D. from Harvard University.

[1] "The Evolution of the Global Energy Market," in *Russia in Global Affairs*, vol. 5, no. 1, January – March 2007, p.9.

[2] In response to the author's question about whether Russia is an energy superpower, Putin said, "I have never referred to Russia as an energy superpower. But we do have greater possibilities than almost any other country in the world." See: President of Russia, "Transcript of Meeting with Participants in the Third Meeting of the Valdai Discussion Club," <http://www.kremlin.ru/eng/speeches/2006/09/09>.

[3] For a discussion, see Angela Stent, *From Embargo to Ostpolitik: The Political Economy of West German-Soviet Relations 1955 – 1980*, (Cambridge: Cambridge University Press, 1981), ch.7.

[4] See Robert L. Larsson, *Russia's Energy Policy: Security Dimensions and Russia's Reliability as an Energy Supplier*, (Stockholm: Swedish Defense Research Agency, 2006).

[5] For an excellent discussion of these issues, see: Vladimir Milov, Leonard L Coburn, and Igor Danchenko, "Russia's Energy Policy, 1992-2005," in *Eurasian Geography and Economics* 2006, 47, no. 3, pp.285 – 313, and two dissenting responses-Matthew Sagers, "Russia's Energy Policy: A Diverging View" (*Ibid.*, pp. 314 – 320) and Anders Aslund, "Russia's Energy Policy: A Framing Comment," (*Ibid.*, pp. 321 – 328).

[6] *Long-term Outlook for Russian Oil Production to 2030*. Cambridge Energy Research Decision Brief, June, 2006.

[7] "The Evolution of the Global Energy Market," *Ibid..*, p.20.

[8] *Gazprom's New Upstream-Downstream Model*, Cambridge Energy Research Associates Private report, 2007.

[9] Financial Times, November 21, 2007.

[10] Vladimir Milov, "Russian Power and Gas Sectors: Status and Policies," (Moscow: Institute of Energy Policy, November 30, 2006).

[11] "The Evolution of the Global Energy Market," op. cit.

[12] Milov, et al; op. cit., p.300.

[13] Larsson, op. cit., pp. 224 –235.

[14] "Yushchenko Accuses Yanukovych Government of Sellout to Russia or Energy," Open Source Center Report, 21 June, 2007.

[15] For a discussion of RUE, see *Global Witness, It's a Gas: Funny Business in the Turkmen-Ukraine Gas Trade*, April 2006.

[16] EU Commission, "A European strategy for Sustainable, Competitive and Secure Energy," CON (2006) 105, Brussels, 6 March 2006.

[17] Piebalgs speech to Cambridge Energy Research Associates conference, East Meets West, Istanbul, June 2007.

[18] For further discussion of these issues, see: Securing the Future: Making Russian-European Gas Interdependence Work, (Cambridge Energy Research Associates, 2007).

"We should treat the related problems of energy inefficiency and environmental degradation in China as if they were our own problem — because in fact they are."

— JEFFREY A. BADER

Rising China and Rising Oil Demand: Real and Imagined Problems for the International System

Jeffrey A. Bader
Director, John L. Thornton China Center,
The Brookings Institution

China's emergence as a major economic, military, and political power in the last decade has produced strains in the international system. China's global trade surplus is causing imbalances in developed and developing economies and anxieties among U.S. manufacturers and in the Congress. Its military build-up has caused concern especially but not exclusively in Japan and Taiwan and prompted the U.S. Defense Department to label China as the country most likely to become a peer competitor of the United States. China's "soft power" has launched a thousand articles on the "threat" to U.S. hegemony in Southeast Asia, Africa, even Latin America. Its inadequate regulatory system has allowed a host of inferior or dangerous products ranging from pet food through tires to medicines and fish to be distributed in international markets.

Among the areas where China's impact has been felt, and where its presence has prompted interest, concerns, and misconceptions, is the international energy market. China's demand for oil moves short-term markets and long-term prices. Its demand for imported oil has skyrocketed and shows no sign of abating in the coming decades. Its national oil companies — exploring, buying, and investing — are players in a field once reserved to the major international oil companies. China's overseas oil investments have sparked warnings of possible conflict or even wars for energy resources. Its energy presence in countries like Iran, Sudan, Venezuela, and Burma has complicated U.S. policies seeking to isolate them or alter their behavior. The ubiquitousness of Chinese national oil companies' investments and contracts has raised fears that they are distorting or constraining the operation of international oil markets. The Chinese oil companies are commonly seen as soldiers marching in lockstep to the commands of a dictatorial government calling the shots. There are fears of the impact of

China's consumption of hydrocarbons on the international environment and more particularly on the global climate.

These concerns are a mixture of the reasonable and the unreasonable. Some, such as the alleged distortions of international markets, are vastly overstated. Others, such as the impact on U.S. foreign policy objectives, are real, but manageable. In the face of these challenges, U.S. policymakers need to understand and to analyze, but above all to build mechanisms of cooperation with China to deal with these developments in ways that strengthen the international system as well as protect American interests.

China's Energy Mix and Magnitude of Its Energy Growth

The rise of China has profoundly affected the global economy in the last decade, and the energy sector certainly has not been exempt. The impact on global energy has been primarily owing to:

- The pace of China's economic growth, notably industrialization and a booming automotive sector;
- Inefficiency in China's energy use;
- Increased Chinese imports of oil in its energy mix because of flat domestic reserves.

China's 10% annual GDP growth rate has contributed to a doubling of its demand for oil in the last decade, from 3.3 million barrels per day (bpd) in 1995 to 6.6 bpd in 2005. From 2000 to 2005, China was responsible for about 25% of world oil demand growth. Experts' projections of China's future oil demand vary, ranging from 10 million bpd to 13.6 million bpd for 2020. That would move China's demand from about one-third to about one-half of that projected for the U.S. The anticipated increase in China's automotive population from about 25 – 30 million today to about 120 million will contribute importantly to this growth.[1]

China's domestic oil production is expected to remain flat or increase marginally for the next 15 years. That will mean, according to expert projections, that China will need to import 6 – 11 million bpd in 2020, constituting 60 – 80% of demand requirements.[2]

Estimates are that China requires about three times as much energy for each unit of GDP growth as the United States, five times as much as the EU, and eight times as much as Japan. The reasons are multiple, including less advanced technology than utilized by developed countries. Chinese energy efficiency

ENERGY DEMAND, HISTORIC AND **RECENT FORECASTS**

(by BP's *Statistical Yearbook 2006* and the IEA's *World Energy Outlook*)

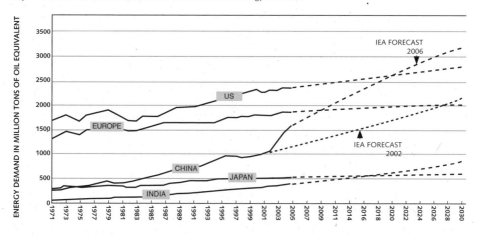

Source: BP Statistical Yearbook 2006, IEA WEO 2002, IEA WEO 2006. Excludes biomass and waste. *Europe refers to OECD Europe.

Source[3]

improved from 1980 to 2001. Since then, it has regressed, in large measure because of growth in energy-intensive industries such as steel and aluminum spurred by incentives offered by governments for investment in such sectors, and by preservation of small, inefficient, heavy production facilities by local protectionist officials.[4]

China's oil imports have gathered international attention, but its principal source of energy remains domestically mined coal, accounting for two-thirds of energy production. Most of China's coal is in the north. Most of its water is in the south. As a result, most coal leaves the mine unscrubbed, and 40% of China's railroad traffic consists of coal shipments, which are in fact substantially dirt. The consequences are clear to any visitor to urban China. China has 16 of the 20 cities with the dirtiest air in the world. The World Health Organization's (WHO) standard for healthy air is 60 – 90 micrograms of solid particulate per cubic meter. China's cities average about 400. Coal production is the principal reason why China will overtake the United States as the leading emitter of greenhouse gases perhaps as early as this year.

China is diversifying sources of energy away from coal and oil. It is making a heavy bet on nuclear energy, aiming to have up to 40 gigawatts on line by 2020. But even if this number is achieved, it would provide only 4% of China's energy consumption. China also is seeking to increase natural gas production and imports, building liquefied natural gas (LNG) terminals and discussing pipelines from Russia and Central Asia. Projections are that gas will provide 6% of China's energy mix in 2020, compared to 3 – 4% at present.

These facts and figures lead to a number of conclusions:

- China will be increasingly and heavily reliant on oil imports, especially from the Persian Gulf;
- China's oil demand will be second only to America's through 2020;
- It is in the interest of the oil-consuming world, including the United States, to help China improve energy efficiency so as to decrease its burden on world markets, and to assist China in constraining its use of dirty coal.

China's Energy Policy: Is There One?

Does China have an energy policy? It is commonly asserted that it does. Its leaders, notably Premier Wen Jiabao, have articulated goals that could be construed as a policy. The steps announced by Premier Wen last year include the goal of reducing energy consumption per unit of GDP by 20% and major pollutants discharge by 10% by 2010. He has outlined a series of measures designed to achieve these goals, including curtailing growth in energy-intensive industries, terminating tax incentives for energy-intensive production, eliminating preferential land and electricity discounts to energy-intensive industries, assessing new projects for energy consumption and environmental protection standards, and closing down

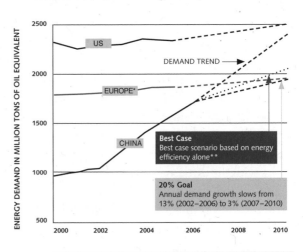

CHINA ENERGY DEMAND SCENARIOS, 2006–2010

(by BP's *Statistical Yearbook 2006*, the IEA's *World Energy Outlook* and the *Economist Intelligence Unit*)

Source: BP Statistical Yearbook 2006, IEA WEO 2006 for U.S. and Europe. Excludes biomass and waste. China economic growth projections are from EIU. *Europe refers to OECD Europe. **Best case scenario based on LBL estimates of potential demand elasticity improvements using aggressive industrial efficiency measures.

Source[6]

backward production facilities.[5] However, China in fact did not come close to achieving its energy efficiency reduction target of 4% for 2006, and instead of a 2% drop in emissions, they rose last year. Thus, it is fair to ask whether it has a coherent strategy for meeting those goals.

Compared to the United States, whose energy policy beyond a broad reliance on market structures is hard to describe, China's authoritarian system is widely presumed to provide a political environment facilitating the articulation and implementation of a coherent and coordinated, if not necessarily wise, energy policy. And indeed, if one looks at the ownership structures of the major players in China's energy sector and the sector's organization chart, one might readily assume that to be the case.

The Role of the State and the Party in Running China's Power Sector

The companies that dominate China's oil sector — China National Petroleum Corporation (CNPC), China Petroleum and Chemical Corporation (Sinopec), and China National Offshore Oil Company (CNOOC) — all are state-owned. The state's shares in the energy companies, like all shares in central state-owned companies, are held by the State Asset Supervision and Administration Commission (SASAC). Their top executives are members of, and are appointed by, the Party. Their career advancement lies in the hands of the Party's Organization Department. An executive's next move may be within the company, or it may be to a different entity entirely. For example, former president of CNPC, Zhou Yongkang, is currently Minister of Public Security. The Organization Department's control over personnel decisions inevitably creates strong incentives for the top executives to be responsive to the directives of the Party.

The same is true in the power sector. Until 2002, one state-owned power company — the State Power Corporation (SPC) — controlled all power generation and distribution in China. The SPC's monopoly was broken up in that year, and five separate state-owned power generation companies were established, dividing up the assets of the state monopoly. The five compete nationally, though the assets of each tend to be concentrated geographically. The distribution of power is controlled by a separate state-owned company, the State Grid Corporation. All nuclear-powered plants are under the supervision of the China National Nuclear Corporation, also a state-owned company.

China does not have a Ministry of Energy, though there is discussion of creating one at next year's National People's Congress. Bureaucratic supervision of the energy sector has gone through a series of organizational chart reshuffles over the last 20 years, without much impact on performance or effective supervision. At the present time, the energy sector is overseen by the powerful National Development and Reform Commission (NDRC), which is the former State Planning Commission. The NDRC, which can be thought of as a Chinese counterpart to Japan's Ministry of Economy, Trade and Industry (METI), still has the instincts of a planning agency. Managers of the energy companies frequently cycle through senior positions in the energy bureaucracy in a Chinese version of the Beltway's revolving door.

Because of general dissatisfaction with the NDRC's stewardship of energy policy, particularly during the widespread brown-outs of 2003 – 04, the leadership created two new bodies: the Energy Leading Group of top officials led by Premier Wen Jiabao, and its secretariat, the State Energy Office, which reports directly to Premier Wen. But the establishment of these two new bodies has not fundamentally weakened the role of the NDRC. The Leading Group meets infrequently and concerns itself with broad coordination. The Chairman of NDRC, Ma Kai, is a member of the Leading Group and also serves as Director of the State Energy Office, so he is well-positioned to preserve NDRC's place at the table. The State Energy Office has only about two dozen staff members and is basically a research office, not a policymaking body.

Countervailing Forces

Power in the oil and gas sector is exercised primarily by the "big three" companies, all of which operate with substantial autonomy. Since the reforms of the late 1990s that created the companies in their present form, each has been expected to operate on commercial principles — to maximize profit, to make investment and pricing decisions based on profit-seeking, and to finance investment from retained earnings and commercial loans. The two largest, CNPC and Sinopec, are behemoths, with over 1 million and 775,000 employees respectively. CNPC is ranked the 39th largest company in the world by *Fortune* magazine. Neither the NDRC nor the SASAC, to which the companies nominally report, has the ability, the expertise, the staffing, nor the mandate to dictate their decisions, and neither is involved in their day-to-day operations. The chief executives of the oil companies have the rank of Minister or Vice Minister, which further limits the ability of bureaucracies headed by officials of comparable rank to direct them.

Each of the three has set up subsidiaries containing most of the best assets of their companies. These subsidiaries are listed on overseas exchanges — Petro-China (CNPC's subsidiary) in Hong Kong and New York; Sinopec Corp. and

CNOOC Ltd. in Hong Kong, New York, and London. — The subsidiaries must meet the prudential standards of their listing exchanges and be responsive to shareholders, so they operate with a greater level of transparency and commercial integrity than their parent companies, which still hold unprofitable businesses and branches they cannot close.

The three companies all have established joint ventures with international oil companies (IOCs) — for example, Petro-China with Total/Fina/ELF; Sinopec with Exxon-Mobil; and CNOOC with BP, Shell, and Chevron. As the Chinese companies have become involved in multi-billion dollar ventures operating with the IOCs, they have increasingly adopted the work styles and professionalism of their partners.

In serving domestic markets in China, the national oil companies (NOCs) and the power companies are subject to the same market forces, and increasingly to a degree to the political forces, operating in the West. The power generation companies are free to choose the type of fuel powering the new generators they are building. Pricing factors and potential for profit drive such decisions. Domestic oil prices have crept up along with global prices over the last several years, albeit with a time lag because of Government anxiety over impact on social stability. When the NDRC has dragged its feet in adjusting retail prices, such as in 2003 when it held back diesel and gasoline price hikes, Chinese NOCs responded by exporting unrefined oil, producing long gas lines before the Government responded. A Chinese version of NIMBY (not in my backyard) has emerged as power generation companies find it increasingly complicated to build new generating capacity. NGOs, angry farmers, and occasionally an inquisitive press have resisted confiscation of property and disruption or pollution occasioned by proposed power plants, delaying or in some cases derailing proposed projects.

"Going Out:" The Chinese NOCs Abroad

In the early 1990s, when China became a net oil importer, the Chinese national oil companies began to explore overseas for new sources of crude oil. It was almost a decade later, in 2002, that Hu Jintao articulated the "going out" strategy, under which Chinese companies would henceforth be encouraged and provided incentives to find new sources of commodities and minerals abroad. The energy companies were the chief practitioners and beneficiaries of the new strategy, though they had already started "going out" well before Hu's public encouragement.

The national oil companies give lip service to the national security goals that were used to justify the Government's new strategy, but their motives have been different. They realized that potential profits from domestic reserves were shrinking because of the absence of new fields and domestic price controls, and they needed new foreign fields, bringing the opportunity to sell on international markets at international prices, to sustain profitability. Listing on international stock exchanges, they were looking to become modern, integrated oil companies that could compete with the international oil companies. They were happy to sell to international markets, not exclusively to the Chinese market.

The NOCs have substantial internal resources to finance investment. In 2006, for example, PetroChina's net profit was $19.2 billion, Sinopec Corp.'s $6.5 billion, and CNOOC Ltd.'s $4 billion.[7] But they do not have to rely exclusively on their own resources in their overseas investments. The Chinese Government frequently has provided assistance of various kinds. China Export Import Bank has reportedly offered loans at favorable interest rates for investments in Africa. China's Development Bank and its state-owned banks also have provided substantial credits. Chinese development assistance, administered by the Ministry of Commerce, is frequently tied to investments by NOCs. China's top leaders frequently visit oil-producing countries in support of NOC investments.

China's NOCs, with the encouragement of the Government, have sought to diversify geographic sources of supply, believing that the companies and the country both benefit by hedging their bets on any one particular place. The Chinese NOCs are rarely competitive in terms of technology, reputation, or ability to manage a sophisticated, large, complex energy investment with the IOCs, so they have had to find other ways to win deals. In some cases, that has meant going to places that the IOCs have avoided for political reasons, such as Sudan and Iran. In other cases, it has meant relying on Beijing's financial largesse, such as the billions of dollars in loans that China Export Import Bank has provided to Angola to rebuild its economy (including reconstruction of the Benguela Railroad, in disrepair since the civil war of the 1970s), which helped Sinopec secure exploration and production assets. In other instances, China has been willing to pay what their IOC competition deemed excessive amounts for exploitation rights.

Chinese companies also have agreed to deals involving downstream infrastructure, such as a Sinopec-Aramco-Exxon Mobil agreement to build a $3.2 billion refinery in Guangdong province to process Saudi crude, or the construction of a pipeline from Kazakhstan to western China to transport 200,000 barrels of oil per day in association with a CNPC acquisition in Kazakhstan. Each of these deals was attractive to the producer in part because of the desirability of locking in a Chinese commitment to a long-term oil purchasing agreement.

Where around the globe have the Chinese NOCs been active? CNPC's largest investments have been in Sudan and Kazakhstan. The company also has assets in Peru, Indonesia, Venezuela, Nigeria, and Chad. Sinopec signed a Memorandum of Understanding (MOU) in 2004 with Iran's national oil company that would entail Chinese control and exploitation of the Yadavaran field plus the import of 10 million tons of LNG per year for 25 years, but Iranian and Chinese officials and executives have yet to sign a final agreement. Sinopec also has investments in Angola, Nigeria, Kazakhstan, Canada (Alberta), Russia, and Colombia. CNOOC Ltd. has assets in Australia, Indonesia, Canada, and Nigeria.

Is China "Locking Up" Oil Supplies?

Particularly in the wake of CNOOC Ltd.'s unsuccessful attempt to acquire Unocal, there has been speculation about the danger of China "locking up" energy supplies around the world, to the detriment of the United States. Energy economists generally have given such arguments short shrift. The amount of oil available for equity investments around the world is only about 23% of global reserves, since the remainder is controlled by national oil companies and closed to foreign acquisition. The production of China's NOCs, like that of the IOCs, generally goes into the international marketplace, not into some private cache controlled by the Chinese Communist Party. In any event, supplies China acquires from its production in, for example, Sudan, simply displace purchases that China might otherwise make from, for example, Saudi Arabia. The impact of the foreign investments of China's NOCs is indeed positive to the extent that they put on the market supplies that otherwise would remain underground.[8]

The debate in the United States over the supposed risks posed by China's "going out" strategy and "locking up" of oil supplies has been mirrored by arguments within China. Some within the leadership, the NDRC, and the People's Liberation Army (PLA) believe that having equity shares and investments in far-flung corners of the globe provides China with "energy security" that would be in peril if they relied on the tender mercies of the IOCs. They variously contend that energy security lies in ownership of oil reserves, pipelines from Central Asia to circumvent American sea power and possible blockade, and a challenge to

American patrolling of sea lines of communication by development of a Chinese blue water navy.

On the other hand, increasing numbers of Chinese energy experts are openly questioning this line of argument. Economist Mao Yushi has written, "The only reliable method to ensure China's energy security is to maintain political neutrality when reaching agreements through business negotiations on the basis of fair competition and market mechanisms…Privatization of the natural resources sector is the best path to rationalize the distribution of resources… Undoubtedly, the U.S. deployment of aircraft carriers to safeguard the sea lanes of communication has greatly benefited Japan, Taiwan, New Zealand, as well as the Chinese mainland and India…What is the most important task facing political leaders all over the world? It is to protect and sustain the global market."[9] Another leading energy expert, Zha Daojiong, wrote, "Oil diplomacy is simply not a zero-sum game…Major oil importers shouldn't be overly threatened by the reality of America's dominant influence over the production and supply of the world oil market because suppliers and consumers of oil do not fundamentally have a confrontational relationship…." In addition, arguing against economically dubious construction of pipelines to Russia and Central Asia, Zha wrote, "Instead, awareness about China's geographical vulnerability should be turned into a powerful strategic motivation for cooperation with the powers that have the capacity to adversely affect China's oil supply security. More specifically, China must pursue confidence-building measures with the major powers in the Pacific…Pursuing land-based means of transporting foreign oil and gas to China, for the sake of minimizing the risk of maritime attack or blockade, is not only against economic logic but also risks turning fear and the psychological element of energy insecurity into self-fulfilling prophecy."[10]

Not Energy Consequences, but Foreign Policy Consequences

The more serious issues for the United States raised by China's oil investments are the foreign policy consequences where the United States is seeking to alter the behavior of particular states or to isolate them. The major such cases are Iran, Sudan, Burma, and Venezuela.

Iran is China's third largest supplier of oil. Chinese NOCs have signed MOUs for investment in Iran, principally for a 51% stake in the Yadavaran oil field which is expected to produce 300,000 bpd, but thus far the MOUs have not been turned into actual functioning operations, in part because of disputes over pricing. In the meantime, China continues to urge a "go slow" approach toward UN Security Council sanctions against Iran, agreeing along with the Russians periodically to tighten them when Iranian defiance becomes too manifest and Western impatience too strong to ignore.

Sudan is China's second largest source of foreign oil production. CNPC has a 40% stake in the Greater Nile Petroleum Operating Company (the other 60% is held by companies from India, Malaysia, and Sudan). Chinese-invested companies in Sudan produced between 200,000 and 300,000 bpd last year, but have the potential to produce upwards of 500,000 bpd in the near future. China has argued against sanctions on Khartoum and for a long time resisted UN command of control over the African Union forces in Darfur without Khartoum's blessing. Recently, China has shifted its stance toward advocacy of a UN force and has urged Khartoum to accept one.

Venezuela's oil is not well-suited for China's refineries. Chávez has pursued the Chinese with greater vigor than they have pursued him. People's Republic of China (PRC) diplomats have told Americans they respect U.S. interests in South America. China's imports from Venezuela are increasing rapidly but are still rather small overall. Whether China will eventually import the substantially larger volumes envisioned by Chávez will depend on whether China — perhaps with help from Venezuela — invests in the necessary refining capacity.

Because of the difficulty the Chinese NOCs face in competing with the IOCs in stable oil-producing states, and because of the willingness of Chinese NOCs to venture where IOCs can't or won't, it is likely we will continue to see Chinese investments in problematic states. This will create foreign policy challenges for the United States, and the answers will not always be the same. The Chinese may be prepared to slow-walk investments in countries such as Iran where the U.S. has a strong national security interest. In Sudan, where China's investments are substantial and where the U.S. national security interest is less in evidence, China will continue to invest. The United States should seek to persuade China to use its influence to affect Khartoum's behavior, rather than pursue a strategy aiming at Chinese disinvestment sure to fail. In the case of Venezuela, China is likely to keep a modest relationship on a commercial basis and not risk incurring U.S. wrath by developing a strategic relationship. In the case of Burma, China's neighbor, Beijing is unlikely to pay much attention to outside blandishments since it sees its own strategic interests as engaged more than America's.

Climate Change

China will soon become the world's leading emitter of greenhouse gases. On a per capita basis, the Chinese produce about one-third the level of residents of Organisation for Economic Co-operation and Development (OECD) countries (and about 1/5 the level of Americans). China's emissions are as high as they are primarily because of China's heavy reliance on coal, the source of 68% of its energy production, compared to the global average of 28%.

China signed the Kyoto Protocol in 2002 as a developing country, with no obligation to limit emissions. It has announced its intention to participate in negotiations on a post-2012 framework to replace Kyoto.

After years of giving global warming scant attention, Chinese scientists, and more recently officials, have begun to acknowledge both its reality and potential cost to China. The Government issued "China's National Climate Change Programme" in June 2007 laying out in detail the risks China faces in the future:

- Water scarcity in northern China, and floods in southern China;
- Increased typhoons along coastal areas;
- Increased instability in agricultural production;
- Increased potential of desertification and shrinking grassland area;
- Shrinkage of glaciers in Tibet and the rest of western China, along with drying of lakes and wetlands.[11]

Despite acknowledging the problem, Chinese leaders do not agree they should assume the kinds of responsibility for addressing it that Western countries should. They have explicitly rejected the idea that China accept mandatory emission caps, arguing that Western countries have caused the problem, that they must provide financing and technical assistance to developing countries to allow them to reduce emissions, and that China cannot accept constraints because of its level of development.

Chinese leaders advocate measures short of acceptance of mandatory caps, including promotion of renewable energy, improved energy efficiency and conservation, rationalization of energy-intensive industries such as steel and aluminum, and above all reliance on technological innovation.

Polls show that the Chinese are disturbed by the appalling levels of environmental degradation, especially in their cities. Pollution ranked as the fourth most important issue in a poll taken by a Chinese polling organization.[12]

Environmental protection has crept up the list of national priorities. Governments and developers are building environmentally friendly features into new projects, not because of concern over global warming but because the public increasingly demands it to cope with air pollution. Many of the same measures China is taking to mitigate air pollution will reduce CO_2 emissions, so national environmental policy will have a tangential positive effect on climate change.

Chinese leaders will continue to regard climate change as a low priority, even while acknowledging the reality and costs. China's other problems not only are daunting, but the solution to many of them requires rapid and continuous economic growth. China cannot sustain that kind of growth without continued heavy use of hydrocarbons. There will be marginal increases in the place of renewables in the energy mix, but coal, the only energy source in which China is richly endowed, will continue to be king.

PROJECTIONS OF **CHINESE** AND **U.S. CO$_2$ EMISSION COMPARISONS** FROM **1980–2025**

(by the IEA and the Energy Information Administration of the U.S. Department of Energy)

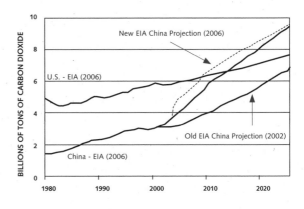

Sources: U.S. EIA *International Energy Outlook 2006*; World Resources Institute; Oak Ridge National Laboratory.

Source[13]

What Should We Do?

The array of challenges posed by China's emergence as a factor and player in international energy markets and the global environment should prompt American policy makers to respond, not with fear-mongering, but with initiatives to manage them.

The response in some instances should be public education to ensure we do not go down the wrong path. The hysteria triggered in the Congress by CNOOC's effort to acquire Unocal was an excellent example of what to avoid. Energy experts need to try to make the public and the Congress understand that oil markets function effectively to distribute resources and that the system is not threatened by occasional acquisitions or company sales, or by changing the flag flying over a field.

We need to use the strategic dialogues established by Treasury Secretary Paulson, Energy Secretary Bodman, and Deputy Secretary of State Negroponte to deal with the real foreign policy consequences of some of China's investments, e.g., vis-à-vis Iran and Sudan. At the same time, we should assure the Chinese that short of a conflict between our two countries, such as in the Taiwan Strait, the United States has no intention of constraining China's access to energy.

We should either amend the rules for membership in the International Energy Agency (IEA) or tie China as an observer firmly to its operations so that its management of its strategic petroleum reserve is firmly coordinated with that of the IEA members.

We should encourage U.S.-based IOCs to work with Chinese NOCs not only to expand sources of supply but to expose the NOCs to the operations of Western multinationals. The Chinese NOCs are climbing a steep learning curve on matters like corporate governance, transparency, and conformity with international codes of conduct. If we fall victim to politically inspired cries to isolate them, or to de-list them from U.S. exchanges, we can expect their move up the learning curve to slow considerably or even reverse.

Finally, we ought to set up trilateral funding mechanisms — United States, Japan, and China — to transfer technology and promote energy efficiency to China. China's gross inefficiency in energy production is a threat not only to the health of its people but to global prices, global health, and global climate. We should treat the related problems of energy inefficiency and environmental degradation in China as if they were our own problem — because in fact they are.

■ ■ ■
―――――――――――――――――――――――――――――――――――

Jeffrey Bader is Director of the John L. Thornton China Center and Senior Fellow at The Brookings Institution. He worked at the State Department, the National Security Council, and the United States Trade Representative's office on U.S.-China relations in a 27-year career with the U.S. government. In his last assignment, he led the U.S. delegation in completing negotiations on the accession of the People's Republic of China, and of Taiwan, into the World Trade Organization. During his career with the U.S. government, Ambassador Bader worked in Beijing, Hong Kong, and Taipei. He served as Deputy Assistant Secretary of State responsible for China, Taiwan, and Southeast Asia; as Director of Asian Affairs at the National Security Council; and as Director of the State Department's Office of Chinese Affairs. Ambassador Bader also has served several tours in Africa, culminating in his assignment as U.S. Ambassador to Namibia from 1999 to 2001. Ambassador Bader received a B.A. from Yale University and M.A. and Ph.D. degrees from Columbia University.

[1] Zhidong Li, Kokichi Ito and Ryoichi Komiyama, "Energy Demand and Supply Outlook in China for 2030 and A Northeast Asian Energy Community: The automobile strategy and nuclear power strategy of China," Institute of Energy Economics, Japan (August 2005) <http://eneken.ieej.or.jp/en/report/view_report.php>, p. 16.

[2] Erica S. Downs, "The Brookings Foreign Policy Studies Energy Security Series: China," The Brookings Institution (December 2006) <http://www3.brookings.edu/fp/research/energy/2006china.pdf>, pp. 9 and 10. The range of 6 to 11 million bpd was determined by comparing the differences between the lowest projected demand and highest projected supply; and the highest projected demand and the lowest projected supply.

[3] Daniel H. Rosen and Trevor Houser, "What Drives China's Demand for Energy (and What It Means for the Rest of Us)," in C. Fred Bergsten, Bates Gill, Nicholas R. Lardy and Derek J. Mitchell, eds., *The China Balance Sheet in 2007 and Beyond* (Center for Strategic and International Studies, Peterson Institute for International Economics, 2007), p. 29.

[4] *Ibid.* pp. 27 – 31, 33.

[5] "Report on the Work of the Government," Delivered by Wen Jiabao at the Fourth Session of the Tenth National People's Congress, March 5, 2006. <http://english.people.com.cn/200603/14/eng20060314_250512.html>.

[6] Rosen and Houser, p. 45. (Energy efficiency projections based on research by Lawrence Berkeley National Laboratory.)

[7] RMB totals taken from 2006 annual reports of CNOOC, PetroChina, and Sinopec. RMB totals converted to USD using currency rate on December 31, 2006 per currency conversion website OANDA <http://www.oanda.com/convert/classic>.

[8] See for example Daniel Yergin, "Ensuring Energy Security," *Foreign Affairs*, vol. 85, no. 2 (Mar/Apr 2006), p. 72.

[9] Mao Yushi, "Politics vs. Market," *China Security* (Summer 2006).

[10] Zha Daojiong, "Energy Interdependence," China Security (Summer 2006).

[11] National Development and Reform Commission, *China's National Climate Change Programme*, June 2007 pp. 16 – 19.

[12] Polling data from Victor Yuan, Chairman of the Horizon Research Consultancy Group.

[13] Jeff Logan, "Surging Chinese Carbon Dioxide Emissions," World Resources Institute, November, 20, 2006, <http://earthtrends.wri.org/updates/node/110>.

Part 3

THE GREAT ENERGY DEBATE: THE NATIONAL
SECURITY IMPLICATIONS OF GLOBAL
CLIMATE CHANGE AND IMPACT POTENTIAL
OF ALTERNATIVES

CHAPTER 6

Climate Change Risks in the Context of Scientific Uncertainty

Jay Gulledge
Senior Scientist and Program Manager for Science and Impacts,
Pew Center on Global Climate Change

CHAPTER 7

Sources of Alternative Energy and Energy Market Innovations

David G. Victor
Director, Program on Energy and Sustainable Development,
Stanford University

CHAPTER 8

The Age of Energy Gases:
The Importance of Natural Gas in Energy Policy

Robert A. Hefner III
Founder and Owner,
The GHK Company

"There is a window of opportunity to avoid tipping points leading to catastrophic events... It is unlikely, however, that uncertainty surrounding the timing and effects of such events will be eliminated before this window closes. Hence, if society is to act to prevent the worst impacts of climate change, it will do so in the face of uncertainty."

— JAY GULLEDGE

▪ Climate Change Risks in the Context of Scientific Uncertainty

Jay Gulledge
Senior Scientist and Program Manager for Science and Impacts,
Pew Center on Global Climate Change

This chapter reviews potential future climate change impacts and identifies key uncertainties and "trap doors" that could result in unanticipated effects and attendant coping difficulties. Because of the potential global consequences, uncertainty surrounding abrupt global sea-level rise and its implications for decisions about the future receive particular attention. This report offers no predictions. Rather, it considers possible outcomes either supported by current scientific understanding or not ruled out because of remaining uncertainty. Assessments of this type require subjective judgments, as uncertainty inherently arises from a lack of solid objective information. The author attempts to clarify his own subjective judgments, as well as those of independent and more authoritative sources. Physically deterministic *predictions* of future climate are currently impossible; this is the unavoidable backdrop of uncertainty against which policymakers must make decisions regarding global climate change.

Two Myths about Climate Change

Some misconceptions have developed from the strained efforts of scientists to communicate knowledge about global climate change to decision makers. This section addresses two broad myths that seem to have propagated through the policy community. Specific areas of miscommunication are addressed in later topical sections.

Myth 1: Future climate change will be smooth and gradual. Climate change projections, such as those produced by the Intergovernmental Panel on Climate Change (IPCC), appear smooth and gradual because they are based on climatology forecasts averaged over space and time (e.g., Figure SPM.5 in ref. (21)). Climate history, however, reveals that climate actually changes in fits and starts, with abrupt and often dramatic shifts (9). Regardless of the causes, which may include global warming (19, 26, 49), the recent dramatic increase in the frequency of North Atlantic tropical cyclones (Figure 1) offers an example of abrupt modern climate change (12, 15). The tendency of climate to change abruptly ensures that surprising changes will occur in the future, even if average climate change is projected

Figure 1

TROPICAL CYCLONE FREQUENCY IN THE **NORTH ATLANTIC**

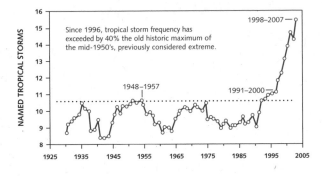

The running 10-year average of annual frequency shows a dramatic and abrupt increase above the previous maximum observed in the 1950s.
DATA: Atlantic Hurricane Database Re-analysis Project;
http://www.aoml.noaa.gov/hrd/data_sub/re_anal.html.

accurately (9). For example, a (hypothetical) projection of one meter of sea-level rise over one century might prove correct, but occur as several quick pulses with static periods between. Such a change is more difficult to adapt to than gradual change, as public works projects of the necessary scale would require several decades to complete. Surprises from abrupt climate change will likely impose a burden greater than expected based on current model projections.

Myth 2: Impacts will be moderate in industrialized countries. To plan effectively for the future, policymakers must overcome the general impression that developed nations will not be seriously affected by climate change. In fact, the United States, southern Europe, and Australia are likely to be among the most physically impacted regions. By virtue of its size and varied geography, the United States already experiences a wide range of severe climate impacts, including droughts, heatwaves, wildfires, flash floods, and hurricanes, all of which are likely to be exacerbated by climate change (20, 21). For example, the United States ranked 7th in the world for the number of people killed by tropical cyclones during the period 1980–2000 (33). Japan and Mexico trailed the United States in deaths despite having similar numbers of people exposed to tropical cyclones. Australia also suffers from severe tropical cyclones. The IPCC projects that climate change will make tropical cyclones more destructive and the most intense storms more frequent (21). The United States is also one of the most susceptible countries to sea-level rise because it has the largest number of coastal cities, as well as two agricultural deltas, near or below sea level. The United States and coastal countries of the European Union are likely to experience some of the greatest losses of coastal wetlands, which support fisheries in the North Atlantic, the Gulf of Mexico, and the Mediterranean Sea (30, 31).

In 2003, central and southern Europe experienced a prolonged heatwave that was the hottest in at least 500 years and led to the premature deaths of 50,000 people (1). The probability of such a severe heatwave occurring again has more than doubled as a result of global warming, and this type of event is projected to be common in the region by 2040 (45). According to the IPCC, the southwestern United States, southern Europe, and southern Australia will experience progressively more severe and persistent droughts and heatwaves in future decades as a result of climate change (43).

The misconception that climate change will spare the industrialized world may stem from confusion between the concepts of *impact* and *vulnerability*. Vulnerability concerns the ability of a population to withstand impacts. Because of their more advanced infrastructures and stronger economies, industrialized countries may be more capable of devoting resources to preparing for and recovering from climate change impacts than developing countries with similar exposure. Even so, the United States and other industrialized countries will be impacted severely, and the potential to devote resources does not imply that the foresight and political will required to divert resources to managing impacts would prevail. Severe climate impacts in wealthy nations portend greater resource commitments — either proactively or reactively — at home and correspondingly less foreign aid. Reduced aid would likely increase the vulnerability of developing nations, generating greater potential for migration of environmental refugees.

Overview of Projected Climate Change

Although artificially smoothed projections of average climate change can be misleading when taken at face value, they allow us to gauge how much change we should expect overall, even if we cannot yet describe the course of change precisely through space and time.

Temperature. According to the 2007 IPCC Fourth Assessment Report (AR4), "best estimates" of the increase of global average surface air temperature during the 21st century range from 1.8 to 4.0°C (3.2 to 7.2° F), depending on future man-made greenhouse gas emissions (21). Temperature over land, particularly in continental interiors, warms about twice as much as the global average, as surface temperatures rise more slowly over the ocean. High northern latitudes also warm about twice as fast as the global average. Extremes change more than averages, leading to fewer freezes, higher incidence of hot days and nights, and more heatwaves and droughts. Larger warming at high northern latitudes leads to faster thawing of permafrost, with consequent infrastructure damage (e.g., collapsed roads and buildings, coastal erosion) and feedbacks that amplify climate change (e.g., methane and CO_2 release from thawed soils) (2). Winter temperatures rise more rapidly than summer temperatures, especially at higher latitudes. Wintertime warming in the Arctic over the 21st century is projected to be three to four times greater than the global wintertime average.

As discussed below, these projections omit a number of potential positive feedbacks in the physical climate system that might amplify the warming from man-made greenhouse gases alone (34). Consequently, actual warming could be larger than the AR4 projections indicate.

Precipitation. A consistent feature of model simulations is an increase in global average precipitation as a result of increasing greenhouse gas concentrations (29). However, the geographic distribution of this change is very uneven, and some regions experience decreased precipitation. In general, areas that are currently wet (i.e. the moist tropics and high northern latitudes) become wetter, while currently dry areas (i.e. the arid and semi-arid subtropics and mid-latitude continental interiors) become drier. Consequently, areas that currently suffer from seasonal flooding and areas that currently suffer from frequent drought will see these problems intensified by climate change (21, 23). South Asia is likely to be the most impacted by increased precipitation. The southwestern United States, Mexico, Central America, the Mediterranean basin, southern Africa, and southern South America will experience decreased precipitation and more frequent drought (29, 41). Decreases in precipitation and related water resources are projected to affect several important rain-fed agricultural regions, particularly in eastern Asia, Australia, and Europe. A decrease in summer precipitation is projected for Amazonia, where the world's largest complex of wet tropical forest depends on high year-round precipitation (14).

Regional Sensitivity. A given change in regional climate, such as a degree of warming or a 10 percent change in precipitation, does not affect all regions the same way. It is useful, therefore, to examine how sensitive different regions might be to changes in temperature or precipitation. Some regions experience a stable climate, and natural and human systems have developed around this stability; in such regions, even a small change may generate significant impacts. In regions with historically large climate variability, however, larger changes are required to exceed the bounds of climate variability to which natural and human systems have adapted. Sensitivity, therefore, can be examined as a function of the degree of future climate change in a region relative to the historical climate variability in that region (4).

A climate change index describing the climate sensitivity of different regions to changes in temperature and precipitation indicates that many of the same regions that support rain-fed agriculture are among the most sensitive areas to climate change (cf. References 4 and 14). The areas most sensitive to a combination of temperature and precipitation change relative to natural variability are in tropical Central and South America, tropical and southern Africa, Southeast Asia, and the polar regions (4). The Mediterranean region, China, and the western United States show intermediate levels of sensitivity. There is a general correspondence between physical climate sensitivity and marginal agricultural lands, such as in the southwestern United States, Central America, sub-Saharan Africa, southern Europe, central Asia — including the Middle East, and eastern China. The most affected region of South America completely covers the Amazonian rainforest. Reduced productivity of this forest would have strong feedbacks on global climate by releasing carbon to the atmosphere and modifying precipitation, and would result in massive loss of biodiversity, including many economically important species (14).

Sea-level rise. Based on model estimates of thermal expansion of ocean water and ice melt from glaciers and continental ice sheets, the 2001 Third Assessment Report of the IPCC (TAR) projected that sea level would rise by 0.09–0.88 meters (0.3–2.9 feet) by the end of the 21st century (22). In 2007, the AR4 projected a narrower range of 0.18–0.59 meters (0.6–1.9 feet) (21). At the upper end of this projection, the potential contribution from future changes in ice flow from the Greenland and West Antarctic ice sheets was not included. The AR4 states that linear acceleration of ice loss (a simple extension of recently observed acceleration) could add up to 0.2 meters (0.7 feet) of sea-level rise in the 21st century, which still leaves the upper end of the AR4 projection range lower than that of the TAR, yet there is no reason to believe that sea-level rise will actually be lower than estimated by the TAR (13), which may have been conservative in the first place (36).[1] Using an alternative method, Rahmstorf (35) projected sea level to rise by 0.5−1.4 meters (1.6−4.5 feet) by the end of the 21st century. This projection was published too late to be considered in the AR4.

The current eightfold range of uncertainty for 21st century sea-level rise is significant. The lower end represents a minor nuisance overall — low-lying island nations notwithstanding — whereas the upper end portends severe global impacts.

Underestimating Climate Change

Climate scientists have long recognized the potential for climate change to be underestimated because of a lack of understanding of positive feedbacks in the climate system. A positive feedback amplifies the rate and amount of change. For instance, if warming causes frozen arctic soils (permafrost) to thaw, and the wet soil emits more greenhouse gases to the atmosphere, these extra greenhouse gases will increase the rate and degree of warming. Although there is evidence that this very feedback is already operating (50), its contribution to future warming has not been incorporated into projections. Another potential positive feedback that is inadequately incorporated into climate projections and may already be proceeding is a decrease in the absorption of atmospheric CO_2 by the oceans and land ecosystems (7). Although negative feedbacks (i.e. dampers of change) are also possible, the Earth's climate system appears to be endowed disproportionately with positive feedbacks (16).

Recent observations indicate that climate models have been underestimating the rates of change of several key aspects of climate change, including ice loss from the Greenland and Antarctic ice sheets (42), arctic sea ice decline (46), global sea-level rise (36), and global precipitation increase (51). All of these changes were predicted before they were detected, but they are occurring sooner or more rapidly than expected (13). The observed rate of temperature change is closer to model projections, but is in the upper range of those projections (36). Although there may be multiple reasons for underestimating rates of change, inadequately treated positive feedbacks are probably involved (34).

Asymmetry of Uncertainty and Elevated Risk

The typical view of uncertainty assumes that the distribution of possible outcomes takes the shape of a bell curve, with equal chance that the actual outcome could be either smaller or greater than predicted (Figure 2). However, the fact that projections have consistently underestimated the rate and magnitude of climate change suggests that the uncertainty surrounding future climate conditions is systematically biased toward more severe climate change (Figure 3). In other words, the probability that climate change will be greater than projected is higher than the probability that climate change will be smaller than projected. Hence, the risk of severe outcomes is greater than the public and policymakers generally perceive.

Figure 2

MODIFIED VIEW OF **UNCERTAINTY SURROUNDING FUTURE CLIMATE CHANGE** BASED ON **RECENT OBSERVATIONS** COMPARED TO **PROJECTIONS**

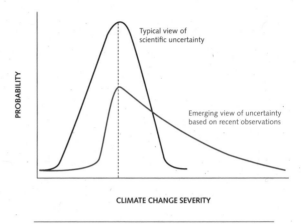

The probability distribution appears to be biased systematically toward more severe climate change. Therefore, the risk to society is probably greater than generally perceived.

Ocean physicist Stefan Rahmstorf illustrates the point in a recent research article about sea-level rise (35):

> Although a full physical understanding of sea-level rise is lacking, the uncertainty in future sea-level rise is probably larger than previously estimated. A rise of over 1 m by 2100 for strong warming scenarios cannot be ruled out... On the other hand, very low sea-level rise values as reported in the IPCC [Third Assessment Report] now appear rather implausible in the light of the observational data.

In the past year, other leading climate scientists have expressed concurring opinions (25).

Potential "Trap Doors"

The greatest risks from future climate change may lie in thresholds of warming beyond which abrupt or irreversible changes in the climate system occur.

Components of the climate system can exhibit nonlinear change, especially under the influence of positive feedbacks. In nonlinear change, a small change in one part of the system stimulates a much larger response in another part of the system. This type of relationship can drive the responding component past a threshold, or tipping point, beyond which the behavior of the system changes abruptly or irreversibly. Such nonlinearities represent potential "trap doors" that could spring open, with surprising consequences for which society is unprepared. Some examples follow.

Trap Door 1: 'Noah's Flood'. Given that ten percent of the world's population currently lives in low-lying coastal zones and that this proportion is growing (28), sea-level rise is a key consideration for society on all time scales from decades to millennia. Unfortunately, what will happen with the largest potential source of future sea-level rise — the polar ice sheets — remains unresolved and it is impossible as yet to estimate realistic upper bounds to future sea-level rise from climate models (21). Until sound physical approaches are available for this purpose, ice sheet-dominated sea-level rise in the past may be our most realistic guide to the future (32).

At the end of the last ice age, sea level rose at rates of $1-2$ meters per century for several thousand years (16). Earlier, during the warmest part of the previous interglacial period, the globe was $1-2°$ C warmer than at present for only a few centuries, yet sea level reached $4-6$ meters higher than it is now (32). We know therefore that ice sheet-dominated sea-level rise can exceed one meter per century and that rapid sea-level rise probably occurred when the Earth was only slightly warmer than it is today.

Regardless of how high the seas rise by 2100, many centuries will pass before sea level equilibrates with the warming realized this century (29). Local warming of about $3°$ C around Greenland above preindustrial level ($1-2°$ C for the global average) would eventually eliminate Greenland's ice sheet, raising sea level by six meters; contributions from Antarctica would add more (21, 32). Moreover, ancient climate records indicate that the equilibrium relationship between global temperature and global mean sea level has been stable for millions of years (Figure 3). This relationship implies that the amount of warming projected by the AR4 for the 21st century would lead eventually to a rise of 50 meters (162 feet) above current sea level (3, 52). The shapes of continents would be redrawn. Equilibration would progress over millennia, but the process would be ongoing and would likely be unstoppable through human intervention after an unknown tipping point, which could occur within the next few decades (17, 18).

Avoiding abrupt sea-level rise entails stabilizing the global temperature this century below a level that would destabilize the polar ice sheets. Warming of not more than 2° C above pre-industrial temperature (about 1.2° C above present), may provide some margin of safety in this regard, although significant uncertainty remains about such "guard rails," and some argue that even 2° C above preindustrial temperature is too risky (16, 52).

Figure 3

THE HISTORICAL EQUILIBRIUM RELATIONSHIP BETWEEN **GLOBAL SEA LEVEL CHANGE** AND **GLOBAL TEMPERATURE CHANGE** RELATIVE TO **PRESENT-DAY CLIMATE**

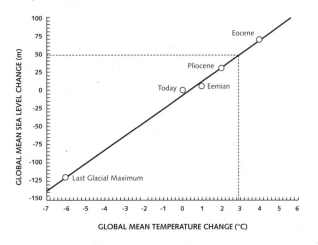

The dotted line represents the mid-point estimate of average global warming for the 21st century relative to 1990 from the AR4. Graphic adapted from (3) and (52).

Trap Door 2: 'Death by a Thousand Cuts'. Another possible trap door scenario is one in which extreme weather events familiar to a given region simply become so frequent that every year is a bad weather year. In the United States, imagine having permanent Dust Bowl-like conditions in the Southwest; widespread wildfires in both eastern and western forests; catastrophic flash floods in California, the Midwest, and the Southeast; intense nor'easters pounding New York, Philadelphia, and Boston; enormous blizzards or thunderstorm systems halting commerce every few weeks from the Rockies to New England; and major crop failures from persistent or repeated drought interlaced with frequent hailstorms and flash floods. Moreover, imagine that most of the countries of the world are experiencing similar "piling on" of extreme weather events in most years. Severe drought, floods, and heat have all plagued Europe in recent years. Asia, Africa, Australia, and Central and South America all face similar possibilities. Add to the direct physical damage of extreme weather events the consequences for health and social systems, the insurance industry, and the economy at large, and the impacts of a nonlinear increase in familiar extreme weather events around the world can mean "death by a thousand cuts."

Trap Door 3: 'The George Foreman Effect'. "Down goes Frazier! Down goes Frazier! Down goes Frazier!," was the stunned cry of Howard Cosell when George Foreman took the world heavyweight championship title from previously undefeated Joe Frazier, knocking him to the canvas six times to score the KO in less than two rounds. The devastation that "Big George" imposed on his unfortunate opponents offers a graphic analog to another potential trap door—repeated severe climatic blows of a particular type against major population centers.

What if New York, Miami, Houston, and Los Angeles were all struck by Katrina-like hurricanes within a decade? What if Europe were plagued every few years by intense, lingering heatwaves like the one that took 50,000 human lives prematurely in 2003 (1)? Urban centers of the Midwestern U.S. may face similar prospects as longer, hotter heatwaves become a regular feature of the regional climate (11). What would be the social, economic, and political consequences of repeated strikes from such enormous climatic events on major population centers around the world? Population centers have developed their infrastructures and emergency response systems under the assumption that such devastating events have very low probabilities of recurrence. Climate change could increase those probabilities dramatically. A one-meter rise in sea level could convert what is now considered a 100-year flood in New York City to a four-year flood for some parts of the city (39). Adapting to this type of change may not be possible, particularly for coastal cities where a combination of sea-level rise, intense storms, shoreline erosion, and saltwater intrusion into water supplies may combine to make many coastal cities unsustainable.

Trap Door 4: 'Breadbasket Bandits'. Most of the staple grains that feed the world are produced in a handful of grain-exporting countries, including Argentina, Canada, Russia, members of the European Union, the United States, Thailand, and Viet Nam. Between 2002 and 2004, at least five of the major grain exporters experienced decreased grain production, causing them to curtail exports in order to hold food prices down at home (6). All of these shortages were related to heat and drought. Luckily, the United States, which supplies more than a third of global grain exports, did not have serious shortfalls during this period. But with climate change, the odds of several of the largest exporters experiencing multi-year shortfalls simultaneously may increase, especially if atmospheric circulation patterns change.

Broadly, climate change is expected to intensify current precipitation patterns, offering some degree of predictability and maintaining current geographic patterns of large-scale food production. A systematic reorganization of the atmosphere that shifts rain belts away from some of the traditional breadbaskets would be a much greater threat to food supplies. Such climate regime shifts could become "breadbasket bandits."

Several rapid climate regime shifts have been observed in recent decades, including a shift in the tropical Pacific sea surface temperatures toward El Niño-like conditions, which carry important implications for the distribution of rainfall throughout much of the world (48). Global precipitation patterns could be altered dramatically by a collapse of the North Atlantic overturning circulation (also called the thermohaline circulation or the ocean conveyor), which could occur suddenly as a nonlinear response to warming, although great uncertainty prevails (40, 53). In Europe, regional cooling would shorten growing seasons, exacerbating the effect of decreased precipitation.

Although formerly less productive regions may become more suitable for crop production under such scenarios, the immense agricultural industrial complex behind world grain production would not reside in those regions initially.

Trap Door 5: 'Self Sabotage'. In 1991, the eruption of Mount Pinatubo—the largest volcanic event of the twentieth century—injected millions of tons of sulfate aerosols into the upper atmosphere (stratosphere). Those aerosols blocked the sun's rays, cooling the Earth by a few degrees. The effect lasted a couple of years, then dissipated (38). This was the first large volcanic eruption ever monitored fully by satellite, and it proved what scientists had theorized for decades—that the climate is very sensitive to the shading effect of short-lived fine particles in the atmosphere.

Intentional injection of sulfate aerosols into the stratosphere as a sunscreen to cool the Earth has been proposed as a form of climate engineering (often called geoengineering) to counter the enhanced greenhouse effect (10). It is technically feasible and would be very inexpensive in comparison to transforming the world's energy system to reduce greenhouse gas emissions (5). Therein lies the danger: if an engineered sunshade were implemented as an alternative to reducing greenhouse gases, the risk of abrupt climate change could be much higher than from unabated greenhouse gas emissions alone.

Because the atmospheric lifetime of CO_2 from fossil fuels is on the order of centuries, and one-quarter remains in the atmosphere for millennia, once sulfate injection has been used to permit continued CO_2 accumulation, the measure must be maintained indefinitely (3). If the sunscreen were allowed to dissipate, the full warming effect of the accumulated CO_2 would be realized instantly, causing abrupt warming twenty times faster than projected from greenhouse gases alone (27). The latest research also suggests that the sunshade approach could cause precipitation to decline worldwide, in lieu of the net global increase expected to accompany greenhouse warming (27, 47).

Irrespective of temperature, continued accumulation of atmospheric CO_2 would acidify the oceans, with possible catastrophic effects on marine ecosystems (37). Hence, quick-fix climate engineering approaches could cause self-inflicted abrupt climate change as well as fishery collapse. The cure could be worse than the disease.

Given that the climate is changing more quickly than anticipated and that irreversible changes may be near, many scientists agree that climate engineering options, including sunshades, should be investigated fully but cautiously. Yet many of the same scientists consider such solutions an absolute last resort because of their unpredictability and potential to harm nature and humanity (8). Economics Nobel Laureate, Thomas Schelling, put it most succinctly: "When I'm feeling pessimistic I think climate engineering may become irresistible. I'd prefer to get carbon dioxide under control." [2]

Avoiding the trap doors: Decisions

The difference between those who contested George Foreman's supremacy in the ring and those who stand to be impacted by climate change is that Foreman's opponents knew exactly what they were up against. But if scientists have consistently underestimated climate change, what is society to expect of the future? If the projections of the IPCC are conservative, perhaps they suggest the least change that society should expect, rather than the most probable.

Because the oceans warm first and equilibrate with the air later, we are already committed to some additional warming based on the current greenhouse gas concentration, as indicated by the gray line in Figure 4 (21). Generally speaking, how far beyond the gray line greenhouse gas concentrations rise, and therefore how much more the temperature rises, will be determined by decisions that society makes during the current decade. By deciding how high to allow greenhouse gas concentrations to rise, society chooses how hard to work to avoid undesirable climate change impacts, including 'trap doors' that carry especially severe consequences. One would hope that these critical decisions will be made with the best possible scientific information in mind, but science cannot identify the correct decisions. These decisions will be based on societal values, and an earnest and difficult social and philosophical debate is required to determine which impacts to avoid and the amount of effort to exert to that end.

Despite lingering uncertainties, science has begun to identify impacts that could be avoided by limiting global warming. Many types of impacts have begun already, such as damage to coral reefs and widespread rapid retreat of mountain glaciers, but the worst effects can still be avoided (Figure 5) (23, 24). There is a window of opportunity to avoid tipping points leading to catastrophic events, such as abrupt sea-level rise and large-scale shifts in the climate system. It is unlikely, however, that uncertainty surrounding the timing and effects of such events will be eliminated before this window closes. Hence, if society is to act to prevent the worst impacts of climate change, it will do so in the face of uncertainty.

Figure 4

RELATIONSHIP BETWEEN **STABILIZED ATMOSPHERIC CO₂ CONCENTRATIONS** AND **GLOBAL TEMPERATURE CHANGE** RELATIVE TO **PREINDUSTRIAL**

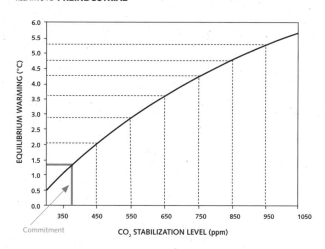

Gray lines show the temperature rise to which we are already committed based on current greenhouse gas concentrations.

Source: Plotted from data in Table SPM.5 in (24).

Figure 5

AVOIDABLE IMPACTS CHART

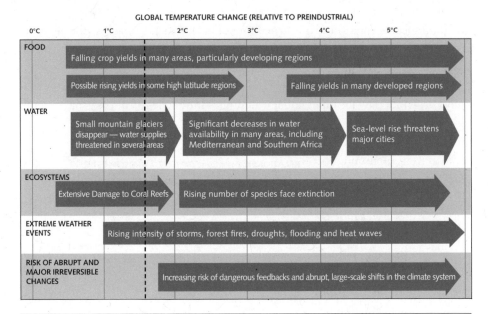

The left end of an arrow indicates at what temperature an impact begins. The dotted line represents temperature change to which we are already committed and examples of potentially avoidable impacts are shown to the right of this line.

Source: Fig. 2 in (44).

■ ■ ■ ──

Jay Gulledge is Senior Scientist and Program Manager for Science and Impacts at the Pew Center on Global Climate Change. Prior to joining the Pew Center he served on the faculties of the University of Louisville and Tulane University, where he developed courses in Global Environmental Change and Ecosystem Ecology. He is currently an adjunct faculty at the University of Wyoming and his research investigates how environmental change alters ecosystem carbon cycling. Dr. Gulledge was a Life Sciences Research Foundation Postdoctoral Fellow at Harvard University as well as a postdoctoral research associate with the Bonanza Creek (Alaska) Long-term Ecological Research Program of the National Science Foundation. He serves on the editorial board of Ecological Applications. Dr. Gulledge received a B.S. and M.S. in biology from the University of Texas at Arlington and a Ph.D. from the University of Alaska Fairbanks in biological sciences.

[1] The AR4 authors never intended for their projections to be compared directly with the TAR projections, noting that "[t]he TAR would have had similar ranges to those in [the AR4] if it had treated the uncertainties in the same way." (29) Nor did they intend to communicate the notion that future sea-level rise would be lower than previously thought, stating that current understanding of polar ice sheet changes is insufficient to "…provide a best estimate or an upper bound for sea-level rise." (29) Unfortunately, these key nuances were lost in translation to the public.

[2] Personal communication with the author by email on July 15, 2007

References

1. Alcamo, J. 2007. Europe. In M. Parry, O. Canziani, A. Allali, J. Stone, E. d. A. Alcaraz, G. Love, J.-P. v. Ypersele, and L. Kajfez-Bogataj (ed.), Climate Change 2007: Impacts, Vulnerability and Sustainability. Contribution of Working Group II to the Fourth Assessment Report of the Intergovernmental Panel on Climate Change. Cambridge University Press, United Kingdom and New York, NY, USA.

2. Anisimov, O. A., D. G. Vaughan, T. Callaghan, C. Furgal, H. Marchant, T. Prowse, H. Viljalmasson, and J. Walsh. 2007. Polar Regions. In S. Solomon, D. Qin, M. Manning, Z. Chen, M. Marquis, K. B. Averyt, M. Tignor, and H. L. Miller (ed.), Climate Change 2007: Impacts, Vulnerability and Sustainability. Contribution of Working Group II to the Fourth Assessment Report of the Intergovernmental Panel on Climate Change. Cambridge University Press, United Kingdom and New York, NY, USA.

3. Archer, D. 2007. Global Warming: Understanding the Forecast, vol. Blackwell Publishing, Malden, Massachusetts.

4. Baettig, M. B., M. Wild, and D. M. Imboden. 2007. A climate change index: Where climate change may be most prominent in the 21st century. Geophysical Research Letters 34:L01705, doi:10.1029/2006GL028159.

5. Brahic, C. 2007. Solar shield could be quick fix for global warming. New Scientist. Available at <http://environment.newscientist.com/article/dn11993-solar-shield-could-be-quick-fix-for-global-warming.html>.

6. Brown, L. R. 2005. Outgrowing the Earth: The Food Security Challenge in an Age of Falling Water Tables and Rising Temperatures, vol. Norton & Co., New York.

7. Canadell, J. G., C. L. Quéré, M. R. Raupach, C. B. Field, E. T. Buitenhuis, P. Ciais, T. J. Conway, N. P. Gillett, R. A. Houghton, and G. Marland. 2007. Contributions to accelerating atmospheric CO_2 growth from economic activity, carbon intensity, and efficiency of natural sinks. Proceedings of the National Academy of Sciences USA 104:18866–18870, doi:10.1073/pnas.0702737104.

8. Cicerone, R. J. 2006. Geoengineering: Encouraging research and overseeing implementation. Climatic Change 77:221–226, doi:10.1007/s10584-006-9102-x.

9. Committee on Abrupt Climate Change. 2002. Abrupt Climate Change: Inevitable Surprises. National Academy Press, Washington, DC.

10. Crutzen, P. J. 2006. Albedo Enhancement by Stratospheric Sulfur Injections: A Contribution to Resolve a Policy Dilemma? Climatic Change 77:211–220.

11. Ebi, K. L., and G. A. Meehl. 2007. The heat is on: climate change and heatwaves in the Midwest. Regional Impacts of Climate Change: Four Case Studies in the United States. Pew Center on Global Climate Change, Arlington, Virginia.

12. Emanuel, K. 2005. Increasing destructiveness of tropical cyclones over the past 30 years. Nature 436:686–688.

13. Engelhaupt, E. 2007. Models underestimate global warming impacts. Environmental Science & Technology 41:4488–4489.

14. Fischlin, A. 2007. Ecosystems, their properties, goods, and services. In M. Parry, O. Canziani, A. Allali, J. Stone, E. d. A. Alcaraz, G. Love, J.–P. v. Ypersele, and L. Kajfez-Bogataj (ed.), Climate Change 2007: Impacts, Vulnerability and Sustainability. Contribution of Working Group II to the Fourth Assessment Report of the Intergovernmental Panel on Climate Change. Cambridge University Press, United Kingdom and New York, NY, USA.

15. Goldenberg, S. B., C. W. Landsea, A. M. Mestas-Nunez, and W. M. Gray. 2001. The Recent Increase in Atlantic Hurricane Activity: Causes and Implications. Science 293:474–479.

16. Hansen, J., M. Sato, P. Kharecha, G. Russell, D. W. Lea, and M. Siddall. 2007. Climate change and trace gases. Philosophical Transactions of the Royal Society A:doi:10.1098/rsta.2007.2052.

17. Hansen, J. E. 2007. Scientific reticence and sea-level rise. Environmental Research Letters 2:doi:10.1088/1748-9326/2/2/024002.

18. Hansen, J. E. 2005. A slippery slope: how much global warming constitutes "dangerous anthropogenic interference"? Climatic Change 68:269–279.

19. Holland, G. J., and P. J. Webster. 2007. Heightened tropical cyclone activity in the North Atlantic: natural variability or climate trend. Proceedings of the Royal Society A (in press).

20. IPCC. 2007. Summary for Policymakers. In M. Parry, O. Canziani, A. Allali, J. Stone, E. d. A. Alcaraz, G. Love, J.–P. v. Ypersele, and L. Kajfez-Bogataj (ed.), Climate Change 2007: Impacts, Adaptation and Vulnerability. Contribution of Working Group II to the Fourth Assessment Report of the Intergovernmental Panel on Climate Change. Cambridge University Press, United Kingdom and New York, NY, USA.

21. IPCC. 2007. Summary for Policymakers. Climate Change 2007: The Physical Science Basis. Contribution of Working Group I to the Fourth Assessment Report of the Intergovernmental Panel on Climate Change. Cambridge University Press, Cambridge, United Kingdom and New York, NY, USA.

22. IPCC. 2001. Summary for Policymakers. Climate Change 2001: The Physical Science Basis. Contribution of Working Group I to the Fourth Assessment Report of the Intergovernmental Panel on Climate Change. Cambridge University Press, Cambridge, United Kingdom and New York, NY, USA.

23. IPCC. 2007. Summary for Policymakers. Climate Change 2007: Impacts, Adaptation and Vulnerability. Contribution of Working Group II to the Fourth Assessment Report of the Intergovernmental Panel on Climate Change. Cambridge University Press, United Kingdom and New York, NY, USA.

24. IPCC. 2007. Summary for Policymakers. Climate Change 2007: Mitigation of Climate Change. Contribution of Working Group III to the Fourth Assessment Report of the Intergovernmental Panel on Climate Change. Cambridge University Press, United Kingdom and New York, NY, USA.

25. Kerr, R. A. 2007. Pushing the scary side of global warming. Science 316:1412–1415.

26. Mann, M. E., and K. A. Emanuel. 2006. Atlantic hurricane trends linked to climate change. Eos: Transactions of the American Geophysical Union 87:233–244.

27. Matthews, H. D., and K. Caldeira. 2007. Transient climate-carbon simulations of planetary geoengineering. Proceedings of the National Academy of Sciences USA 104:9949–9954.

28. McGranahan, G., D. Balk, and B. Anderson. 2007. The rising tide: assessing the risks of climate change and human settlements in low elevation coastal zones. Environment & Urbanization 19:17–37.

29. Meehl, G. A., T. F. Stocker, W. D. Collins, P. Friedlingstein, A. T. Gaye, J. M. Gregory, A. Kitoh, R. Knutti, J. M. Murphy, A. Noda, S. C. B. Raper, I. G. Watterson, A. J. Weaver, and Z.-C. Zhao. 2007. Global Climate Projections. In S. Solomon, D. Qin, M. Manning, Z. Chen, M. Marquis, K. B. Averyt, M.Tignor, and H. L. Miller (ed.), Climate Change 2007: The Physical Science Basis. Contribution of Working Group I to the Fourth Assessment Report of the Intergovernmental Panel on Climate Change. Cambridge University Press, United Kingdom and New York, NY, USA.

30. Nicholls, R. J. 2004. Coastal flooding and wetland loss in the 21st century: Changes under the SRES climate and socio-economic scenarios. Global Environmental Change 14:69–86.

31. Nicholls, R. J. 2007. Coastal systems and low-lying areas. In M. Parry, O. Canziani, A. Allali, J. Stone, E. d. A. Alcaraz, G. Love, J.–P. v. Ypersele, and L. Kajfez-Bogataj (ed.), Climate Change 2007: Impacts, Vulnerability and Sustainability. Contribution of Working Group II to the Fourth Assessment Report of the Intergovernmental Panel on Climate Change. Cambridge University Press, United Kingdom and New York, NY, USA.

32. Overpeck, J. T., B. L. Otto-Bliesner, G. H. Miller, D. R. Muhs, R. B. Alley, and J. T. Kiehl. 2006. Paleoclimatic Evidence for Future Ice-Sheet Instability and Rapid Sea-Level Rise. Science 311:1747–1750.

33. Pelling, M., A. Maskrey, P. Ruiz, and L. Hall. 2004. Reducing Disaster Risk: A Challenge for Development, A Global Report. United Nations Development Programme, Bureau for Crisis Prevention and Recovery, New York. Available at <http://www.undp.org/bcpr/we_do/global_report_disaster.shtml> (accessed June 4, 2007).

34. Pittock, B. A. 2006. Are Scientists Underestimating Climate Change? Eos: Transactions of the American Geophysical Union 34:340–341.

35. Rahmstorf, S. 2007. A semi-empirical approach to projecting future sea-level rise. Science 315:368–370.

36. Rahmstorf, S., A. Cazenave, J. A. Church, J. E. Hansen, R. F. Keeling, D. E. Parker, and R. C. J. Somerville. 2007. Recent climate observations compared to projections. Science 316:709 (doi:10.1126/science.1136843).

37. Raven, J., K. Caldeira, H. Elderfield, O. Hoegh-Guldberg, P. Liss, U. Riebesell, J. Shepherd, C. Turley, and A. Watson. 2005. Ocean acidification due to increasing atmospheric carbon dioxide. The Royal Society, London.

38. Robock, A. 2000. Volcanic eruptions and climate. Reviews of Geophysics 38:191–219.

39. Rosenzweig, C., and W. D. Solecki (ed.). 2001. Climate Change and a Global City: The Potential Consequences of Climate Variability and Change—Metro East Coast (MEC), vol. Columbia Earth Institute, New York, N.Y.

40. Schlesinger, M. E., J. Yin, G. Yohe, N. G. Andronova, S. Malyshev, and B. Li. 2006. Assessing the Risk of a Collapse of the Atlantic Thermohaline Circulation. *In* H. J. Schellnhuber, W. Cramer, N. Nakicenovic, T. Wigley, and G. Yohe (ed.), Avoiding Dangerous Climate Change. Cambridge University Press, Cambridge, U.K.

41. Seager, R., M. Ting, I. Held, Y. Kushnir, J. Lu, G. Vecchi, H.-P. Huang, N. Harnik, A. Leetmaa, N.-C. Lau, C. Li, J. Velez, and N. Naik. 2007. Model Projections of an Imminent Transition to a More Arid Climate in Southwestern North America. Science 316:1181–1184.

42. Shepherd, A., and D. Wingham. 2007. Recent sea-level contributions of the Antarctic and Greenland ice sheets. Science 315:1529–1532.

43. Solomon, S., D. Qin, M. Manning, Z. Chen, M. Marquis, K. B. Averyt, M. Tignor, and H. L. Miller (ed.). 2007. Climate Change 2007: The Physical Science Basis. Contribution of Working Group I to the Fourth Assessment Report of the Intergovernmental Panel on Climate Change, vol. Cambridge University Press, United Kingdom and New York, NY, USA.

44. Stern, N. 2006. Executive Summary. The Economics of Climate Change: The Stern Review. Cambridge University Press, Cambridge, U.K.

45. Stott, P. A., D. A. Stone, and M. R. Allen. 2004. Human contribution to the European heatwave of 2003. Nature 432:610–614.

46. Stroeve, J., M. M. Holland, W. Meier, T. Scambos, and M. Serreze. 2007. Arctic sea ice decline: Faster than forecast. Geophysical Research Letters 34:L09501, doi: 10.1029/2007GL029703.

47. Trenberth, K. E., and A. Dai. 2007. Effects of Mount Pinatubo volcanic eruption on the hydrological cycle as an analog of geoengineering. Geophysical Research Letters 34:L15702, doi:10.1029/2007GL030524.

48. Trenberth, K. E., P. D. Jones, P. Ambenje, R. Bojariu, D. Easterling, A. K. Tank, D. Parker, F. Rahimzadeh, J. A. Renwick, M. Rusticucci, B. Soden, and P. Zhai. 2007. Observations: surface and atmospheric climate change. *In* S. Solomon, D. Qin, M. Manning, Z. Chen, M. Marquis, K. B. Averyt, M. Tignor, and H. L. Miller (ed.), Climate Change 2007: The Physical Science Basis. Contribution of Working Group I to the Fourth Assessment Report of the Intergovernmental Panel on Climate Change. Cambridge University Press, Cambridge, United Kingdom.

49. Trenberth, K. E., and D. J. Shea. 2006. Atlantic hurricanes and natural variability in 2005. Geophysical Research Letters 33:L12704, doi:10.1029/2006GL026894.

50. Walter, K. M., L. C. Smith, and F. S. C. III. 2007. Methane bubbling from northern lakes: present and future contributions to the global methane budget. Philosophical Transactions of the Royal Society A 365:1657–1676.

51. Wentz, F. J., L. Ricciardulli, K. Hilburn, and C. Mears. 2007. How Much More Rain Will Global Warming Bring? Science:doi:10.1126/science.1140746.

52. WGBU. 2006. The Future Oceans—Warming Up, Rising High, Turning Sour. Special Report of the German Advisory Council on Global Change, Berlin.

53. Zickfeld, K., A. Levermann, M. G. Morgan, T. Kuhlbrodt, S. Rahmstorf, and D. W. Keith. 2007. Expert judgements on the response of the Atlantic meridional overturning circulation to climate change. Climatic Change 82:235–265.

"U.S. leadership is badly needed; and perhaps once the United States has adopted its own policies in this area, it will have the credibility to create a better international system for managing the problem at hand."

— DAVID G. VICTOR

Sources of Alternative Energy and Energy Market Innovations

David G. Victor
Director, Program on Energy and Sustainable Development,
Stanford University

Slowing global warming will require very deep cuts in the emissions of carbon dioxide (CO_2) and other so-called "greenhouse gases" (GHGs). Global emissions probably need to be halved, at least, over the next half century, with even more severe reductions to follow. A full strategy to make such deep cuts in emissions requires many elements — such as emission taxes or caps, equipment regulations, and schemes for international cooperation — but most of the effort hinges on the prospects for technological progress. Deep cuts in emissions will require radical transformation of energy technologies and infrastructures — in effect, the creation of a wholly new and different world energy system.

This chapter examines two aspects of the technological challenge. First, it explores the state of the technologies themselves and argues that the most important frontiers for technological change are in low-carbon fuels for transportation and, crucially, zero-carbon schemes for generating electric power. Whether society actually realizes the great potential for carbon reduction will depend on a host of factors, such as whether regulators will allow public utilities to earn a return on investments in unproven promising technologies that are far outside what is normally considered "climate change policy." Second, it explores the larger context that will affect the pace and direction of technological change. It argues that societies will need active technology policies, which will be especially difficult in the United States where there are long-standing libertarian ideologies that discourage meddling in markets and where the track record for energy technology policy is mixed at best. It also argues that climate policy will interact with other policy goals, such as promoting energy security and global trade. There are great dangers of mismanagement if climate change is allowed to eclipse these other goals. Most notably, as the industrialized world struggles to find ways to encourage developing countries to apply advanced technology, the brandishing of trade sanctions will arise as the inevitable outcome. The consequences of that for both deployment of technology and the larger global trade regime under the World Trade Organization (WTO) could be exceptionally harmful.

Energy Technologies that Matter

Figure 1 shows the U.S. emissions of CO_2 from burning fossil fuels, the most important human cause of climate change. About two-fifths of emissions come from electricity, mainly due to the combustion of coal. About one-third of emissions come from transportation, mainly due to oil. Oil is prized in transportation for its high power density and ease of liquid storage and will be particularly difficult to unseat. Successful strategies for controlling emissions ultimately require new technologies in these two sectors — the sharp reduction in CO_2 from burning coal for electricity and the replacement of oil in transportation. While this paper focuses on examples from the United States, the general observations apply to nearly all modern economies. No major economy has escaped the iron law that economic development yields pervasive electrification, and in most of the world, coal is a backbone for electric supply. Nor has any major economy divorced itself from oil for transportation fuels; even Brazil, much in the news as the king of sugar-grown alcohol fuels, still relies on oil for about 90 percent of its liquid fuel. For both — electricity and oil-based transportation — opportunities exist to shrink the carbon footprint by using energy more efficiently as well as decarbonizing the fuel and its combustion systems.

Electric Power

There is great potential for limiting emissions from electric power by using electricity more efficiently. Societies that have invested heavily in efficiency, such as in California, have seen some success. As is the norm with efficiency measures, progress has been made through scores of initiatives rather than

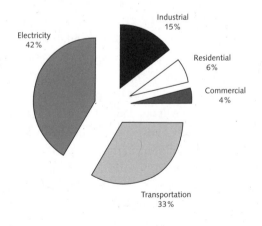

Figure 1

U.S. EMISSIONS OF **GHGs** FROM **FOSSIL FUEL COMBUSTION**

Industrial
15%

Electricity
42%

Residential
6%

Commercial
4%

Transportation
33%

Source: Table ES-3; U.S. EPA, *Inventory of U.S. Greenhouse Gas Emissions and Sinks: 1990–2005* (April)

by swinging a few sledgehammers. Appliance standards, low-power standby modes for televisions and computers, substituting fluorescent for incandescent bulbs in homes, swapping conventional bulbs for energy-sipping LED traffic lights, opening and closing of windows, and many other initiatives explain why California's per capita power consumption has been roughly flat for a few decades even though the economy has swelled. More can be done across the rest of the nation — notably in areas such as the south where historically much less has been done and where power demand is also rising rapidly. It may be possible to make somewhat deeper reductions in power consumption if the country moved more aggressively to a "smart grid" that would deploy smart meters that allow high energy home appliances such as air conditioners to schedule their operations when most convenient (and least costly) for the grid. Such systems are likely to save the most money by shifting load away from peak periods (which does not actually save energy, and in some cases, might increase emissions if they shift the electric grid away from the natural gas used for peak supply and toward higher-emitting coal plants that are used mainly for baseload power supply), but smart grids could also reduce total power consumption. Experience with smart grids is thin, and the hurdles to deployment are high and numerous. Most consumers in northern Italy already have these meters installed, and advanced trials are under way in a few U.S. markets. Utilities and their regulators are cautiously interested in these programs not simply for the efficiency but also because smart meters make meter readers redundant, potentially eliminating a large expense.

At best, such efforts will probably only slow growth in demand and will not, by themselves, allow deep cuts in emissions from the power sector. Significant reduction requires removing carbon from the power source in the first place, and with that in mind, at least four fronts look attractive. One is to switch from coal to natural gas because gas emits less than half the CO_2 for every kilowatt-hour of useful electricity. The EU has been following that strategy, in part, as its power sector grapples with the need to cut emissions and because other low-emission sources of energy are not available on the rapid 2008 – 2012 timetable for the EU to meet its Kyoto commitments. This strategy is costly, however, because gas prices have risen (with oil) in recent years and gas is one of the most expensive ways to generate baseload power. Moreover, most industrialized countries import gas in prodigious quantities, which has raised the concern that gas dependence could be harmful to the economy and undercut foreign policy. Such fears are particularly acute in Europe, which gets about one-quarter of its gas from Russia; the handwringing on gas dependence has been heightened following the decision in early 2006 by the state-owned gas giant Gazprom to cut Ukraine's subsidized gas supply which, in turn, encouraged Ukraine to briefly curtail supplies downpipe to Western Europe.

A second track is to make greater use of renewable power, notably wind which is already nearly cost effective in some markets. Deploying wind on a much larger scale will require new schemes for dispatching power that take into account the intermittency of the weather as well as smarter rules to govern access to the transmission network. Most other renewable sources of electricity are further from economic viability. Solar commands particularly strong public support yet is notably remote from economic viability. In general, solar flourishes only where there are large and generous public subsidies.

A third approach, nuclear power, is attractive because it offers very large quantities of baseload electric supply with essentially no CO_2 emissions. The combination of concerns about energy security and global climate change have combined to catalyze much discussion of a nuclear "renaissance," although the real effort to lay the foundation for that renaissance — improved reactor technologies and improved systems for regulating the construction and operation of new reactors — goes back many years. So far, that renaissance is more evident in the pages of news magazines than in real new investments, not least because the new technologies and regulations remain largely untested in commercial settings and reactor suppliers have not been willing to provide competitive cost and performance guarantees. Many of these problems are likely to be sorted out in the next few years and more than a dozen applications by companies that seek to build new reactors are likely to be filed with the U.S. Nuclear Regulatory Commission in the next year; perhaps four to six actually will be built. For the next decade or two, at best nuclear power will roughly keep its current share of power supply (about one-fifth of electricity in the United States is nuclear). However, if the renaissance proves real, that share could rise steadily from 2020 and beyond. In making projections on nuclear power, it is crucial to look at real projects and engineering capabilities rather than dreams. In Western Europe, just one new reactor is under construction (in Finland); more are on the drawing books in France and the United Kingdom but no firm orders have been placed. In Eastern Europe, there are several new reactor projects in progress, although those owe themselves more to the credible threat of using dangerous Soviet-era technologies than an epiphany about the dangers of CO_2. A surge in nuclear power is already well underway in China where one large new reactor is likely to be commissioned per year for the foreseeable future. This is driven, however, by the Chinese goal of diversifying energy sources, not cutting CO_2.

In all, the nuclear option appears to be very attractive as a way to curtail CO_2. Careful studies by the Electric Power Research Institute (EPRI) and other analysts have shown that with likely improvements in technology over the coming decade, nuclear is more attractive than most other technologies for cutting carbon. However, the extent to which a renaissance really unfolds depends not only on the technology itself but also success in re-crafting the various institutions that are essential to regulating nuclear power worldwide. The nonproliferation regime, in particular, is in tatters and a new system — probably with fuel banks and leasing arrangements, such as has been proposed by the International Atomic Energy Agency's Mohamed el Baredei and also seemingly endorsed by the Bush administration as well as many in the 2008 presidential field — will be needed. Fears of nuclear terrorism will amplify the need for a robust nonproliferation system that goes much further than regulating the behavior of governments, as has been the practice in the past. Efforts to corral "loose nukes" have slowed to an inadequate pace. The most urgent problems exist at the "front end" of the fuel cycle, but longer-term problems remain in the "back end" of waste disposal where some progress could be made through a more international approach. Engineers are fond of noting that none of the problems of waste disposal are "technical," they are all just political. As purely political problems are usually the hardest ones to manage, this does not seem a novel observation. It could be that one of the most important global warming policies is sustained progress on the nuclear fuel cycle, which is one of many reasons why it is crucial to move discussion of climate change policy outside the relatively insulated realm of environmental policy analysts into the hands of institutions whose decisions are truly pivotal.

The fourth alternative is advanced coal — in particular, coal plants that allow the CO_2 effluent to be injected underground in geological storage (GS) where it is safe from the atmosphere for the indefinite future. There are many ways to design such plants, the details of which are beyond the scope of this paper. Rather, three points are crucial about making this concept viable. First, it is essential not to pick winners. Today, most attention has been lavished on coal combustion technologies known as integrated gasification combined cycle (IGCC), but there are many other options that could prove better with experience. The trick for policy, however, is that technologies will not become commercially viable without large-scale demonstration projects, which are costly and thus require picking winners.

Coal plants are not like lab mice that can be ordered by catalog and bred in many varieties for a pittance. Second, most of the components of viable advanced coal with GS are already known individually. However, there is no experience that applies them in integrated systems at commercial scale with the reliability that makes this track comfortable for real power utilities. The utility business is extremely conservative, and lawyers are constantly reminding decision makers that if they commit to risky projects that do not work, then the shareholders will be liable for the consequences. (When utilities invested in nuclear plants in the 1970s they had "guarantees" of rate recovery that are similar to the guarantees being offered today for advanced coal plants, but many of these guarantees unraveled when the economics of these nuclear investments turned sour.) Thus, perhaps the single most important innovation for advanced coal technologies are decisions in many states — such as Colorado, Indiana, Iowa, Nevada, Ohio and a few others — to make "bombproof" promises to utilities that when they experiment with unproven but promising technologies that their investments will be deemed "prudent." For regulated utilities, the promise of prudence is essential since it allows the company to shift some of the risks to ratepayers; this, indeed, explains why the vast majority of large-scale investment in advanced coal and nuclear plants in the United States is likely to occur in regulated settings rather than in purely competitive "merchant" markets.

Third, and perhaps most crucially, applying GS at scale requires injecting a lot of effluent under ground — at pressures typical for injection, all the CO_2 from today's coal plants in the United States alone would sum to about 50 million barrels per day (mbd) of fluid. Building a system to handle such huge volumes is a daunting task. Nevertheless, humanity has some relevant experiences such as the world oil market where the infrastructure handles nearly 90 mbd of fluid, and networks that are even larger in water supply. It is worrisome, however, that there is no settled regulatory framework for injecting these fluids; nor is it even clear which regulators will handle the task. In the United States, that absence will be especially problematic because much subsurface activity is controlled by state oil and gas regulators, most of whom are unaware of the issues, potentially making it difficult for the federal government to lead the way. Fragmented property rights in some states could make it hard to gain clear title on the pore space needed to inject CO_2. If the pollution includes contaminants, which is likely since coal is hardly the cleanest of primary fuels, then the Environmental Protection Agency (EPA) will overlay its own regulatory program that is yet to be adjusted for application to large-scale CO_2 injection. Existing laws governing subsurface injection are probably adequate to ensuring operational safety as CO_2 is pumped underground because oil and gas operations inject similar fluids with similar risks, but nobody knows who will assume long-term liability and stewardship that will stretch on indefinitely. None of this is beyond the realm of technical solution, but many pieces must align for this option to be viable. Moreover, public opinion on this technology is ill-formed and could turn against it with well-publicized early missteps.

The single greatest danger in carbon regulation is irrational exuberance about rates of change in the electric power sector. It is fashionable to embrace a "field of dreams" approach to power regulation — that is, government should just set rules to regulate the effluent and the power companies will find a way. For CO_2, especially if tight rules are best achieved with large new capital investments in advanced coal and nuclear, that approach can be dangerous because real rates of change are slow, especially given the need to build new regulatory systems alongside new technologies. The power industry will cope if it cannot keep pace by building gas-fired power plants which are generally easy to site and quick to build. The implications for gas and power prices, however, could be quite unfavorable. Regulatory uncertainties around CO_2 and a host of other issues could lead the power industry to build a lot more gas-fired units than most of the optimizing models suggest.

Transportation

As with electric power, there are many ways to make transportation more efficient. Nobody really knows how much more efficient vehicles can be made without adverse consequences in performance and safety. The National Research Council, in a consensus study released in 2001, suggested that over one product cycle (about a decade), U.S. automobile efficiency could be roughly doubled; other analysts think the figure is higher. At this writing, Congress is scrutinizing rules that would be more modest, which it might still abandon if they become politically too toxic. Fuel economy regulations, similar to the U.S. tax code, are replete with loopholes that degrade their effectiveness, such as the distinction between cars and "trucks" (which favors the latter) as well as the bogus credit for manufacturers of "flex-fuel" vehicles that can run on nearly pure ethanol even though only a small fraction of those units ever get a sip of ethanol during their lifetime. Since there is so much to be done, it seems that the most cost-effective way to cut oil consumption — and CO_2 from transportation — will be found in efficiency for some time.

In addition to progress on passenger transport, there are great potentials to improve efficiency in freight transportation and jet travel. In general, however, those activities tend to operate already at the margin of what is cost-effective because freight haulers and airlines are large fuel users managed by professionals who keep a constant eye on the bottom line. Thus a whole generation of ultra-efficient aircraft — such as the Boeing 787 — along with new engines are coming into service, accelerated by the spike in fuel costs. Jet travel should be watched especially carefully because all societies shift transportation services away from slow modes (like buses and cars) toward faster systems (notably aircraft but also high speed trains where they are available) as incomes rise. Similarly, small private and semi-private aircraft are likely to become more prevalent as incomes rise.

While there is much potential for improvement through efficiency, making considerable cuts in carbon from liquid fuels in transportation will require removing the carbon from the fuel itself. Two tracks are being followed — one involves shifting from oil to liquid biofuels, and the other envisions a shift from liquid fuels altogether. On the biofuels track, investors are traveling three routes. One is conventional biofuels. This involves growing conventional crops and turning them into alcohol through fermentation, a process known well to distillers and college students worldwide. The main biofuel crop in the United States today is corn, which offers only modest potential to replace oil. The acreage that can be devoted to corn is limited, as is the political tolerance for the impact on food prices. The corn plant itself is biologically inefficient. As a strategy for cutting carbon, the corn option is nearly useless because nearly as much carbon is emitted during processing (which requires heat and thus usually the burning of fossil fuels, including coal in some instances) as is absorbed through photosynthesis during growing.[1] All of these flaws are widely known. They are tolerated, to an extent, because America's corn alcohol program is not an energy program. Instead, it is the product of extremely well-organized special interest groups in agribusiness. Sugar, as in Brazil, offers a better avenue for making conventional biofuels because the sugar plant is biologically more efficient in producing fermentable material. (And thus, the U.S. corn lobby keeps a stiff tariff in place to discourage sugar competitors.)

A second alternative involves biological processes that use the whole plant — including the stalks and other woody cellulose. Most plants devote most of their effort to producing cellulosic biomass, but with conventional technologies that material is hard to convert into combustible fuel. A wide array of "cellulosic" ethanol technologies promise to fix this problem, but none is proven commercially yet. Private investment in this area is massive and growing — spurred, in part, by the promise of creating a rival for costly oil and in part by the large government incentives on offer for biofuels. A third and even more exotic route to biofuels involves engineering new microorganisms that, on their own, can synthesize combustible fuels that, depending on a wide array of factors, could help cut carbon and dependence on oil. In practice, the second and third avenues are deeply intertwined since much of the promise for cellulosic ethanol also involves genetic engineering.

Biofuels raise difficult issues for policy because they require government to play a sophisticated role, especially in light of the rapidly-rising investment by the private sector. At this writing, government policy is probably playing its most constructive role in creating an assured market for biofuels (in the form of fuel mandates) rather than through direct R&D funding, although government funded basic R&D in plant biology and microbiology is an important foundation for some of the applied biofuels research such as in genetic engineering. It may be hard for government to ensure that all biofuels compete on a level playing field if the agribusiness lobby that has been so effective at promoting conventional biofuels learns that other options are more cost-effective. The lobby of farmers and agribusiness will discover that most of the value added in advanced fuels comes from the proprietary enzymes and other intellectual property, not from the growing and handling of crops themselves. Moreover, the term "biofuels" is a stroke of marketing genius because it conjures images of nature when, in fact, the new fuels rely heavily on human-engineered enzymes and crops. The environmental lobby will soon discover this, and it too may split from encouraging biofuels as it learns that replacing large amounts of oil with cellulosic ethanol will require large areas of land devoted to genetically engineered crops, a scenario they have abhorred in the past.

A second track for cutting CO_2 from transportation eschews liquids for electricity stored onboard with batteries. There has been a lively and irrelevant debate about who killed the electric car in the United States because, in fact, the patient was dead upon delivery. Fully electric cars are unlikely to be practical except in niches — such as oddball speedsters, fleet vehicles, and golf carts — because no country has built the infrastructure needed for reliable recharging at every outpost.[2] More promising, however, are so-called "pluggable hybrid electric vehicles (PHEVs)." Using standard household wiring, these vehicles allow the user to charge onboard batteries and drive the first one to two dozen miles on grid power before an onboard engine (as in standard hybrid vehicles such as Toyota's Prius) supplements the stored power. Since most driving is short distance from a home base, pluggable hybrids can move a large fraction of transport energy consumption from oil to electricity. Also, given that central power station generators are more efficient than a vehicle's onboard internal combustion engine, a shift to electric power will save carbon and is roughly cost-effective today. If the electric system is decarbonized as well, the savings in CO_2 could be dramatic.

Any effort to decarbonize oil will interact with the growing debate about energy security that, in the United States, is mainly about dependence on imported oil. All of the strategies outlined above would help cut carbon and also improve energy security. Some strategies—notably the manufacture of synthetic liquid fuels from coal, which is attractive to the Air Force and coal-rich states such as Montana and Illinois—could boost security while amplifying CO_2 in harmful ways. In theory, synthetic fuels from coal could be manufactured in a way that allows for geological storage of the CO_2 underground, although in practice that route is a lot more costly than most rivals for cutting oil consumption and CO_2 emission.

Toward a Technology Strategy

In closing, there are three main points about the factors that could affect whether and how these advanced technologies come into widespread service.

First, even as the advanced industrialized countries attempt to cut carbon through schemes such as "cap and trade" and "carbon taxes," the real price on CO_2 emissions is likely to be lower than the level needed to encourage adequate private sector investment in the wide range of promising technologies for cutting carbon. This occurs because real carbon policies will be limited by political concerns about the impact on competitiveness, and because there are well-known failures in technology markets that cause the private sector to under-invest in innovation. An active technology policy will be needed. This strikes me as unavoidable, but it makes American analysts generally uncomfortable because technology policy is taboo in American economic policy. In addition, conventional wisdom contends that past efforts to promote energy technologies — for example, the Synthetic Fuels Corporation — have been disasters.[3] Yet such history needs a fresh look, because while the past has had numerous disasters, it has also yielded important lessons and success stories. Successes include the ability of National Institutes of Health (NIH) to adjust rules to favor investment in orphan drugs, the partial success of Sematech, and Defense Advanced Research Projects

Agency's (DARPA) general success with its portfolio of investments. Among the lessons is the need for some market pull to ensure that the private sector aligns with the public goal; the merits of independent peer review and management so that government investment decisions are removed by politics; and the need to encourage a broad investment in basic research as well as more applied development and demonstration.

Second, a more active effort will be needed to engage the major developing countries, notably China and India, as they already account for about half of world emissions. Their share will rise in the future as their economies industrialize. Engaging these countries is not only important for gaining full leverage on world emissions but also because it will be difficult to sustain political support for emission controls in the advanced industrialized countries without some credible effort by their economic competitors. So far, little progress has been made on this front. The Kyoto Protocol includes a Clean Development Mechanism (CDM) that rewards developing countries on a project-by-project basis for activities that would be uneconomic if not for the side-payment. Thus, it encourages marginal projects for which it is easy to demonstrate that the investment otherwise would not have been made. The scheme has encouraged substantial flows to projects in developing countries, but it is laden with perverse incentives. Because it only rewards projects that would otherwise be uneconomic it, in effect, promotes activities that are not in the host country's interest. Moreover, it pushes countries to lie about their underlying intentions. For example, countries might reject a binding law requiring the use of efficient power plants because such a law, once in place, would make any investment in efficient power plants ineligible for CDM credits. The CDM is not a viable way to encourage transformation to carbon-sipping energy systems.

A different track could focus on major infrastructure investments that align better with the host countries' core interests. For example, power companies in both China and India are experimenting with advanced coal combustion technologies, driven partly because those technologies are more efficient than traditional technologies (and thus could be less costly to operate), and partly because they make it easier to tame severe local air pollution.[4] Both countries are also in the midst of building gas pipeline and distribution networks, which allow for greater use of gas in generating electricity — efforts they are pursuing because gas helps to cut local air pollution. The West can help through broad packages of incentives to help these countries apply the latest technologies. These packages would focus on areas where local interests align with the Western interest in cutting CO_2. This complementary approach to the CDM could have enormous leverage on CO_2 emissions and will force western governments to look far outside the "traditional" areas of climate change policy to find the deepest cuts. For example, the U.S.-India nuclear partnership could prove to be one of the most important CO_2 policies in recent years because it will help India build a commercially viable zero-carbon nuclear industry.[5]

Finally, all these efforts to impose limits on carbon and craft elaborate technology strategies will be hard to sustain without progress in convincing firms and people in the advanced industrialized world that developing countries will be part of the solution (and, before that, convincing the rest of the world that the United States is part of the solution). Frustration with "free riders" will inevitably lead politicians and analysts to look for sticks that can be used to enforce compliance with international norms, such as trade sanctions. The French government has already mooted this idea early in 2007, and a growing number of analysts are looking into the options. A coalition of labor unions, industries, and politicians have centered on such a mechanism that the United States could apply to enforce its own carbon standards on the rest of the world.

Most difficult problems of international cooperation usually end up on the WTO's doorstep because the WTO is one of the only successful examples of sustained international coordination. It has also delivered massive benefits to nearly all its members. It will be important to resist the temptation to graft carbon onto the WTO and to use trade sanctions as strong enforcement tools because most WTO members (the developing countries) dislike such usage and because trade sanctions will be difficult to contain once deployed. With the WTO's "development round" headed for dormancy and the institution already fragile, adding carbon to the mix could be politically lethal. Instead of looking to the WTO, it will be important to build a more effective mechanism for international coordination that is focused on the CO_2 problem itself. So far the Kyoto framework has not offered that mechanism. Better ideas are found by working with a small number of the largest emitters — for example, through the G8+5 process or the L14 system that former Canadian Prime Minister Paul Martin has advocated — but to date not much real effort has been made to craft these "minilateral" institutions into a scheme that could be effective. U.S. leadership is badly needed; and perhaps once the United States has adopted its own policies in this area, it will have the credibility to create a better international system for managing the problem at hand.

■-■-■——

David Victor is Professor of Law at Stanford Law School and Director of the Program on Energy and Sustainable Development at the Freeman Spogli Institute for International Studies, which he came to Stanford University in 2001 to start. Previously, he directed the Science and Technology program at the Council on Foreign Relations in New York, where his research focused on the sources of technological innovation and the impact of innovation on economic growth, global forest policy, global warming, and genetic engineering of food crops. Professor Victor is a Senior Fellow at the Stanford Freeman Spogli Institute for International Studies and a Senior Fellow (by courtesy) at the Woods Institute for the Environment. He received a B.A. from Harvard University and a Ph.D. from the Massachusetts Institute for Technology in political science.

[1] Here I am focused on alcohol fuels that can be blended (up to about 85%) into gasoline, which is the main motor fuel in the United States. For brevity I will not give much attention to oil-producing plants that can serve a similar function through blending with diesel fuel — so-called "biodiesel." Most conventional oil plants, for example, technologies are an ecological horror because they are inefficient and thus require large amounts of land and other inputs (including primary rainforest, which is cut for palm oil plantations in a few parts of the world). A few oilseeds fare better because they can thrive on degraded lands and thus do not compete with food crops, although the ecological consequences of cropping degraded lands rather than just leaving them to Nature could be just as harmful as devoting large areas of more productive land to agriculture.

[2] One could imagine technological pathways that undercut this statement, such as quick-charge batteries that are already in advanced development. However, a large number of technological advances as well as many tens of billions of dollars in public and private investment would need to align before an all-electric vehicle infrastructure became feasible.

[3] Even this case is less disastrous than often thought. It was created at a moment when most analysts expected oil prices to stay high and supplies scarce and politically charged, and it was correctly disbanded shortly after it became clear that those plausible assumptions were incorrect. Predicting those oil price movements would have been difficult.

[4] In all these efforts, China is ahead of India. The really big news in the debate over developing countries and global warming may be that India is a harder case to address than China because India's energy sector is so sprawling and undisciplined.

[5] The Bush administration has proposed a strategy along these lines — first through its "Asia Pacific Partnership" and most recently in the context of the G8 meetings — though like much of what the administration proposes it is a sound idea that seems likely to falter in implementation. Elsewhere my colleagues at Stanford and I have quantified the effect of various large-scale energy infrastructure investments could have on emissions from major developing countries <http://iis-db.stanford.edu/pubs/21061/China_and_India_Infrastructure_Deals.pdf>. So far, we have looked at sharing of advanced coal technology, the construction of a natural gas pipeline network in China (along with a supportive air pollution regime that would encourage gas over coal), and the creation of a commercially viable nuclear power industry in India. We have focused on options that align with what countries already seek and thus are prone to yield self-enforcing strategies because both parties want them to succeed. The leverage is huge. For example, the U.S.-India nuclear partnership alone would save about 100 million tons of CO_2 per year by 2020, which is more than half of all the EU efforts to cut carbon under the Kyoto Protocol.

"For more than a hundred years, free markets and the ingenuity of mankind worked efficiently to decarbonize our energy systems."

— ROBERT A. HEFNER III

■ The Age of Energy Gases:
The Importance of Natural Gas in Energy Policy

Robert A. Hefner III
Founder and Owner, The GHK Company

History will record 2007 as the tipping point for energy and environmental consideration by leaders and policymakers around the world. Each day it becomes more and more apparent that the rapidly increasing use of coal and oil in a 'business as usual' scenario is unsustainable. Britain's *Stern Review on the Economics of Climate Change*[1] estimated that such a coal and oil scenario could lead to economic contractions and societal costs equivalent to the Great Depression and both World Wars. The globalization of the world's economies and the vast quantities of energy they require has created globalized pollution, brought to the forefront climate constraints on economic growth, increased global financial imbalances and economic volatility, escalated geostrategic tensions, and increased the energy system's vulnerability to terrorist attacks that would severely disrupt global commerce and create mega financial shocks. As I will describe in this chapter, these forces have brought civilization as we know it to the point of no longer being able to resist the next great energy transition, one as fundamental as the 19th century transition from wood to coal and the 20th century transition to oil. I will make the case in this chapter that the transition to 21st century smart and efficient energy technologies will be fueled principally by natural gas (natgas). For the long-term, natgas will be the bridge to environmentally benign hydrogen.

Natural Gas and Its Competitors
Before continuing, I would like to make the following introductory "bottom line" points about natgas and its competitive fuels that will be expanded upon further in the text:

- Coal and oil are the problem. Natgas and profitable efficiency are the principal solutions.

- Solar and wind are excellent solutions but will not become a principal source of energy over the next 30 years.

- Nuclear is a workable "clean" technology but because of proliferation, the potential for terrorist acts, unresolved waste storage and "not in my backyard" issues, nuclear must be subsidized by governments and is difficult to finance and site. As a result of these issues and the necessity of significant mandatory retirements for existing plants, it will be difficult for nuclear to maintain its current 17%[2] of the world power market over the coming decades.

- Biofuels have many full-cycle economic and environmental problems and are not a long-term sustainable alternative for gasoline. The recent rush to biofuels has been more of an emotional rather than a technological response to the climate and geostrategic constraints of oil.

- Natgas is a distinct fuel and is not a part of the "oil and gas" industry. Natgas is a principal part of our energy solution because natgas produces 50% less CO_2 than coal when used for electric generation and, when used for transportation about 25% less CO_2 than gasoline.[3] Natgas should not be included with coal and oil as simply another "fossil fuel" whose use should be significantly reduced or eliminated; rather natgas use over the near-term should be encouraged to displace coal and oil use. Natgas should be a principal part of America's near-term solution for reducing CO_2 emissions.

- Natgas is globally abundant. Natgas resources may equal coal or even exceed the world's energy value of coal. (Of course, natgas abundance is critical to my Age of Energy Gases Theory and will be addressed further in this chapter.)

- Natgas can substitute for gasoline, so natgas has the potential to immediately begin to reduce both oil imports and CO_2 emissions by converting America's automobile and truck fleet to dual-fueled vehicles. Natgas consumption technology for vehicles is already in-hand, in wide use and well tested. Today, there are about five million vehicles around the world running on natgas. In America, we have a million mile pipeline grid in place that is connected to over 56% or 63 million American homes,[4] so with a small compressor appliance in the garage and a scuba-like tank in the trunk (it is safer than gasoline) you are ready to go with a dual-fuel natgas/gasoline vehicle. Additionally, the majority of urban gasoline filling stations are connected to the natural gas grid, so it is relatively easy and inexpensive to add a natural gas fueling station. The conversion cost is less than trading up for a hybrid automobile, so for significant near-term reductions in oil use and CO_2 emissions, natgas vehicles should become a significant part of America's energy planning.

- "Clean coal." I don't believe there is such a thing. Even if sequestration technology—the capturing, liquefying and pumping of CO_2 into the earth—is proven and coal plants are actually able to capture all of coal's sulfur, mercury and ash emissions and successfully bury the waste in toxic waste dumpsites, "clean coal" is highly inefficient, very cumbersome and cannot be economically competitive with natgas when all the external costs of coal are included. To sequester 60% of America's CO_2 emissions from coal-fired power plants would require the pumping of 20 million barrels of liquid CO_2 per day into the ground[5] or four times the U.S. daily oil production.[6] Natgas produces only one-half or less the CO_2 emissions of coal when used for electric power generation, so if sequestration works, it is better to start with natgas and half the CO_2 emissions.

- Coal to liquid and coal to gas technologies are dinosaurs and already proven difficult, cumbersome, noncommercial and polluting. America's last attempt with coal to gas was a complete $10 billion bust[7] ($25 billion 2007 dollars). And coal to liquid would require large government subsidies for a technology that will produce about twice the CO_2 emissions as gasoline.[8]

A Brief History of Energy

Keeping the above thoughts in mind let me begin with a brief history of energy. Civilization began around the fire, and wood fueled the first power plant—the open pit fire. From the beginning of civilization it has been the increasing quantity of non-human energy consumption that has freed increasingly large numbers of humankind from the daily struggles of manual labor and initiated the complex interconnected global society that is being created today. History will look back at the beginning of the 21st century as a time of unprecedented and rapid human change. The world economies are globalizing, over 3 billion people in Asia are entering the economy, and information technology has exploded around the world and is connecting billions of people to each other and to all human knowledge. Vast Quantities of Energy Consumption (VQEC) are required to fuel and power today's global standard of living. Also, for the first time in human history, the use of vast and increasing quantities of coal and oil are becoming globally unsustainable and are creating economic, environmental, and geostrategic limits to growth. Global oil consumption is running about 84 million barrels per day[9] or 31 billion barrels per year. That equals nearly 1,000 barrels per second or about one cubic mile of oil per year[10] that release about 12 billion metric tons of CO_2 to the atmosphere.[11] Oil consumption in a 'business as usual' scenario is estimated to be well over 100 million barrels per day by 2030,[12] which would release about 17 billion metric tons of CO_2 each year. Global coal consumption is about 16 million tons per day, or 6 billion tons per year,[13] a cubic mile of dirty black rocks that release about 10.5 billion metric tons of CO_2 to the atmosphere each year. A "business as usual" coal scenario calls for the consumption of nearly 10 billion tons per year by 2030[14] that would release over 16 billion metric tons of CO_2 annually. In 2007, our global economy will consume two cubic miles of coal and oil that will release over 20 billion tons of CO_2 or nearly 80% of all the world's human-produced CO_2 emissions.[15] Unfortunately, our existing energy infrastructure and its principal fuels of coal and oil are basically 18th, 19th and 20th century technologies that have not changed that much and can no longer meet our 21st century needs. Over the coming decades, these aging technologies will not be able to sustain the economic growth that will be needed for the continuing development of our globalized economies and increasing standards of living required to give hope for a better future to all of our global society's growing number of participants.

It is my premise that energy transitions are enormous and powerful long-term waves, and that civilization has recently entered the next great energy transition that, once again, will have the potential to unleash tsunami waves of technological innovation, economic growth and prosperity. I call this transition The Age of Energy Gases.[16] The Age of Energy Gases will certainly continue to require increasing VQEC, even with the considerable efficiency savings that will come with smart 21st century energy technologies. These accelerating trends are unprecedented in human history and only become possible because of VQEC. VQEC is not a bad thing in itself; what is bad, what will not be sustainable for humanity, is the *inefficient* use of bad *forms* of energy. What I mean by bad forms of energy are fuels that by their use create economic, environmental and geostrategic limits to economic growth. My decades of energy studies have led me to the conclusion that the energy necessary to sustain an economy is as fundamental as money. We can barter and trade without money on a grand scale, such as arms for oil, or on a small scale, a barber trading haircuts for accounting work, but not without the use of energy. All barter transactions require the use, or I like to use the word expenditure, of energy. The money/energy inputs to all economies are a complex interactive system that may be the most important aspect to understanding energy and the economy. What must be clearly understood is that energy use is never a neutral input to the economy because its use either tends to diminish or restrain economic growth and pollute the environment, or tends to enhance growth and economic productivity and clean the environment. I have coined the word "econergy" to mean "the forces of energy operating within the economy and the environment." So as leaders, central bankers and policymakers tackle the problems of formulating policies for sustaining economic growth while limiting CO_2 emissions, cleaning the environment, and enhancing energy security, they must keep clearly in mind that to achieve successful outcomes, the econergenic effects must be an essential component of their thoughts, model-making and policy decisions.

If our children and grandchildren are to experience the next tsunami wave of technological and economic growth within a sustainable environment we must begin now to enact energy policies that will facilitate rather than inhibit our transition to 21st century high tech, smart, highly efficient energy technologies that run on clean fuels that will also reduce the world's CO_2 emissions. Our aging, outdated and often worn out (most American oil refineries are about 50 years old) energy infrastructure is simply not capable of meeting our 21st century needs and must be replaced.

I believe that natural gases will fuel the next great energy wave. Even without policies to encourage natgas use in the large consuming nations, natgas has been the fastest growing primary source of energy during most years since the 1970's[17] and is estimated by many energy experts, myself included, to continue its leading rate of growth. This wave begins with clean methane, commonly called natgas, and during the second half of the 21st century, a transition will accelerate toward totally clean hydrogen. In a climate-constrained world, natgas is a positive step forward because when consumed it releases about one half or less CO_2 to the atmosphere than coal and about 30% less CO_2 than oil. And because natgas is only one carbon atom and four hydrogen atoms, it will be the transition fuel to the hydrogen economy.

Hydrogen and the hydrogen economy should become civilization's energy endgame. Only within a hydrogen-based economy that produces virtually no energy pollutants and releases no CO_2 to the atmosphere can forecasted levels of global population and its required increases of economic growth be sustained environmentally. For more than a hundred years, free markets and the ingenuity of mankind worked efficiently to decarbonize our energy systems.[18] The path toward civilization's ultimate goal is clearly marked by a series of energy waves that decarbonized our energy sources over the past 100 years by shifting from wood, composed principally of carbon, to coal, with a little less carbon and a bit of hydrogen, to oil, again, less carbon and more hydrogen, to methane, composed of only one carbon and four hydrogen atoms. Over the past 100 years, it has been Adam Smith's "invisible hand" and the natural imperative of humanity to seek a higher quality of life and not government policies or intervention that has cleaned and greened our energy consumption. We began civilization with carbon and as we enter the 21st century, about two-thirds of the energy atoms we burn are actually hydrogen.[19] Today, because we are facing serious global climate and geostrategic constraints that are occurring because of the large and increasing quantities of coal and oil consumption, we are compelled to accelerate our transition to hydrogen. A policy principally composed of taxes on CO_2 emissions from the use of coal and oil will speed this next great energy wave. The price signal will encourage the use of natural gas, wind, solar and other renewables to displace coal and oil and will stimulate the drive to profitable efficiency in the consumption of energy which will, over time, create a more efficient energy infrastructure. If taxes from CO_2 emissions are recycled and used to reduce the tax burden upon society, we can achieve our goals of significantly reduced CO_2 emissions and oil imports without the massive economic burden and contractions that are often described as a necessary evil for meeting our environmental and security goals.

Natural Gas Abundance

In order for my theory of The Age of Energy Gases to be credible, the global supplies of natgas must be large. The large or even vast supplies of natgas around the world are becoming more apparent each year as more and more very large natgas fields are discovered. However, in order to fully appreciate and understand the abundance of natgas, we must abandon the historic misconception that "oil and gas" are one energy source and one energy industry. My life's work as a geologist and natgas, not oil, explorationist has led to my belief that global natgas resources are much more abundant than oil and at least as abundant as coal. As you contemplate the abundance of natgas, keep in mind that wherever coal is found natgas is present and wherever oil is found natgas is also present and often in equal or larger quantities and, even more important, the largest natgas fields in the world contain little and sometimes no oil.

We must abandon the long-held concept of "oil and gas" where "gas" comes second, as a little-valued by-product of oil. Natgas is different from oil in almost every way except how it is generally explored for, and even then success in natgas discovery requires thinking outside the parameters of oil exploration.[20] Natgas is lighter than air and cannot be seen or smelled; oil is a viscous smelly liquid easily seen and difficult to clean up when spilled. Oil spills devastate vast stretches of oceans and beaches whereas huge but as yet unmeasured quantities of natgas have been leaking from the Earth's land masses and oceans over geologic time for millions of years and, although a so-called greenhouse gas,[21] without apparent adverse environmental impact. Natgas is compressible and oil is not, allowing a natgas reservoir of identical size but at deeper depths to hold twice as much or more natgas as the same reservoir at a shallower depth. Natgas is chemically simple, with four hydrogen atoms and only one carbon. Oil is chemically complex and contains much more dirty carbon.

One of the most significant differences between oil and natgas is that natgas is commercially produced from many reservoir rocks that could not commercially produce one drop of oil. Commercial supplies of natgas are always present within the geological structures that produce oil but are also found in large geologic volumes of rock that do not contain oil. Because natgas can be commercially produced from all the volumes of rocks that contain oil, as well as vast volumes of rocks, particularly tight sandstones, shales and coals that contain no oil, the global volumes of sediments capable of producing natgas commercially are at least twice and probably closer to several times the volume of rocks capable of oil production. Additionally, because natgas is lighter than air, it flows naturally from its reservoir to the surface. Because oil is a viscous liquid it generally does not flow to the surface unless assisted by natgas contained in the oil. As a result, most conventional natgas fields produce 70% to 80% of the natgas originally in place while most oil fields only produce 15% to 30% or less of the oil in place unless secondary and tertiary recovery methods are used that sometimes can increase oil field recoveries up to 40% or 50%. These natural gas characteristics account for the fact that at depths in the earth below 8,000 feet, the same reservoir full of natural gas will nearly always produce more usable BTU's than if it is full of oil.

Another significant difference between oil and natgas is that in most sedimentary basins of the world, very little oil is produced below a depth of 15,000 feet (the U.S. Gulf Coast is an exception), yet very large and giant natgas fields exist below these depths. Because throughout its history natgas has been priced at a large discount to oil, very little exploration of the vast quantities of potential reservoir rocks at these depths have been explored, yet sedimentary basins exist to depths of at least 50,000 feet and potentially commercial quantities of natgas have been found below 30,000 feet. As a result, there are hundreds of thousands, if not millions, of cubic miles of deep sediments within the world's gas- and oil-producing basins that remain unexplored below 15,000 feet. The point here is that as the price of natgas rises to parity with oil, very large supplies of natgas exist that will be discovered and developed, often within highly populated and large consumption areas of the world such as the USA, China and India. By adding together the vast quantities of unexplored deep sediments and possibly even larger quantities of sediments at shallower depths that can commercially produce natgas but not oil, there are at least several times if not an order of magnitude more volumes of rocks capable of producing natgas than those that produce oil within the geological basins of the world that already produce gas and oil. And with natgas recoveries from those reservoirs averaging about twice those of oil, it becomes a reasonable assumption that the global supplies of natgas are at least twice, if not several times, those of oil. Fundamental to the development of these abundant natgas supplies is price. Over the coming decade, natgas will need to take its place in the world's pricing regime as a primary fuel needed to reduce the use of coal and oil with all the external costs I have described. For the first time in its history, natgas will need to be priced on parity with oil and eventually at a premium that I believe it deserves because of its superior environmental and security characteristics. Of course, this will not happen without a meaningful CO_2 tax system.

A recent, important and good example of large volumes of rocks that have historically produced virtually no oil are shale reservoirs that have become the number one target for natgas development in the U.S. Over the last decade, new, real-time 3-D seismic, massive fracturing, horizontal drilling techniques and higher natgas prices have created commercial natgas resources from shale reservoirs that have increased America's natgas potential by more than 50%,[22] and these technologies continue to improve each day (Figure 1).

Natgas is pervasive around the world, whereas about 65% to 70% of all oil reserves[23] are located under a relatively small and concentrated area of the earth's surface. Natgas is significantly more distributed around the world and can provide consumers a much larger diversification of supplies than can oil. An interesting sideline story to shale gas is that America's first natgas production and

Figure 1

AMERICAN SHALE GAS DEPOSITS

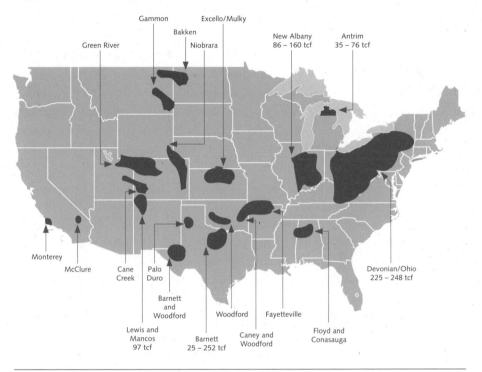

Gas shale deposits appear in basins from the east to the west coast across the United States. Although recovery percentages are low, total volumes are high.

Map courtesy of Schlumberger.

commercial use was from shale near the town of Fredonia, New York in 1821, 38 years before America's first oil well.[24] And over 900 years ago in Sichuan, China, a commercial and residential natgas infrastructure was connected to natgas wells up to 1,000 meters deep.

Another significant difference between natgas and oil is that oil is trapped in very specific geological structures whereas natgas is contained in vast volumes of sediments, particularly tight sands, shales and coals over very large areas within geologic basins. This geologic distinction means that recoverable natgas resources rapidly expand with price increases as more and more natgas becomes commercial to produce. This phenomenon has been clearly demonstrated over the past decade by the expanding areas of commercial natgas production added to America's Barnett Shale natgas play as the price of natgas increased. On the other hand, increases in oil price will only achieve limited additional reserves realized principally through the use of costlier secondary and tertiary recovery methods from existing fields and the possibility of commercially opening new, very high-cost provinces for oil exploration such as very deep-water offshore basins, the Arctic, Antarctica, and in the U.S., the Arctic National Wildlife Refuge.

Natgas requires a significantly different infrastructure than oil and is cleaner and generally more efficient. The U.S. is blessed by the existence of a million mile pipeline system that provides natgas distribution for easy access to most Americans. For this reason, in America, the displacement of coal for power generation and oil in the transportation sector will be relatively inexpensive and easy to accomplish in very little time.

Nonetheless, most people today think of "oil and gas" as one industry. My grandfather and father were in the oil industry, but I separated myself from the "oil industry" while at the University of Oklahoma. Unfortunately for natgas understanding, the world's universities have taught "petroleum" geology and "petroleum" engineering; the dictionary defines "petroleum" as hydrocarbon *liquids*, not gases, and the "petroleum" courses follow the name, with students learning basically about oil, not natgas. Although natgas has recently begun to come to the forefront, most of the senior people in the industry today were educated with the semantic connotation of "petroleum," a liquid, and the natgas they most understand is the natgas associated with oil and found by the "oil and gas" industry.

Most of the natgas available for consumers today was found by oil geologists searching for oil with capital budgets targeted toward expanding oil supplies. International comparative measurements of natgas and oil are most often expressed in "Barrels of Oil Equivalent (BOE)." Yet, during the last decade or so the world's "oil and gas" exploration results passed into the era of natgas *followed* by oil. By studying the world's "giant oil and gas fields"[25] found between 1990 and 1999, we learn that 37 giant oil fields were found containing 36,800 million barrels of oil equivalent (BOE) and 40 giant gas fields were found containing 119,387 million BOE — over three times as much natgas as oil found in the giant fields. An even closer look shows that usually about 30% to sometimes as much as 40% or more of the BOE in the giant oil fields were actually natgas. So, in reality, at least five times more natgas was found as oil. This is a clear indication that the future is natgas, not oil.

Natgas is not part of the oil industry. The natgas industry is only now beginning to exist as an integrated global industry. Historically, natgas has at best been priced as a cheap by-product of oil in spite of its environmental and security-of-supply advantages, or worse, flared away as a nuisance. For decades, the brightest spots on earth at night have been the giant natgas flares from "oil" fields in Siberia, Saudi Arabia and West Africa. Only in the past few years has the market begun to price natgas as an important commodity but at a price still mostly discounted to oil. Likewise, only in recent years have capital budgets begun to target the expansion of natgas reserves and natgas infrastructure. A good example is Qatar that is on its way to building one of the first truly integrated global natgas companies. And today, I would estimate that the lion's share of the "oil and gas" industry's capital budgets are still targeted on oil.

In America in the mid-1970's, natgas production began to be outstripped by natgas demand because, since 1955, the price of natgas had been government-regulated at very low prices, a fraction of the equivalent oil price (Figure 2). It was during this period of price-regulated shortages of natgas and the oil shocks of the early 1970s that Congress last took a hard look at energy. During President Carter's campaign, he pledged to work to deregulate the price of all newly produced natgas. I testified before Congress 18 times attempting to refute statements by

Figure 2

U.S. NATURAL GAS WELLHEAD PRICES (ON A BTU BASIS)

AS A PERCENTAGE OF **U.S. CRUDE OIL WELLHEAD PRICES, 1947–2006**

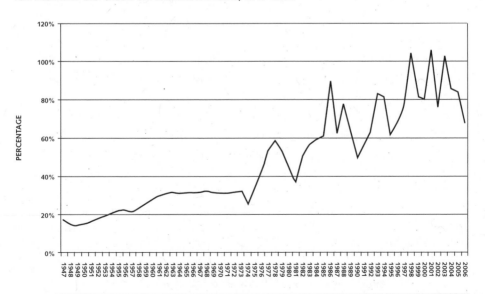

Natgas price, on a BTU basis, as a percentage of oil.

Exxon, Mobil and Shell and other oil companies that America was running out of natgas. The liberals of Washington, led by Senator "Scoop" Jackson, made these authoritative oil company predictions of scarcity the basis of their opposition to price deregulation saying that any deregulation in times of long-term shortage would lead to "unconscionably" high prices and windfall profits. My testimony was that the U.S. had vastly abundant natgas supplies and that the oil companies only understood oil and oil geology and were only estimating the natgas that would be found by oil exploration and that was associated with oil production. In 1976, Exxon stated in two widely circulated papers that remaining natgas in the lower forty-eight states was 287 trillion cubic feet (Tcf)[26] and as late as 1984, Exxon's Charles B. Wheeler testified before Congress that natgas resources were about 300 Tcf.[27] In other forums, the renowned King Hubbard of Shell Oil Company, who correctly forecast peak oil in the United States, estimated remaining natgas resources of 100 Tcf. Even though his oil estimate was correct, his natgas estimates were linked to his understanding of oil and at least an order of magnitude too low. In August 1978, a number of high-level policymakers and "oil and gas" representatives attended The Aspen Institute's "Workshop on R&D Priorities and the Gas Energy System," where Exxon reiterated its estimate of 287 Tcf. When I presented my forum paper, "The Future for Conventional U.S. Natural Gas Supply," I countered by saying that Exxon's estimates were "unrealistically low" and biased by its "view through the window of oil." My 1978 natgas resource estimates were between 1,500 and 2,000 Tcf depending upon price. Phased deregulation of new natgas was signed into law by President Carter in 1978. Unfortunately, because Congress and the Carter Administration believed the oil company estimates of impending natgas shortages to be credible, the Fuel Use Act was also passed that *prohibited* the use of natgas in new power generation plants, then natgas's fastest growing market, and severely restricted its use in new industrial facilities. What followed were 20 years of natgas supply surpluses and a 30-year resurgence of coal-fired plants. History has proven that the oil company estimates were indeed unrealistic. Since 1975, 584 Tcf[28] of natgas has been produced in the U.S., and today, most analysts estimate remaining natgas to be over 1,000 Tcf.[29]

Although the natgas market is only now in its infancy as a global commodity, the past few decades have seen natgas to be the fastest growing primary energy during most years. So, when you hear people talk about "oil and gas" in one breath, remember that they are "oil" people and are limited in their understanding of natgas by their long-held views of oil. However, in spite of the heavy oil bias that I believe keeps the natgas reserve and resource estimates at less than half of what they realistically must be, the consensus of world natgas supplies is certainly adequate to provide significant increases in global natgas consumption. The International *Petroleum* Encyclopedia (my emphasis) estimates between 6,686 Tcf to 9,708 Tcf of "conventional" natgas has been discovered[30] and with an annual consumption rate of about 100 Tcf [31] that gives us 67 to 97 years of natgas at current rates of use. One credible estimate of the worldwide unconventional natgas resource base is over 30,000 Tcf.[32] These large, unconventional supplies could be increased 2 to 3 times by commercial hydrate natgas production. Taken together, the global conventional and unconventional natgas resources are certainly ample to fuel The Age of Energy Gases. I would like to point out here that the terms "conventional" and "unconventional" were established by the "oil and gas" industry and that "unconventional" simply means natgas supplies that are produced from geological conditions that are outside what is considered a "conventional" oil trapping structure. Since the first U.S. natgas production was from shale, shale could be considered a "conventional" natgas source.

The key to natgas reliance is to define with credible confidence that the world's undeveloped natgas resources are indeed abundant and sufficient for long-term energy policy. It is not surprising that there is very little information about global natgas resources. So, I believe what is needed today to differentiate natgas understanding from oil and to alleviate the fears of insufficient natgas resources is an appropriate international institution that can organize a global effort for the collection of natgas resource and production data and mount a well-financed program for research and study of natgas and natgas technology.[33] Natgas resource estimates must no longer be limited by oil thinking. To understand natgas, we must begin the task of analyzing the significance of many recent natgas facts and discoveries before realistic, unbiased global natgas estimates can be formulated. We must recognize such natgas facts as:

- The non-biologic origin of natgas is becoming more probable by the discovery of vast quantities of methane on Titan, one of Saturn's moons (Figure 3), as well as on Jupiter, Saturn itself, Uranus and Neptune—and here on Earth, methane venting from the 40,000 mile long mid-oceanic rift system (Figure 4). Natgas should not be thought of as just another "fossil fuel," as we are learning that there is an increasing possibility that large quantities of natgas may not be of biologic origin and may even be continuously forming as part of the great continental subduction movements occurring on earth today;

Figure 3

TITAN — METHANE ATMOSPHERE, LAKES

A lake of liquid methane surrounded by mountains of solid ice on Titan.

Source: Huygens probe, ESA. (Courtesy of Jesse Ausubel).

- Natgas is produced by the degradation of biological waste and garbage landfills and is to that extent a "renewable" fuel;

- The discovery of natgas hydrates in all the world's oceans and their potential for commercial production. The world may contain more energy in the form of natgas hydrates[34] than all the energy contained in the world's coal and oil combined (Figure 5), and only in the past several years have very limited experiments begun to test how natgas hydrates can be commercially produced;

- The recent commercial development of shale gas in the U.S. that may well have doubled America's natgas resources,[35] yet shale gas has not been explored for and commercially developed in the other continents of the world.

Figure 4

GLOBAL OCEANIC RIFT SYSTEM

40,000 mile mid-oceanic rift system.

Source: *Discover Magazine*, June 2007.

Policymakers commit a tragic mistake when they dismiss natgas as simply another "fossil fuel," because doing so ignores that natgas is considerably environmentally cleaner than oil and coal, natgas has the potential to significantly reduce global CO_2 emissions by its use for power generation, natgas is cheaper and cleaner than gasoline and can fuel a large segment of the global automobile fleet, global natgas reserves are potentially massive, and large quantities of natgas may have non-biological sources and commercially significant amounts are renewable. We need to learn to distinguish between natgas — a principal solution to global energy problems — and coal and oil, which are the principal problems.

Figure 5

GLOBAL NATURAL GAS HYDRATES

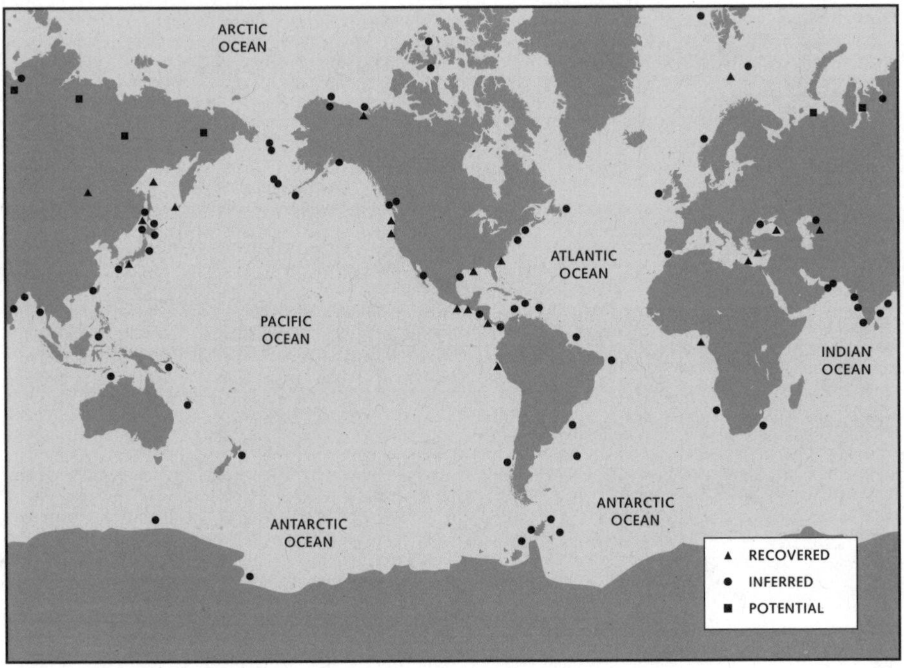

Source: U.S. Geological Survey.

The Age of Energy Gases

Computer projections of natgas[36] forecast that natgas will move toward supplying about 80% of the world energy market, as did coal in the 19th century. But how could that be realistic, particularly recognizing that oil never attained 50% of the world's energy marketplace? Oil peaked in 1973 at 48% and has subsequently declined to about 36% of today's global demand for energy,[37] yet natural gas has been consistently the fastest growing energy source since the 1970's. That fact fascinated me, particularly because energy transitions are better defined by the *percentage* of the market each fuel holds and tend to be obscured by the quantities of the fuel consumed. I wondered why a fuel as efficient and competitive as oil, when compared to coal, only managed to achieve just less than 50% of the global energy market. It dawned on me that possibly the big picture of energy transitions may well be elegant simplicity. In the big picture, matter in the universe exists principally in two forms — solids and gases. Liquid is a transitional and minimal state of matter. There is not much liquid in the universe, in our solar system or on earth. If one drained all the water and oil from the Earth it would become a little ball of water with an oil film less than the size of the end of your thumb as compared to a two foot diameter earth (Figure 6).[38]

Figure 6

WATER PLANET?

Water Planet? We frequently hear that more than 70% of the world is covered by water. But how much is there really? On the left is an image of the Earth with all water removed. On the right is a sphere representing all the water on Earth (oceans, icecaps, glaciers, lakes, rivers, groundwater etc.). To the far right (tiny sphere) is the *fresh* water that is readily available to humanity to sustain life.

Courtesy of Woods Hole Oceanographic Institution.

The earth is mostly solid, saturated and surrounded by gases. As liquid is a transitional and minimal state of matter, it could therefore be a clear indication that oil, a liquid, may be a comparatively limited global energy resource as compared to coal, a solid, and natgas, a gas. If you think of it this way, the energy sources that fueled civilization from the beginning through the Industrial Revolution were solids, then a liquid transition took us to the "modern world." Then what would be the future? I call it The Age of Energy Gases, as depicted in the next figure (Figure 7), which has the capacity for the first time in human history to transition civilization to fully sustainable growth for millennia to come.

The Age of Energy Gases begins with a common natgas, methane or CH_4—only one carbon and four hydrogen atoms. Further out in the wave of energy gases, say 2050 or even later in the 21st century, after the natgas infrastructure based upon the use of gas, not solids or liquids, is in place, we will accelerate a transition through a similar and largely in-place methane infrastructure, to a hydrogen (also a gas) based economy. By studying Figure 7, we can see that as we move across these energy waves over time we have been de-carbonizing or we might say we have been "hydrogenising" our energy consumption. Today, we have already reached the point that only one-third of the coal, oil and natgas atoms we burn are carbon and two-thirds are hydrogen. Indeed, the past 150 years has seen a greening and cleaning of our energy sources.

Figure 7

THE AGE OF ENERGY GASES GLOBAL ENERGY TRANSITION WAVES

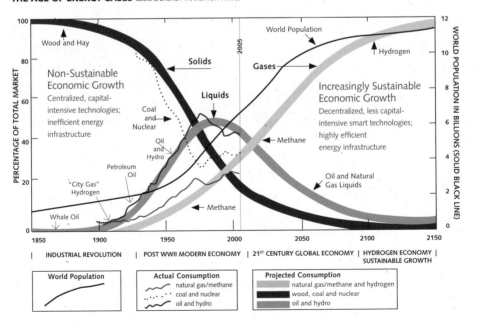

It is my long-term concept that for millennia civilization existed with only the basic technologies, then grew with waves of accelerating technological innovation originally fueled by dirty, inefficient solid fuels, mostly wood and coal. Then, in the 20th century, a rapid and what will become a relatively short-lived liquid oil transition began that once again provided the fuel for another exponential technological pulse that began at the close of WWII and spurred the creation of the modern connected and globalized society that we live in today. This technological pulse, fueled by cheap energy, allowed for the exponential growth in population that also began at the close of WWII.[39] We have been caught in a conundrum where low-priced energy, resulting from decades of supplies far in excess of demand, provided for exponential population growth that must be fueled by more energy consumption. As long as the energy input was cheap, the cycle accelerated. But now, because of large increases in the price of energy as a result of supply and demand balances, and even more important, the dramatic acceleration of external costs of coal and oil, human creativity will once again seek technological innovation that will be fueled by a less costly (including externalities) primary energy source at an exponential rate of growth. This time the principal source is gases, beginning with methane. This wave has already begun, as can be clearly seen on The Age of Energy Gases and the Earth Energies for the Millennia charts (Figures 7 & 8). And this time the transition will once again last for millennia because the hydrogen economy will allow the earth to sustain its forecasted population growth as well as the economic growth created by waves of technological innovation to come.

Hydrogen is a totally clean and fully sustainable form of energy. Hydrogen, one of the basic elements of nature, is the universe's simplest and most abundant element, accounting for more than 90% of the observable universe. Hydrogen bound in water and organic forms accounts for more than 70% of the Earth's surface.[40] When hydrogen is burned with oxygen only heat and water are produced.[41] The hydrogen economy is technologically possible today; cars, planes, boats, power plants and towns have already been fueled with hydrogen, so the technology is basically in hand and is not something that is yet to be invented. What is needed is a *long-term* commitment by governments to provide research and development funding for natgas, hydrogen and hydrogen technology, with incentives like those given in the past to coal, oil and nuclear, and commitments by nations equal to the one that put man on the Moon. India offers an example by way of its "National Hydrogen Energy Road Map." The Road Map emphasizes the development of a total hydrogen energy system and recommends two major

Figure 8

EARTH ENERGIES FOR THE **MILLENNIA**

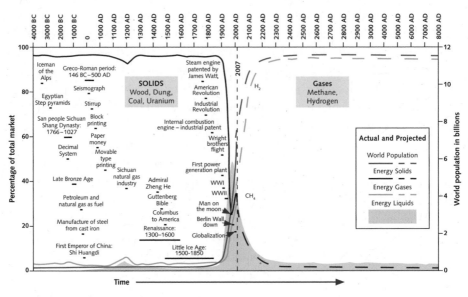

Sources: Robert A. Hefner III, © 2007, The GHK Company

initiatives for promoting the use of hydrogen as a fuel — for Green Transportation and Green Power Generation. The Road Map visualizes that by 2020, one million hydrogen-fueled vehicles and 1,000 megawatts (MW) of hydrogen-based power generation capacity would be established in the country.[42]

Today's emotional rush to biofuels, nuclear and "clean coal" are not solutions but rather only unsustainable attempts to continue along the "business as usual" scenario by adding some modern but generally uneconomic, inefficient solid and liquid technologies that will increasingly be subsidized by governments and paid for by society in the form of increased taxation. Corn ethanol and other food crop biofuels are already driving up food costs that literally hit the poor "where they live." If subsidized and mandated by policymakers, these biofuels are likely to continue to push up inflation, causing central bankers to raise interest rates, and we will all suffer the macroeconomic consequences of higher costs and fewer jobs. So why mandate that biofuels must compete with food for land, farmers, fertilizer and equipment, particularly when they are not that good at reducing pollution and in many cases require nearly as much energy to make as is produced? As to cellulosic ethanol, the idea is certainly better but it continues to need significant advances in technology as there is no commercial technology yet developed, so I don't think it will be a quick fix. It is certainly easier and quicker to convert an automobile to clean compressed natural gas (CNG).

Nuclear works, however, we do not yet know the real cost of nuclear terrorism, nuclear proliferation or nuclear waste storage; so one way or another, nuclear energy will need to be subsidized by the taxpayer. Planners and policymakers would be negligent if the economic and social costs of a dirty bomb were not carefully considered in the formulation of energy policy. Today, there are 442 nuclear plants in operation worldwide[43] that produce about 17%[44] of the world's electric power and even if over the coming three decades the 29 nuclear plants now under construction and the additional 100 planned plants[45] are actually built, nuclear energy would only then supply about 22% of the world's electric power. However, because of the large global requirements for nuclear plant retirements, an even more ambitious program of nuclear development would be necessary to keep nuclear's percentage of power from actually declining. Nuclear will be increasingly capital intensive, difficult to license, site and finance, and a new plant will take most of a decade or more from decision to build to completion. Realistically, I cannot see nuclear becoming a principal energy source in the world for electric power in the next 30 years.

The words "clean coal" are nothing more than a dirty trick used by a 19th century industry willing to do almost anything to keep from going out of business. The only so-called "clean coal" will require sequestration — underground storage, a technology whose cost cannot be yet realistically measured. And even if commercially attainable, sub-surface geological reservoirs can be accessed to store all the CO_2, it is questionable how long the CO_2 will stay in place. As mentioned earlier, to sequester 60% of America's CO_2 emissions from coal-fired power plants, 20 million barrels a day of liquid CO_2 would need to be pumped into the ground.[46] To physically and economically pump these volumes will be no easy task as they equal about four times America's daily crude oil production.[47] And, even if the CO_2 is sequestered, what will happen to coal's toxic pollutants of sulfur, mercury and ash? Suffice to say there is no such thing as "clean coal." Jeff Goodell, in his excellent book, *Big Coal*, eloquently describes how coal-generated electric power is a major impediment to a revolution in power generation, "Old coal plants are more than just relics of an earlier era; they are giant bulwarks against change, mechanical beasts that are holding back a flood of ideas and innovation."[48]

Totally clean power can only be produced from solar, wind, hydro, tides, geothermal and hydrogen. Unfortunately, although each clean energy source has an important market to supply and the two principal sources, solar and wind, will continue to grow rapidly and be supported by policymakers, none of these other than hydrogen will be capable of providing to humankind a principal energy solution. And hydrogen, like each fuel before it, will require a long-term transition, so that is why natgas, a fuel already in transition to becoming a principal global energy source and already composed of mostly hydrogen, is the natural bridge to the hydrogen economy. Additionally, because natgas-fueled power emits only half the CO_2 as coal and almost none of the other pollutants, there is a reasonable possibility that CO_2 sequestration from natgas power generation could become commercially feasible. If so, then natgas can be added as a source of totally clean electric power generation.

Follow The Technology

Instead of heading off in so many different energy directions believing in the need for all forms of energy and energy diversification, as has recently been the case, what we must rather do as we enter the 21st century is to *"follow the technology."* Technology is clearly leading us from complex chemistry of dirty, carbon rich solids (coal: $C_{135}H_{96}O_9NS$), through a carbon rich liquid transition (oil: C_5H_{12} to $C_{36}H_{74}$), to simpler and simpler chemistry (natgas: CH_4) with less and less carbon, and pointing us toward the simplest chemistry and cleanest source, with no carbon at all, hydrogen itself (H_2). *We are going from centralized, highly capital-intensive, inefficient power plants that burn dirty, chemically complex solids, toward decentralized, less capital-intensive, highly efficient, smaller, smart power systems that burn chemically simple, clean natgases.* Our future will have smaller and smaller forms of energy converters, located closer and closer to energy demand and decision making. We will have smart energy technology with computers moving toward nanotechnology implanted throughout the energy system from production through transportation to consumption. And possibly most important to the efficiency of consumption, we will move from regulated and bureaucratic, centralized, top-down highly inefficient energy decision making to flexible, cost-saving smart systems efficiently controlled by the individual, family, neighborhood or office building and tailored to meet continuously changing local needs. These new technologies will spawn new waves of efficiency, conservation and savings that will once again increase productivity within our economic systems by orders of magnitude. Consumption itself will become vastly more efficient. But, none of this is possible without basically a new energy infrastructure built for The Age of Energy Gases.

The Age of Energy Gases is the path that will move civilization away from coal-fueled unsustainable growth and environmental degradation, as was the case during the Industrial Revolution in England, the Pittsburgh killer fogs in the 1940's in America and in most of China today, toward fully sustainable economic growth. In the case of oil, we will be moving from a fuel with impending limitations that is largely concentrated in politically less stable regions to a fuel — natgas — that, unlike oil, is abundant and more widely distributed globally. Once again, those who think of "oil and gas" as one industry, also think because Russia, Iran and Qatar currently have the largest measured quantities of natgas[49] that we will be jumping from an oil OPEC frying pan into a natgas OPEC fire. I doubt this because natgas's widely spread global abundance will provide for significantly more diversification of supplies than is the case with oil. The natgases wave will move us away from strategic instability, unsustainable CO_2 emissions, polluted cities, degraded environments and global climate warming to less and less CO_2 emissions with more sustainable and secure growth. The barriers to entry into The Age of Energy Gases will not be issues of supply, technology or economics, but the lack of natgas understanding and the will of policymakers to end our unsustainable and addictive use of coal and oil.

About Energy Policy

Finally, some of my thoughts about how energy policy must be put in place to accelerate our transition to The Age of Energy Gases. To be effective, energy policy must first take into consideration that the energy input required to sustain the economy is as fundamental as money. And much like money, the energy input is the net result of each person's daily energy expenditure habits. Every individual within the economic system is using, or I prefer to say "spending" energy 24 hours per day, 365 days per year. Therefore, it is the result of the combined habits of all the people within the economy that create national and global patterns and quantities of energy use. During the year 2006, global and U.S. energy consumption by fuel (in million tons oil equivalent)[50] was:

	Global	U.S.
Coal	3090.1 (28.4%)	567.3 (24.4%)
Oil	3889.8 (35.8%)	938.8 (40.4%)
Natgas	2574.9 (23.7%)	566.9 (24.4%)
Nuclear	635.5 (5.8%)	187.5 (8.0%)
Hydro-electricity	688.1 (6.3%)	65.9 (2.8%)

Of course, we each know just how hard it is to change our life patterns and daily habits; basically there are only three effective ways to change:

I Leadership and the moral imperative to leave the world a better place than it was at our birth.

II Government intervention and mandates; these policy tools certainly work, sometimes well and sometimes not so well, as has clearly been demonstrated by various policies enacted during the last major energy legislation in 1978. The CAFE gasoline mileage standards worked well by significantly increasing the average mile per gallon for passenger cars, whereas, the $10 billion ($25 billion in 2007 dollars) spent for the "Synfuel" coal to natural gas program was a complete bust and waste of taxpayer money. Luckily the entire $88 billion allotted ($220 billion in 2007 dollars) was not spent.[51] The Fuel Use Act, part of the comprehensive 1978 legislation, prohibited the use of natgas in new electric power plants and thereby created a 30-year resurgence of coal plants. If the Fuel Use Act had never existed and all the coal-fired electric generating capacity added in the past thirty years had been fueled instead by natural gas, U.S. CO_2 emissions would have been reduced by at least 20%.[52]

III Most all consumers and economists agree that if the price of something goes up you use less of it. Increased prices are always the most effective, productive and efficient way to reduce consumption habits. However, increased prices in both developed and developing economies are fiercely resisted by leaders and policymakers. As a result; all governments in some way or another, sometimes massively and others moderately, subsidize energy consumption. The "inconvenient truth" is that we are not going to get people to change their energy use habits as long as governments subsidize energy. Excellent examples of large subsidies are the price of gasoline in Venezuela and the U.S. and the price of natgas in China and Russia. Unfortunately, because habits are so fundamentally linked to price signals and because energy transitions are so long-term, government subsidies create long-term macroeconomic distortions that can not easily be changed. We must recognize and act upon the reality that energy price subsidies encourage consumption and price increases diminish consumption in the most effective manner because the price signal causes each individual to either conserve or use energy in the most efficient manner for their daily lives.

When I talk about subsidies, many are direct (gasoline in Venezuela, natgas in Russia and China through price controls) or indirect as a result of government policies that require the external and social costs of energy consumption to be paid by the general taxpayer. For instance, the cost America pays for its access to and protection of oil production, transportation and consumption equals at least the entire price of a gallon of gasoline.[53] So the American policy of not taxing the gasoline consumer for the considerable costs of a blue-water navy to the extent it is used to protect oil's sea lanes, Desert Storm to protect oil supplies along with some portion of the Iraq War, or health costs related to gasoline pollution, create the economic forces that stimulated the SUV boom and mass migration to the suburbs. And once the SUV fleet and suburbs exist it becomes very difficult to make changes that will reduce gasoline consumption. Once an inefficient energy infrastructure is in place it becomes very difficult to replace in less than a generation. By not taxing these well-known but difficult-to-measure external costs of energy consumption in America, it became by default American energy policy to allow Americans to become addicted to oil and to build an oil infrastructure for gas guzzlers, often driving hours to and from homes in the suburbs to urban offices, creating enormous inefficiencies and terrible urban traffic problems that in themselves reduce economic productivity. What U.S. policy has done is to stimulate oil consumption on the one hand and then on the other hand give direct subsidies to the oil industry to stimulate oil production.

As to electric power in the name of the rural poor and the consumer, America has subsidized electric power generation directly and indirectly since Roosevelt's New Deal. The nuclear industry receives large direct subsidies in many forms including loan guarantees, R&D subsidies, waste disposal/storage subsidies, limited liability for accidents, insurance subsidies, and decommissioning subsidies. Some reports indicate federal subsidies would comprise 60–90% of the generation cost for new nuclear plants.[54] Over the years coal has received billions of dollars in R&D subsidies but I would say the largest "subsidies" are in the form of the coal industry not paying the externalities of coal mining and coal power plants that can pollute the air and foul the earth, and the commensurate health costs, all of which are paid by society as a whole. Coal is not held to the same environmental standards as natgas. Additionally, coal subsidies include tax breaks such as capital gains treatments of coal royalties and mining reclamation deductions, and direct subsidies such as coal R&D programs, plus the Clean Coal Technology Program which has funded dozens of projects, the Clean Coal Power Initiative, and FutureGen, the ten-year $1.5 billion public-private partnership to build a first-of-its-kind coal-fueled near-zero-emissions power plant. As I write, the coal lobby is asking for billions more taxpayer dollars to pay for coal gasification. Additionally, one of the recently-introduced energy bills would create a variety of financial incentives for the coal companies, including giving free pollution credits to coal-burning power companies based on past pollution levels.[55]

In order to begin to create a level playing field, these large subsidies to oil and coal must end and the large and very real external costs of the consumption of coal and oil now paid by government and taxed to society must be internalized through a system of consumption taxation. Otherwise, consumers who pay less than the full cost of the gasoline or the electricity they use will not change their consumption habits. Pollution or CO_2 taxes could take many forms; however, the most direct and simplest form will always be the best. The direct approach to the reduction of CO_2 emissions is to start where the problem is – nearly 80%[56] of the world's and the U.S.'s CO_2 emissions are the result of coal and oil use. Therefore, the best and most direct way to reduce CO_2 emissions in the world is a direct tax on CO_2 emissions from coal and oil use, not a cap and trade system where many *incentives to consume more energy are left in place* and an often volatile market is created that can be easily gamed by the multinational oil companies, coal companies and financial institutions. Within this sort of market it will be difficult for industry and utilities to make long-term decisions because of a lack of certainty in long-term prices. Cap and trade will hold us back from the fundamental changes and innovations that must be accomplished to reduce carbon use at a rate to meet our global climate challenges. Of course you ask, "Why not tax natgas?" presuming that I do not advocate a CO_2 tax on natgas use because I am in the natgas business. Even though such an assumption is certainly reasonable I can assure you that this is not my intent. My intent is good policy that works. So let me explain. Natgas is not the principal energy problem and a policy that facilitates its use to replace coal and oil will be by far the most rapid (the infrastructure is in place), least expensive and least economically disruptive method of lowering CO_2 emissions and reducing America's demand for imported oil.

We must realize that in spite of the fact that America is the "Saudi Arabia of coal" as the coal companies like to say, coal use is not a viable long-term fuel for a modern 21st century society. Coal currently produces 36% of America's CO_2 emissions.[57] Attempts to sustain the use of coal simply hold back progress and put up large barriers to a coming revolution in energy efficiency. The entire coal infrastructure is a dirty, environmentally degrading, unconscionably inefficient technology that is destined for Schumpeter's "creative destruction."

Natgas is a highly efficient, clean fuel with half or sometimes much less the CO_2 emissions of coal. Natgas use can begin to create a modern efficient system of electric power generation that will create very large savings in power use. Natgas power plants can also meet the growing need for electric power in a timely manner as it takes much less time to site, build and put on-stream a natgas plant than a large coal facility. A fast-track natgas-fired plant can take about three years or less in America, less in other countries, versus a coal plant at about five to ten years.[58] Natgas use must be encouraged to take the place of coal, and therefore coal CO_2 emissions should be taxed at rates that begin to internalize the real cost of its use and natgas should not.

Oil use in America has become an unwelcome "addiction." Oil use produces 44% of the U.S. CO_2 emissions.[59] Over the past decade, America's oil imports have been the largest component of America's trade deficit, larger than its trade deficit with China. Oil imports to the U.S. are costing about $300 billion per year[60] and will likely rise significantly. Regarding total energy consumption, on a per capita basis, America's long-term subsidies to energy use are reflected by the fact that Americans use about twice the energy per capita than other developed economies. Americans use 59 BOE per year as compared to 28 for Germans, 29 for Japanese and 9 for Chinese.[61] In addition to the trade deficit and its related financial problems, oil is also a massive long-term strategic problem with enormous military costs. America is the world's oil policeman. One of the best examples is Desert Storm and the U.S. military intervention to remove Saddam Hussein from Kuwait's oil fields. A coalition of countries paid the U.S. to protect the free flow of oil. Unfortunately for America, this was the exception, so the protection of the world's free flow of oil has cost the U.S. taxpayer hundreds of billions of dollars.

"Business as usual" oil consumption in America and the entire world is no longer sustainable. The entire energy system related to oil is, like coal, facing Schumpeter's "creative destruction." Due to the physical limits of oil's ability to continue to meet demand, because of geostrategic and security problems and tensions that are created by its increased use, and because of the old age of its infrastructure, particularly in the U.S. (many refineries are 50 or more years old), oil's phasing out as a principal energy system will occur either by design, as a result of well-planned policy initiatives such as CAFE standards and CO_2 taxes, or by necessity, as the result of severe economic shocks. These economic shocks will be caused by reaching oil's limits of global production capacity and the subsequent large and sustained price shocks to well over $100 per barrel, or continuing non-related events such as terrorist attacks, the catastrophic collapse or failure of one or two U.S. refineries, a tanker accident and massive oil spill or another Gulf hurricane, any of which would cause very large spikes in oil prices, insurance costs and unwanted economic volatility.

Certainly Americans will be better served by their leaders and policymakers if they recognize these very clear signals and enact a policy to phase out the use of addictive quantities of oil through a system of mandates on gasoline efficiency and phrased in CO_2, or, best of all, gasoline consumption taxes. Natgas should not be taxed. Instead, its use should be encouraged by policy as natgas, through conversions of fleets of automobiles and trucks, can begin nearly immediately to reduce CO_2 emissions and lessen demand for foreign oil at a price no more and probably less than gasoline. Additionally, because of the existing million mile-plus natgas pipeline distribution system, a large number of the over 100 million automobiles that come home each night to a garage already connected to natgas will convert to dual-fuel natgas/gasoline. The use of natgas in the U.S. vehicle fleet can and should be an important component of meeting America's goals of reducing both CO_2 emissions and foreign oil imports. In 2006, net natural gas imports accounted for 16% of U.S. natural gas consumption, so 84% of U.S. natural gas consumption was met by U.S. natural gas production and over 14% came from Canada, so about 98% of the natural gas consumed in America by the U.S. was North American. North American natural gas resources are abundant, so natural gas consumption in the U.S. will continue for the long term to be a domestic North American fuel.

Likewise, as the natgas price increases to a price equal to that of oil and gasoline, Adam Smith's "invisible hand" also goes to work. As the price of natgas increases not only are more domestic natgas resources available but the individual consumer also begins to use less, the quantities of profitable efficiency increases and more and more alternative fuels become profitable without the need for subsidies. As a consequence of the price increases to no more than oil equivalency, more natgas will become available for the market and at the same time, less will be used and more renewable fuels will become competitive in the market so less natgas will be required for the same economic growth. The tax burden on society must also be reduced by the elimination of subsidies for coal and oil. Additionally, because natgas has, with the exception of NOX emissions that are much lower than those of coal and oil, virtually none of the external costs of oil and coal. As more and more natgas replaces the use of oil and coal the tax burden to society for paying the costs of the externalities is also reduced; these cost benefits are rarely included in future economic projections. So, because the tax burden is a drag on the economy, the increased use of natgas and renewables, made possible by higher natgas prices, can offset its higher cost to the consumer as long as the savings the government realizes by not paying the cost of subsidies and externalities for coal and oil are passed along to the consumer in the form of less taxation or are earmarked for such programs as Social Security or health care. With the enormous tax burden of the Iraq War, this is not a time to be subsidizing fuels, particularly coal and oil which cannot become part of America's long-term energy solution. The point here is that because natgas is clean and has few externalities it is a positive input to the economy and the environment. Coal and oil are negative inputs. Coal and oil tend to limit economic growth, reduce economic efficiency and productivity and foul the environment; and, in the case of oil, create increasingly long-term and costly security problems. Therefore, because most economic models only consider the higher cost of price increases and not the often hidden but real offsetting savings and increased productivity induced by natgas use, these models are flawed and always make the economic outcome look worse than it will be in reality. Energy's input to the economy is either positive or negative; government policy should always, to the extent possible, be formulated to encourage or facilitate the energy input that stimulates economic growth and, where possible, reduces pollution and CO_2 emissions.

So why is it not far better to tax energy inputs to the economy that create limits to economic growth by their use and reduce taxes upon labor and capital which stimulate economic growth? A consumption tax on coal and gasoline use is an economically beneficial way to pay for government and it is fair when government uses the revenue to reduce income, payroll and capital taxes.

The forces of energy have long-term effects and are always at work within the economy and the environment and must be accounted for in full in order to create the best possible energy policy for America. For these reasons, I advocate a U.S. energy policy that taxes the use of oil and coal, America's principal energy problems, and not natgas. Natgas is one of the principal solutions and its use to replace coal and oil reduces pollution and CO_2 emissions, helps preserve the environment, reduces the general tax burden created by external costs for all Americans, increases economic productivity, and enhances economic growth. Natgas is econergenically positive; coal and oil are econergenically negative. So, because we all agree that we will use less of what costs more and that we can not sustain increased use of coal and oil, we should phase in taxes on coal and oil and, by doing so, we will give a clear signal to all energy users, entrepreneurs, and venture capitalists that we want to use more of all the cleaner, lower carbon sources and less coal and oil.

I recognize that this chapter includes many statements and thoughts that require much additional study and work, so I highly recommend that the U.S. government create an organization to study natgas as a fuel and natgas qualities, characteristics and potential supplies separate and apart from oil. We need a Department of Natural Gas. For the best in-depth review of natgas by the U.S. government, see the 1993 volume produced by the U.S. Geological Survey (Professional Paper Number 1570) entitled "The Future of Energy Gases."

■ ■ ■ ──

Robert Hefner is Founder and Owner of The GHK Company, a private natural gas exploration and production firm with offices in Oklahoma City, Oklahoma, USA. Mr. Hefner founded GHK in 1959 and, from the 1960's through the 1980's, GHK led in the development of technology necessary to successfully drill and produce many of the world's deepest and highest pressure natural gas wells. Mr. Hefner was also a leader in the industry's successful efforts to deregulate the price of natural gas and he appeared 18 times before Congressional committees testifying on energy matters in the 1970's and 1980's. In 1997, Mr. Hefner discovered one of America's larger onshore natural gas fields. GHK continues as one of Mid-Continent America's active natural gas exploration and production companies. Over the past three decades, Mr. Hefner has authored numerous articles concerning natural gas and its abundance, natural gas's difference from oil, and the importance of natural gas for sustainable long-term economic growth. He is currently writing a book on his theory of "The Age of Energy Gases." For over two decades, Mr. Hefner has actively pursued his interest in China in the areas of energy, foreign affairs, and art. He and his wife, MeiLi, have a collection of contemporary Chinese oil paintings that are amongst the world's most important. Mr. Hefner received a B.S. degree in geology from Oklahoma University.

[1] *Stern Review on the Economics of Climate Change*, 700-page report released October 30, 2006, by economist Sir Nicholas Stern for the British government.

[2] "Nuclear energy to power China," PRLog.Org, June 1, 2007.

[3] Clean Energy Fuels website, "Clean Energy Supports California Governor's Proposal for Reducing Greenhouse Gas Emissions in Motor Vehicles," January 9, 2007; <http://www.cleanenergyfuels.com/07/01-09-07.html>.

[4] *Gas Facts: A Statistical Record of the Gas Industry with 2005 Data*, American Gas Association, Table 8-2; *Statistical Abstract of the United States: 2007*, Table 57.

[5] "The Future of Coal," an interdisciplinary MIT study, summary report, 2007.

[6] U.S. Department of Energy, Energy Information Administration, *Monthly Energy Review*, March 2007.

[7] "Sunset for Synfuels Corp.?", *The Energy Daily*, January 4, 1984.

[8] "Worse Than Gasoline," *Scientific American*, August 2007.

[9] "Energy Demand Will Outstrip Supply, Oil Industry Says," *Wall Street Journal*, July 16, 2007.

[10] "Getting off oil," by Amory Lovins, *The Economist's The World in 2007*.

[11] Carbon Dioxide Information Analysis Center spreadsheet "Global CO_2 Emissions from Fossil-Fuel Burning, Cement Manufacture, and Gas Flaring," with 3.667 multiplying factor.

[12] "Energy Demand Will Outstrip Supply, Oil Industry Says," *Wall Street Journal*, July 16, 2007.

[13] U.S. Department of Energy/Energy Information Administration, *Annual Energy Review 2005*, Table 11.15.

[14] International Energy Agency, *World Energy Outlook 2006*, page 125: "Coal use rises by 59% by 2030 (expressed in tonnes)."

[15] Carbon Dioxide Information Analysis Center spreadsheet "Global CO_2 Emissions from Fossil-Fuel Burning, Cement Manufacture, and Gas Flaring," with 3.667 multiplying factor.

[16] "The Age of Energy Gases," in *International Journal of Hydrogen Energy*, Vol. 27 (2002) 1-9.

[17] Data collected from *Oil Economists' Handbook*, various editions of *International Energy Statistics Sourcebook* and various editions of *BP Statistical Review of World Energy*.

[18] Robert A. Hefner III quote from "Power to the People" by economist Vijay V. Vaitheeswaran, 2003.

[19] Amory Lovins, Rocky Mountain Institute, E-Mail communication July 9, 2007.

[20] "New Thinking About Natural Gas," *U.S. Geological Survey Professional Paper 1570: The Future of Energy Gases*, December 1993.

[21] "Because the atmosphere is rich in oxygen, any methane released into it will spontaneously transform into carbon dioxide and water on a time scale of about ten years." *From The Deep Hot Biosphere*, by Thomas Gold, published 1999 by Springer-Verlag New York Inc., pg. 15.

[22] "Shale gas plays expand," *E&P magazine*, March 2007; "When your gas reservoir is unconventional so is our solution: Shale gas," Schlumberger white paper, October 2005.

[23] *BP Statistical Review of World Energy*, June 2006.

[24] "Unconventional Gas Reservoirs" Power Point presentation by Chris Hopkins, President, Data & Consulting Services, Schlumberger Oilfield Services at 2007 Aspen Institute Forum on Global Energy, Economy and Security.

[25] AAPG Memoir 78, *Giant Oil and Gas Fields of the 1990's*, 2003.

[26] "U.S. Oil and Gas Potential," Exxon Company, U.S.A., Exploration Department, March 1976; "A New Look at the U.S. Oil and Gas Potential," by J.D. Langston, Vice President, Exploration, Exxon Company, U.S.A., presented to The Sixteenth Annual Institute on Petroleum Exploration and Economics, The Southwestern Legal Foundation, Dallas, Texas, March 10, 1976.

[27] Charles B. Wheeler, Senior Vice President, Exxon Company, U.S.A., before the Committee on Energy Regulation, Subcommittee of the Full Committee on Energy & Natural Resources, April, 26, 1984, Washington, D.C.

[28] U.S. Department of Energy/Energy Information Administration, *Monthly Energy Review*, December 2001 and May 2007.

[29] Examples include the U.S. Department of Energy/Energy Information Administration, *Annual Energy Review*, 2006: 1431 Tcf; the Potential Gas Committee's *Potential Supply of Natural Gas in the United States*, 2005: 1,323 Tcf, with reserves added; and others.

[30] *International Petroleum Encyclopedia 2005* with charts indicating estimates of future recovery of natural gas to be between 6,686 Tcf and 9,708 Tcf.

[31] *BP Statistical Review of World Energy*, June 2007.

[32] "Unconventional Gas Reservoirs" PowerPoint presentation by Chris Hopkins, President, Data & Consulting Services, Schlumberger Oilfield Services at 2007 Aspen Institute Forum on Global Energy, Economy and Security.

[33] The Gas Technology Institute (GTI) spends about $25 million per year on natural gas research.

[34] "Potential Supply of Natural Gas in the United States," Report of the Potential Gas Committee, Potential Gas Agency, Colorado School of Mines, published September 2005, page 111; "Methane on Ice," *Chemical & Engineering News*, August 22, 2005, Volume 83, Number 34, pp. 16–17; E-Mail communication from Arthur H. Johnson, Hydrate Energy International, May 21, 2007: "The best global estimates of gas hydrate in place come from the USGS World Energy Assessment. The estimates span three orders of magnitude: 100,000 to 270,000,000 Tcf."

[35] "When your gas reservoir is unconventional so is our solution: Shale gas," Schlumberger white paper, October 2005: The prize is an estimated 500 Tcf to 780 Tcf of natural gas in place.

[36] Cesare Marchetti and Nebojsa Nakicenovic, 1979, "The dynamics of energy systems and the logistic substitution model," RR-79-13, 73 p. and Nebojsa Nakicenovic, 1986, "Patterns of change: Technological substitution and long waves in the United States," WP-86-12, 32 p., International Institute for Applied Systems Analysis, Laxenburg, Austria.

[37] *BP Statistical Review of World Energy*, June 2006.

[38] Woods Hole Oceanographic Institution; Dave Gallo.

[39] "World Population Estimates and Projections by Single Years: 1750–2150," Population Reference Bureau.

[40] "Hydrogen Futures: Toward a Sustainable Energy System," Worldwatch Institute Paper 157, August 2001.

[41] "Hydrogen as an energy carrier," <http://www.hydrogenassociation.org/general/faqs.asp>, April 10, 2007.

[42] "National Hydrogen Energy Road Map" approved by India's National Hydrogen Energy Board in January 2006

[43] "Nuclear energy is resurgent," *Washington Post*, January 6, 2007.

[44] "Nuclear Energy to Power China," PRLog.Org, June 1, 2007.

[45] "Nuclear energy is resurgent," *Washington Post*, January 6, 2007.

[46] "The Future of Coal," an interdisciplinary MIT study, summary report, 2007, page ix.

[47] U.S. Department of Energy, Energy Information Administration, *Monthly Energy Review*, March 2007.

[48] *Big Coal: The Dirty Secret Behind America's Energy Future*, by Jeff Goodell, 2006.

[49] *BP Statistical Review of World Energy*, June 2006.

[50] *BP Statistical Review of World Energy*, June 2007.

[51] "Conceptual Perspectives on Energy Policy," by Llewellyn King, *International Association for Energy Economics Newsletter*, Spring 1996; "Sunset for Synfuels Corp.?", *The Energy Daily*, January 4, 1984; "Congress kills the U.S. Synfuels Corp.," *Science News*, January 11, 1986.

[52] If all the coal-fired electric generating capacity added since 1979 had been fueled instead by natural gas, U.S. CO_2 emissions would have been reduced by eight billion metric tons. Data compiled from 31 U.S. Department of Energy/Energy Information Administration sources, six Edison Electric Institute sources and one Carbon Dioxide Information Analysis Center source; extrapolated for current decade.

[53] "The Real Price of Gasoline," International Center for Technology Assessment, Report No. 3: An Analysis of the Hidden External Costs Consumers Pay to Fuel their Automobiles, 1998, page 34, with low estimate of the external and social cost of gasoline at $4.60/gallon.

[54] "Nuclear Power in the US: Still Not Viable Without Subsidy," Earth Track, November 2005; "Nuclear Subsidies: $7.1 billion a year," Third World Traveler; "The Energy Bill HR6: A gift that keeps on taking a billion dollar budget buster at taxpayer expense," Nuclear Information and Resource Service; "Analysis of Nuclear Subsidies in Lieberman-McCain Climate Stewardship and Innovation Act of 2007, Public Citizen, January 2007.

[55] "Who Owns The Sky?", by Frank O'Donnell, June 28, 2007, www.TomPaine.com; "Will Congress' New Enviro Legislation Sell Us Out to the Coal Industry?", by Frank O'Donnell, July 20, 2007, <http://www.alternet.org>; "No Clean Coal," July 24, 2007, *Laurence Journal World* & 6 News; "FutureGen — Tomorrow's Pollution-Free Power Plant," U.S. Department of Energy, <http://www.fossil.energy.gov/programs/powersystems/futuregen>; "About FutureGen," June 2007, <http://www.futuregenalliance.org>; "An Overview of Senate Energy Bill Subsidies to the Fossil Fuel Industry," May 2, 2003, Taxpayers for Common Sense.

[56] Carbon Dioxide Information Analysis Center, Spreadsheet "Global CO_2 emissions from Fossil-Fuel Burning, Cement, Manufacture, and Gas Flaring: 1751 – 2004," with necessary 3.667 multiplier.

[57] U.S. Department of Energy/Energy Information Administration, "U.S. Carbon Dioxide Emissions from Energy Sources, 2006 Flash Estimate," online from Office of Integrated Analysis & Forecasting, printed July 11, 2007, <http://www.eia.doe.gov/oiaf/1605/flash/flash.html>.

[58] Conversations, C.H. Guernsey & Co.

[59] U.S. Department of Energy/Energy Information Administration, "U.S. Carbon Dioxide Emissions from Energy Sources, 2006 Flash Estimate," online from Office of Integrated Analysis & Forecasting, printed July 11, 2007, <http://www.eia.doe.gov/oiaf/1605/flash/flash.html>.

[60] Trade Deficit Rises to Record $763.6B," by Martin Crutsinger, The Associated Press, February 13, 2007.

[61] BP *Statistical Review of World Energy*, June 2006; population numbers via online information from *The World Factbook*, Central Intelligence Agency.

Part **4**

A GLOBAL ENERGY CONSENSUS: NEW POLICY DIRECTIONS AND THE WAY FORWARD

CHAPTER 9

New Energy Paradigm, New Foreign Policy Paradigm

David Rothkopf
Visiting Scholar,
Carnegie Endowment for International Peace

CHAPTER 10

The ~~Global~~ AMERICAN Politics of Energy

Stephen E. Biegun
Vice President, International Governmental Affairs,
Ford Motor Company

CHAPTER 11

A Blueprint for Energy Security

John Podesta
President and CEO, Center for American Progress

Peter Ogden
Senior National Security Analyst, Center for American Progress

"We must acknowledge that energy policy, environmental policy, economic policy, national security policy, and foreign policy are all inextricably linked."

— DAVID ROTHKOPF

New Energy Paradigm, New Foreign Policy Paradigm

David Rothkopf
Visiting Scholar, Carnegie Endowment for International Peace

I f you go to a psychologist and outline the problems in your life, the first advice you will likely receive is that you cannot change the world. Instead, you should focus on changing what you can — yourself.

It seems the moment has come for U.S. foreign policy to spend a little time on the couch. An examination of U.S. energy policies and their close links to U.S. foreign policy may offer a useful place to start this process of re-evaluation.

For most of the years since the end of the Cold War, U.S. foreign policy has focused on using our great national power to influence or effect change in the world. We have often been accused of trying to remake the planet in our own image. While this claim is something of an exaggeration, it is not an overstatement to suggest that the typical agenda of U.S. presidents, secretaries of state, national security advisors, and their associates has been full of initiatives and proposals to promote U.S.-style democracy and markets, defeat "enemies," prop-up or advance "friends," extend influence, and alter behaviors that we found unsettling. We have sought to coax, buy, bully, cajole, and battle the world into changing, continent by continent, decade by decade.

As for changing ourselves, well, as Jon Stewart might say, "not so much." We have remained stagnant despite the fact that the vision for U.S. national security policy offered by its first framers in the post-Cold War years (whether through the structure they created as part of the National Security Act of 1947 or through key documents like George Kennan's "Long Telegram") underscores the recognition that national security and foreign policy — whether through the cultivation of strength, character, or the most basic framing of national interests — begin at home.

In general, we have exhibited outward-focused, "we-can-change-the-world" behavior. This has been consistent with a deep-seated American worldview that we offer the world the best of all possible systems and that we should be both a model and an example to everyone else. A corollary has been an enduring suspicion of things foreign and a sense that most threats to our security and our position originated beyond our borders. In turn, our international policies had to be oriented accordingly. What is more, as Henry Kissinger has ruefully observed, we have tended to believe that given the chance to change, any country would automatically seek to be more like us.

But early in the 21st century, we face a starkly altered reality that should, it may be hoped, produce a dramatically different U.S. foreign policy stance. Our leverage has diminished on many fronts. While still the world's richest and most powerful nation, some of our greatest strengths faded with the end of the Cold War. Notably, we experienced the absence of an enemy that drove some into our arms and the diminution of the edge we once gained by being the nation best-prepared to fight a global thermonuclear war. Furthermore, other nations have gained economically and militarily; new alliances and different kinds of threats have evolved; and we have proven ourselves unable and, to a large degree, unworthy of imposing our will even on much smaller, weaker nations such as Iraq or Afghanistan. Our stature has diminished; our ability to offer ourselves as a potential example to others has been compromised; and the clout of others, such as the rising giants of Asia and the emerging world, has grown.

Finally, it seems clear that something else has altered that is just as significant and should have equally great implications for the future of U.S. national security and foreign policy formation. Despite all the changes noted above, most of the greatest threats to the U.S. and the most promising solutions to the priority "global" problems actually lie in the place over which we have the most control: here at home.

Nevertheless, this is not a "blame-America" argument intended to let wrong-doers overseas off the hook. There are real bad actors out there and there are worrisome trends that threaten America's global interests. Furthermore, despite America's size or influence, it is clear that unilateral action at home will not, in many areas, be a sufficient policy response. Nonetheless, it is hard to deny that in most — if not all — of the top priority areas of U.S. international policy, an increasingly large component of sensible foreign and national security policy lies in the conception and implementation of creative and courageous domestic policies.

Superpower, Heal Thyself?

This fact has already been recognized in the area of homeland security. However, our policies and the institutions created to implement them remain flawed. In addition, a hugely disproportionate component of our expenditures on securing the U.S. against terror threats have been diverted to overseas misadventures or to bureaucratic bloat at home. But the reality extends well beyond the misnamed, mismanaged "war on terror" as it is currently conceived and touches literally every major international priority that the U.S. maintains. The following section considers these priorities one by one:

First, some priorities concern moderating and diversifying U.S. energy demand:

- *Combating Islamic Extremism.* Vital funding for regimes that support terror, extremism, and interests at odds with the United States comes from the purchase of petroleum products. Reduce demand for those products, and reduce resources on which they depend.

- *Managing Unrest in the Middle East.* Our interests in the Middle East are heavily dominated by our dependence on oil supplies from the region. Reduce dependence on those supplies, and both enhance energy security and reduce the need for costly, fruitless interventions in the region.

- *Combating Nationalism and Anti-Americanism.* International leaders of organized resistance to American goals and key actors in advancing goals contrary to U.S. interests are also dependent on oil sales and the high price of petroleum products to sustain their regimes and augment their influence. These include Russia's Putin, Venezuela's Chávez, and Iran's Khatami and Ahmadenijad. Reduce dependence on the products they sell, create downward pressure on their revenues, and reduce their influence and contain their threat.

- *Reducing the Likelihood that Resource Competition Will be a Future Source of Conflict.* The surging demands of rapidly growing countries like China and India, not to mention those of the rest of the developing world, could turn resource competition, which is currently heating up across Africa, the Middle East, Latin America, and elsewhere, into a source of international tension for the United States. Fostering the proliferation of alternative energy sources, especially turning to those for which there is effectively limitless supply (e.g., sun, wind, water, hydrogen), mitigates the factors behind these growing concerns.

- *Building New Relationships.* Cooperation in the development of new global markets for alternative forms of energy or on changing environmental and technological standards is a chance to build new cooperative relationships. The U.S.-Brazil effort to cooperate on biofuels development qualifies as just one example.

- *Moderating the Threat of Global Warming.* Given scientific acknowledgement of the global warming threat and the potential implications for low-lying regions or those most vulnerable to climate-related disasters, moderating U.S. production of greenhouse gases (GHGs) through alternative energy policy has important international consequences. This is especially salient given the U.S. role as the world's leading producer of GHGs.

- *Reducing Vulnerability to International Economic Pressure.* Reducing dependence on foreign oil helps reduce the trade deficit, fight inflation, and restore U.S. policymakers' influence over our own economic destiny.

However, the area of top foreign policy and national security concerns in which U.S. domestic action is a vital yet neglected lynchpin extends to areas far beyond just those associated with energy and environmental policy. Some illustrations include the following:

- *Maintaining American Military Strength.* A strong military is not feasible unless there are funds to support it. Moreover, if the costs of health care and the issues of an aging society are not addressed, the next President will be facing budget constraints unparalleled in U.S. history. According to the Center for Budget and Policy Priorities, absent solutions to the growth of Social Security and health care costs, by 2017, paying for entitlements and even somewhat reduced defense costs will leave no room in the U.S. budget for anything else. In all likelihood, this will cause both substantial defense cuts and substantial tax increases.

- *Reducing Dependence on Foreign Lenders.* The fact that the United States is heavily dependent on foreign lenders to meet its national fiscal requirements is often cited as a threat on several levels. With nearly 50 percent of U.S. Treasuries held by two major Asian borrowers, we are vulnerable both to changes in their circumstances and/or their policies.[1] The way to reduce this threat is to reduce our borrowing and to increase the U.S. savings rate.

- *Moderating the Negative Impact of Foreign Competition.* The rise of China and India is often cited as a threat to U.S. workers whose jobs are at risk of being shipped overseas. In reality, their rise is good for us in many respects including the creation of export-driven jobs, reducing poverty, stabilizing unstable regions, and aligning international interests. Rather, we must realize that to compete, to attract investment and create jobs, the key is better educating Americans and ensuring we have the infrastructure and regulatory policies we need to draw companies seeking our high-levels of productivity and innovation.

- *Combating the Flow of Drugs Into the United States.* The "war on drugs" has been a war on drug supplies. After decades of failure despite committing major resources and costing hundreds of thousands of lives, it remains clear that the only way to win this war is through reducing U.S. domestic demand. This includes the legalization of some drugs that are more dangerous as illicit commodities than they would be as legal, regulated ones.

- *Restoring U.S. Legitimacy Worldwide.* If the United States fails to honor the principles outlined in its own constitution, which has been mimicked worldwide due to its clear articulation of such values, it cannot be taken seriously when proposing higher standards internationally.

- *Reducing Proliferation of Weapons of Mass Destruction.* A cornerstone of the idea underlying the nuclear Non-Proliferation Treaty (NPT), the essential key to providing support for limiting the spread of weapons, was that those countries that had such weapons would begin to eliminate them in a serious fashion. The United States, as the world's nuclear weapons leader, must lead this effort if future efforts to create an NPT 2.0 that is more effective than the current, crumbling regime are to work.

One problem we face is that foreign policy specialists tend to seek foreign policy solutions for problems. In the same way, Middle East specialists tend to look for Middle East solutions. But with remarkable regularity today, we find international issues with important domestic components to their solution. In addition, there are traditional foreign policy problems with significant technical or economic components required. The system actually produces biases — through the nature of training and the compartmentalization of efforts and incentive structures — that make holistic assessments difficult and arrival at optimum strategies almost impossible. Someday, perhaps for another discussion, one solution will be to emulate Goldwater-Nichols requirements for intra-military jointness among non-military agencies of the U.S. government so that policymakers have a broader, less-territorially defined basis for their deliberations and decision-making.

The New Energy Paradigm

For the purposes of this chapter however, it is worthwhile to focus on the emerging new energy paradigm as a powerful, and perhaps the most useful, near-term driver of this new, more introspective approach to managing policy issues. Also, the energy paradigm encourages us to focus our efforts in those areas over which we have the most control.

A "perfect storm" of developments has led to the emergence of this new energy paradigm. First, rising oil prices have increased pressure on consumers and national accounts. Next, the wars in Iraq and Afghanistan as well as broader instability in the Middle East have underscored the importance of reducing our dependence on that region's oil. Third, the scientific consensus that global warming is a real, man-influenced phenomenon with potentially serious near-term consequences has mobilized many to call for a retreat from our dependence on fossil fuels. The destruction in New Orleans resulting from Hurricane Katrina, seen by many as a consequence of global warming or at least as a wake-up call regarding its potential consequences, was catalytic here. Finally, a series of technological developments has made alternative energy sources more affordable and more commercially viable. The massive increases in investment in alternative energy during the past several years, up 43 percent in 2006 alone,[2] have fueled innovation and placed on the near horizon a growing array of viable, high-impact alternative energy options. These alternatives range from plug-in hybrid vehicles to biofuels produced much more efficiently through cellulosic processes or through alternative feedstocks such as algae, from much·cheaper solar cells to new technologies such as wave to smart grids that manage electricity distribution much more efficiently.

The Critical Steps

The first step consists of recognizing that U.S. energy policy is neither something to focus on only during crises nor is it something to be left primarily to a small clique of special interests. We must also acknowledge that energy policy, environmental policy, economic policy, national security policy, and foreign policy are all inextricably linked. As a consequence, they must be viewed by specialists from every area and especially by a new cadre of experts that are steeped in a variety of disciplines and that understand the interactions of such disciplines.

Beyond these initial steps, three more are required, each of which is actually a process tied to a principle:

DIVERSIFICATION

The first critical step — from a national security, environmental and economic perspective — must be a diversification away from fossil fuels. These currently account for 85 percent of our energy mix, are responsible for over 80 percent of U.S. GHG emissions, and are drawn largely from unreliable partners worldwide. Additional supporting arguments include the inflationary impact of price changes, the size of oil supplies, and the relative costs to innovation and job creation that results from putting all of our energy eggs in one basket. Forty percent of our oil comes from OPEC, primarily Saudi Arabia and Venezuela.[3] Perhaps more important, according to the International Energy Agency's most recent Oil Market Report, annual non-OPEC production growth is low, at just 0.9 mbd (million barrels per day), and it is driven almost entirely by the Former Soviet Union and Africa. This leads to an increasing concentration of oil supplies in politically volatile regions.[4]

Nonetheless, at this juncture, it is important to underscore the point often made by Cambridge Energy Research Associate's Chairman Daniel Yergin among others: energy independence defined as doing away with the need for oil imports, or even imports specifically from high risk areas, is a false promise. He correctly notes that there is but one global oil market. Thus, turbulence in the Middle East or Nigeria or Venezuela will impact oil supplies and prices around the world. The answer is not found primarily in altering where we get our oil;

instead, it derives from reducing its share of our energy mix by diversifying into other energy sources.

In the long term, creating a more balanced national energy portfolio calls for a significant investment in innovation. In the short to medium term, this means promoting and drawing upon the immediate options available to us beginning with conservation and extended through the use of existing technologies and resources in biofuels, clean coal, solar, and wind. Already biofuels are being promoted through aggressive targets, but policies are still being bent to the specifications of domestic political interests rather than the public good. To pick just one example, our ethanol policy could be simplified and made more effective at a lower cost to the U.S. government by eliminating the 54-cent-a-gallon tariff on imported ethanol, which is already avoided by most eligible imports, and transferring the blender's credit to a producer's credit to ensure that only domestically produced ethanol benefits from it. These policy changes would allow sustainably-produced biofuels to enter the United States and compete with imported oil. However, there are no panaceas. No single energy option is going to be the silver bullet that ends our dependency on fossil fuels. Technological advances are affording us a wider range of energy choices, including clean renewable energies that have the added bonus of reducing our green house gas emissions.

CONSERVATION

Diversification of energy sources can only take us so far. As noted above, the most important immediate and ongoing step is to promote conservation and enhanced energy efficiency throughout our economy, from our cars to our homes to our industry. This is no easy task, but it is possible. We have proven countless times that when faced with a national security imperative, our country can adjust to meet it. Rationing during World War II went far beyond fuel to goods as diverse as sugar and shoes. Reducing our energy consumption today should be considered as a similar imperative. Likewise, it should be approached in the same way, underscoring that every unit of energy saved makes us safer, makes the planet healthier, and, given the technologies that may be associated with such conservation, could drive economic growth and job creation.

For example, our homes account for nearly a quarter of our total national energy consumption. They also cause more pollution than our cars because 68 percent of the electricity comes from fossil fuel-fired power plants. As the majority of that electricity goes to appliances, it is estimated that new appliance efficiency standards, already in place in some states, could eliminate the need for up to 40 power plants nationwide by 2020, thus cutting emissions equal to 12 million cars.[5] Such changes are possible with appliances already available on the market thanks to the commitment of individual states and manufacturers to energy efficiency.

INNOVATION

Such ambitious diversification and conservation goals will not be achieved without a commitment to innovation and a transformation in our way of thinking. Renewable energy scientists and engineers have already created efficient technologies for natural gas, biofuels, and others that, if put to full use in all applications, could halve American barrels burnt per dollar of GDP to 25 percent of 1975 levels, according to estimates made by the Rocky Mountain Institute's Amory Lovins.[6] However, the benefits of these technologies are being lost, as they remain underutilized by public and private entities alike.

The increase in investment dollars flowing into this segment of the industry in recent years illustrates that the private sector is willing to dedicate resources to clean energy alternatives. But in order for the United States to fully capture the benefits of this emerging market and enhance its competitiveness under a new energy paradigm, both the public and private sectors must employ their own energy saving strategies as well as expand the country's technological and scientific resource base. Initiatives, such as the U.S. Department of Energy's (DOE) Building Technologies Program which collaborates with the private sector, state and local governments, and national research institutions to develop and implement cutting edge technologies and efficiency solutions, can be expanded and serve as a model for other energy consuming sectors such as transport and industry.

Enhancing U.S. energy security over the long term will necessitate a renewed and concerted focus on science and technology that will most certainly require sustained political will and the strategic allocation of resources. Lovins also estimates that it would require investment of $180 billion over the next decade to eliminate oil dependence, and that doing so will revitalize strategic industries enabling them to save $130 billion gross, or $70 billion net, per year by 2025. In the automotive industry alone, the impact of incorporating existing efficiency technologies into cars and trucks in order to reach 35 miles per gallon by 2018 would create 23,900 protected jobs by 2020, with the benefits from investments in fuel efficiency creating 241,000 more jobs throughout the country, according to recent analysis from the Union of Concerned Scientists. The technology would save a net $37 billion in 2020 alone, cut national oil use by 1.6 million barrels of oil a day in 2020 and reduce CO_2 emissions by 260 million tons.[7]

The government has taken initial steps toward this end, highlighted by the recently announced $23.6 billion dollar DOE[8] spending plan for renewable fuel technologies. But the country can and should certainly do much more to fortify U.S. leadership in the field. For example, the Defense Department is one of the largest energy consumers in the country, accounting for nearly two percent of consumption.[9] Dedicating defense dollars toward developing competitive alternative energy resources would contribute to substantial savings to the national budget as well as improve security positions within the field. Such ideas are gaining momentum as U.S. Defense Advanced Research Projects Agency's (DARPA) Biofuels Program just awarded Honeywell a $6.7 million contract to develop a process to convert vegetable and algal oils to jet fuel.[10] This program is being expanded to include cellulosic conversion and to tackle the critical hurdles in algal oil production efficiency — an indication of the growing understanding of the scope of the challenge and the variety of paths that can be developed to meet it.

On the private sector side, major companies are already responding to market forces and trying to capture the cost and efficiency benefits associated with greater efficiency. Major U.S. retailers such as Kohl's, Target, Macy's, and Tiffany & Co. have incorporated solar and energy efficiency strategies into their nationwide operations. Tiffany's solar projects in the company's New Jersey retail distribution centers will supply an estimated 30 percent of required peak electricity; the strategy is expected to save the company $0.5 million annually.[11] Wal-Mart is constructing experimental 'green' stores aimed at energy efficiency and conservation. As one of the largest private heavy-duty truck fleets in the country (approximately 6,800 trucks), Wal-Mart has also announced plans to double the fleet's fuel efficiency by 2015 by incorporating auxiliary power technologies and other efficiency innovations, such as aerodynamic tractor packages. The company expects to save $494 million a year from efficiency measures by 2020.[12]

Despite the reticence of some U.S. automakers, hybrid technologies are taking hold and gaining greater presence within the United States, expanding the choices for U.S. consumers. While hybrids have not yet made a significant dent on oil imports, saving only 5.5 million barrels of oil in last five years,[13] market penetration will contribute to the country's energy diversification. Within the last five years alone, hybrid sales have grown 72 percent[14] and will likely increase as technological innovation makes alternatives more readily available and affordable to consumers.

Ten Ideas: An Energy Policy Sampler

No alternative energy plan in any country worldwide has worked without government involvement. This is due to the nature of energy market regulation and the reluctance of major energy companies and their partners, such as the auto industry and the power generation industry, to voluntarily make a major push toward changes that might be seen as serving environmental and related security interests. But there are also many successes to highlight. Wind energy prices would certainly have not fallen by thirty-fold since 1980 if it were not for European government incentives to invest in this area. Similarly, Brazil's ethanol subsidies program not only has saved the country an estimated $50 billion in imported oil costs in three decades and created over a million jobs, but the ethanol industry is thriving in Brazil today, over a decade since the subsidies were lifted. The "free market" energy policy of the Reagan Administration resulted in negative effective tax rates for alternative energy investment, favoring gas and oil investments.[15] Since the administration of George H.W. Bush, there has been a much more activist energy tax policy and a greater emphasis on alternatives and conservation.[16] Progress has been made, but it has not been proportional to our needs. Our efforts must be redoubled to confront today's energy and national security challenges.

The complexity of our energy mix makes it a mistake to focus on overly-simplistic, one-size-fits-all solutions, despite the tendency of debaters and the framers of debate to pit one approach against another. We can ill afford to rule out any approaches that make sense, and as noted above, diversity is an important goal. Consequently, thoughtfully coordinated policies that extend across market segments are vital. They also must be harmonized with policies assessing the international impact of each approach, including: identifying the significance of having new partners; seeking to avoid future dependencies; and promoting global markets in new technologies and feedstocks.

A few areas and ideas that should be factored into the new energy policy mix include the following:

PROMOTING CONSERVATION

The decreased energy intensity of the U.S. economy draws much attention. That our economy has grown at a rate six times faster than our energy consumption over the past thirty years is impressive and promising. Nonetheless, we are still consuming 25 percent more energy than we did in 1980; we still lead the world in energy consumption and emissions; and we are still by far the number one consumer in the global petroleum markets.[17] Decreased energy intensity thus allows us to falsely congratulate ourselves on a statistic that is in large part the consequence of the rise of less energy-intensive industries, such as services and high tech, as a share of our total productivity. Services have grown from 60 percent of our GDP 30 years ago to 77 percent today. Also, within industry, manufacturing has shifted into less energy-intensive products.[18] Further, the United States remains the world's largest source of GHGs, responsible for 25 percent of global emissions.[19] The Bush administration's climate policy — announced in February 2002 — has the goal of reducing GHG emissions intensity by approximately 18 percent over the 2002 to 2012 time period. Simply put, this misses the target. We do not need to become proportionally less dependent; rather, we need to reduce our overall dependence on fossil fuels.

That said, a similar goal in the 1990s successfully triggered investment in technological change and alternatives, demonstrating the important role that the government can play in creating incentives for action in the private sector.[20] Our circumstances today call for a real departure from policies that can be best described as more of the same. We must develop policies to encourage consumers and companies to opt for existing clean, efficient technology, to promote innovation to improve the cost-effectiveness of going green, and to develop new alternatives. Just a few of these proposals are outlined below, but they should be framed with an aggressive overall target such as Senator Bingaman's recent proposal to reduce our emissions to 2006 levels by 2020. In the context of proposals such as Angela Merkel's, which calls for reducing Germany's overall emissions by 30 percent by 2020, the most aggressive U.S. proposals look modest.

GAS/BTU TAX

Despite historical resistance, support continues for increasing the federal gas tax as a means of efficiently and directly reducing gas consumption and decreasing our oil dependence. The average gas tax in the United States is a mere 41 cents a gallon, of which 18.4 cents is federally mandated. According to the Congressional Budget Office, a tax increase of just 46 cents a gallon would achieve a 10 percent reduction in consumption.[21] Also, by each penny the tax is raised, the government will gain more than $1 billion in revenue that could be applied to investment in alternatives and efficiency. Even doubling or tripling our gas tax, it would still be dwarfed by those in Europe, which average around $4.00 a gallon. In the United Kingdom, where the gas tax is $4.24 a gallon, drivers use their cars 46 percent less than Americans.[22]

Again, we should not underestimate the will of the American people to make sacrifices. A recent poll found that while 85 percent of Americans would oppose a gas tax increase, this number dropped to just 55 percent when the question was tied to a reduction of the U.S. dependence on foreign oil.[23] There is also bipartisan support; a growing number of opinion leaders on the right and left have come out in favor of a gas tax, including Alan Greenspan, Gregory Mankiw, Charles Krauthammer, John Tierney, Gregg Easterbrook, and Tom Friedman.

A 50 cent increase in the gas tax will likely be proposed in Congress this fall and merits serious consideration. However, gas taxes can be regressive, placing a disproportionate burden on low-income and middle-class Americans. Measures to alleviate this should be embraced. Thus, there should be deliberation of proposals waiving the tax for low-income Americans as well as creating incentives within the tax structure to reward purchasers and operators of more efficient vehicles.

Such a tax is the litmus test of whether we are serious about changing energy behaviors. Political candidates from both parties wince at the suggestion of introducing such a tax even as they offer rhetoric calling for the kind of changes that only such a tax can bring. One such change would come from the introduction of the tax in the form of a price floor for gasoline, thus ensuring the economic viability of alternative energy programs and taking the pricing levers out of the hands of major energy companies. Such companies have repeatedly proved that their own talking points about leaving pricing to the markets are hollow. A recent example involves the statement by the secretary general of OPEC that the West should stop considering plans to invest in biofuels or OPEC would retaliate by reducing investment in new petroleum productive capacity. This one statement alone compromises the idea that normal rules of supply and demand pertain in the cartel dominated world of oil prices.

CARBON CAP AND TRADE

Carbon cap and trade proposals are among the more controversial in the energy policy debate, but also among those most worthy of serious contemplation. Europe's carbon market is valued today at $28 billion, and London School of

Economics Professor Nicholas Stern has predicted this will rise to $40 billion by 2010. By 2012, the EU is seeking to reach a target of emissions eight percent below 1990 levels.[24] Is the system flawed? Certainly. Weaknesses range from high levels of market volatility to excessive influence of lobbying in the designation of industry targets. However, as we saw with a similar U.S. initiative to control sulfur dioxide emissions (the cause of acid rain) through tradable permits, markets of this sort have achieved desired goals in the past. A study published in *Nature* revealed that $132 million worth of equipment upgrades could accomplish the same positive environmental impact as the $6 billion already spent on projects to curb GHG emissions.[25] For these upgrades to make economic sense, carbon must have a cost.

Instituting a carbon cap and trade system would have a material impact on our economy. To be successful, it must be developed with an eye to minimizing the costs and risks already recognized in these systems: namely, reducing effective industry pressure; establishing a well-calibrated system for determining the number of permits; and allowing for adjustment based on the business cycle to minimize volatility.[26] In the United States, the diversity of our geography and natural resources will also call for some thought to be given to those areas with less access to renewable sources of energy, such as wind and solar.

CARBON SEQUESTRATION

Policies to encourage carbon sequestration should be introduced, ideally in tandem with the cap and trade system. A study by the DOE found that integrating an allowance allocation incentive for carbon sequestration into a cap and trade system could result in an additional emissions impact of four percent of covered emissions.[27] Carbon capture is a process that is well understood and relatively straightforward to implement at large point sources. Sequestration, which goes beyond capture to separation and storage or reuse, needs much more intensive research. Today, the DOE has estimated the cost of sequestration for one ton of carbon to be between $100 and $300.[28] Reducing these costs should be a top priority.

Worth attention in the carbon sequestration discourse is the potential for algae scrubbers to absorb the CO_2 from power plant emissions. These algae processes have the potential to produce a range of products for our economy, from fuels to animal feed. At a time when land use and commodity price inflation are becoming serious concerns, algae's potential biofuel yield of 5000 gallons per acre makes the case for investment in this alternative all the more compelling.

CAFE

Corporate Average Fuel Economy (CAFE) standards are also a highly contentious political issue today, pitting the logic of raising standards against a struggling auto industry. The average car in the United States puts more than 1.5 tons of carbon into the air every year, and the transport sector accounts for 27 percent of total U.S. emissions, according to the Environmental Protection Agency (EPA). CAFE standards have not been increased since 1990 for passenger cars and there are gross loopholes in the system, such as the exception of large vehicles weighing more than 8,500 pounds from fuel economy standards and the gas-guzzler tax.[29] This encourages the proliferation of massive SUVs on the roads that we see today and discourages manufacturers from investing in fuel efficiency.

The current Senate bill to raise CAFE standards to 35 miles per gallon by 2020 is a step in the right direction. The Union of Concerned Scientists found that raising the average fuel economy of new passenger cars and light trucks from today's level of 24 miles per gallon to 37 miles per gallon within 10 to 15 years would be technically feasible and cost effective for the consumer with gasoline at $2.50 a gallon.[30] With gasoline prices topping $3.00 a gallon and a dismal outlook for oil supplies, improving standards at this rate would actually produce savings. Given the national security imperative we are faced with, however, Americans must be prepared to go further. More aggressive proposals for a CAFE standard of 40 miles per gallon have been repeatedly introduced in Congress. The projected targets have been for 2010, for 2016, and now by Senator Stevens for 2017, and even these are well below what is technically and commercially feasible with existing technologies.

LIGHT RAIL

Investing in light rail and similar commutation infrastructure is also a critical component to reducing our oil consumption by freeing Americans from their cars and high gas prices. Our federal transportation policy today pumps billions of dollars into new roads each year. A fundamental paradigm shift is required, focusing on mass transit as the clean and efficient means of transport in urban areas. According to a February 2006 Pew Poll, 68 percent of the public supported spending more on subway, rail, and bus systems.[31]

POWER GENERATION

Power plants consume roughly 40 percent of all raw fuel used in the United States today.[32] Moreover, a construction boom is forthcoming, with $50 billion in new investment projected. As in many areas of energy policy, individual states are leading the charge in transforming the power industry, with 20 already implementing laws requiring major electric utilities to produce 15 percent of their power from wind, solar, geothermal, and other clean alternatives to fossil fuels by 2020. A new analysis by the federal Energy Information Administration has said that this policy, if implemented on the national level, would raise energy prices by less than one percent.[33] Around the world, countries are pursuing far more aggressive targets; Scotland is targeting 40 percent renewable power generation by 2020 and Spain seeks 30 percent by 2010. China shares our goal of 15 percent renewable power generation by 2020, but with a rate of electricity demand growth more than double our own.

ALTERNATIVES NOW

The United States needs to aggressively pursue and develop alternatives to oil imports that are available now or that promise to be available in the near future. They include clean coal, nuclear, and biofuels.

Clean Coal

In addition to seeking non-fossil fuel alternatives, clean coal presents an excellent intermediate solution to our energy security challenge. More than half of electricity generated in the United States today is coal powered, and the United States remains a net exporter of this natural resource. Clean coal generally refers to a range of technologies that would make the production of energy — be it electricity or fuels — from coal a cleaner and greener process. Already, there have been successful government-led efforts to reduce the emissions of sulfur dioxide from coal plants, driven by the concern over acid rain in the 1980s and 1990s. Today, research efforts are shifting over to carbon emissions. Clean coal is also an area with great potential for international cooperation, something the United States has sorely lacked in the energy arena. The Asia-Pacific Partnership on Clean Development brings together the world's four biggest coal producers — the United States, China, India, and Australia — in addition to Japan and South Korea, with the aim of maintaining the use of this fossil fuel while reducing its environmental impact.[34] China's commitment to spend over $180 billion on cleaner energy technologies is likely to include a heavy investment in this area and cooperation is therefore likely to be fruitful between the two countries. (In fact, U.S.-China energy cooperation is likely to be one of the links that might help draw us together in our complex relationship ... and will be an important offset to the simultaneously growing challenges of resource competition, concern about Chinese environmental degradation, and concern about nuclear proliferation — all of which shares some links to bilateral energy cooperation with that country.)

Nuclear

Nuclear power is in the midst of what industry advocates are terming a renaissance. After nearly 30 years without a new nuclear project, 20 projects are in various stages of development around the country.[35] Nuclear's rebirth, after being crippled by the public's safety concerns and the private sector's economic concerns, is due primarily to its potential to produce baseload power without relying on fossil fuel and with zero GHG emissions. The concept of nuclear power as "green" is hard for some in the environmental community to swallow, but already leaders like Patrick Moore, a founder of Greenpeace, have been won over. New activity in nuclear energy is being encouraged by government policies to reduce the financial risk borne by investors, through the allowance of up to 80 percent leverage in new projects, insurance for delays in construction, and a production subsidy.[36] However, it is important to keep in mind that the current projects, if they move forward, would just begin to replace the current nuclear power base. Our 66 nuclear power plants and 104 reactors contribute approximately 20 percent of our total electricity production. Given the age of plants today, without new projects the United States would be without any nuclear energy by 2050.[37] With solar and wind still unable to produce electricity reliably, economically, and at scale, losing nuclear would mean a greater dependence on fossil fuels.

Despite the recent resurgence, the long-term future of nuclear power in the United States is still uncertain. While investment interest is real, it has yet to be really tested by opposition. Americans may be open to nuclear power in concept, but having a new plant in your community is another thing all together. Moving nuclear power forward requires heightened safeguards for plants, communities, materials, and waste. An effective, high-functioning homeland security apparatus will be important here, as will educating the public about the benefits and trade-offs involved.

Biofuels

Biofuels represent a proven, commercially viable, green means of reducing our dependence on oil. However, our policies in this area to date have been misguided. Ethanol accounts for 3.5 percent of our fuel consumption, but its use is increasing by 25 percent a year thanks to heavy subsidies.[38] Congress is now on track to mandate a seven-fold increase — to 35 billion gallons — in the amount of biofuels that refiners must use by 2022. Driven by policy support, the U.S. ethanol industry is experiencing double digit growth rates and at least 73 plants are under construction. When plants currently under construction are complete — projected for 2008 to 2009 — total capacity of the U.S. industry will exceed 11 billion gallons per year.[39]

The fundamental flaw in the U.S. biofuels policy is that it is primarily agriculture policy, not energy policy or climate change policy. Corn producers are enjoying record prices, but with the effect of significant food inflation. The U.S. ethanol industry is enjoying record returns, receiving a subsidy of 51 cents per gallon, without reference to the price of oil.[40] America's ethanol subsidy costs taxpayers somewhere between $5.5 billion and $7.3 billion a year.[41] These producers are further protected by a 2.5 percent tariff, as well as a second duty of 54 cents per gallon, on all imported ethanol, which is then largely refunded to oil companies through a loophole in the regulations.[42] If the United States is genuinely committed to replacing fossil fuels with clean, green alternatives, it should open its market to biofuels imports and set an example for global markets.

Wind

Wind is the fastest growing and lowest cost source of renewable energy for the power sector, but still accounts for less than one percent of our electricity supply.[43] According to its advocates, using existing technology, wind power could provide the United States with 20 percent of its generation needs, using one percent of its land; and of this one percent, only five percent would have installed equipment, with the rest open for agriculture or ranching.[44] Wind's potential is in part constrained by policy uncertainty. The only federal incentive available, the production tax credit, was allowed to expire three times between 1999 and 2004, leading to a boom and bust cycle in the industry.[45] The credit is now set to expire again in 2008; renewing it before it expires is critical to maintaining investment and growth in wind power.

Today, the expansion of wind displaces the use of coal, and to some degree natural gas, in our electricity matrix. Wind's greatest weakness as a source of energy, although not one that cannot be mitigated, is variability. While nuclear power plants cannot be turned off, we can regulate the amount of electricity produced in conventional power plants, allowing for flexibility in the system.

However, thinking ahead to a future with inexpensive and efficient renewable power sources and the roll out of technologies like the plug-in hybrid, we could reach a moment when technologies like wind and solar are displacing imported oil, as we shift into an electric economy.

Solar

Solar energy demand has grown about 25 percent annually over the past 15 years, but the pace is escalating, with demand growth in 2006 up 33 percent. Over this same time period, the price of solar energy has fallen about four percent each year thanks to conversion efficiencies and economies of scale. Still, costs remain relatively high, averaging between 22 and 40 cents per kilowatt hour, for large photovoltaic (PV) systems without incentives.[46]

If prices continue to fall at their average rate, large-scale power generation from solar will not become realistic until the middle of this century. Speeding this process through more aggressive targets and R&D support is warranted. However, there are solar technologies already available today that should be promoted. A recent National Renewable Energy Laboratory study found that solar water heating, which fell out of favor in 1985 when government tax credits expired, has the potential to displace between 2.6 percent and 4.1 percent of U.S. natural gas consumption, provide $8.4 billion in savings to consumers each year, and reduce total GHG emissions by one percent.[47] As a country we need to be looking toward the future, but also capturing the potential of existing technologies and providing incentives for consumers to invest in the unfamiliar.

NEXT GENERATION

As we look out into the future, it is going to be innovation in next generation technologies that allows to not only reduce, but ultimately to end our dependence on oil. Among the most promising technologies include plug-in hybrid vehicles, next generation biofuels, and hydrogen.

Smart Power Grids

Smart power grids optimize power generation and distribution and have the potential to improve the efficiency and security of our power sector. However, significant testing is still needed and the transition to a smart grid could require 15 years and dramatically change the public utility business model. Government support and leadership will be needed for pilot projects and to create new frameworks for the deployment of this technology.

Plug-in Hybrid
The plug-in hybrid (PHEV) represents perhaps the most feasible and promising of the next generation technologies existing today, enabling cars to run on an electric battery on short-distance trips and then switching to fuel. The vehicles were the stars of this year's auto shows, but no models are currently in production nor have roll-out dates been announced. The Department of Transportation has projected that PHEVs could replace more than 45 billion gallons of gasoline per year by 2025, replacing one third of U.S. light vehicles.[48] The cost savings for U.S. consumers would also be dramatic; they would spend only one to three cents per mile for electricity, compared to ten cents per mile for gasoline.[49]

Biofuels 2.0
Next generation biofuels, namely the development of commercially-viable cellulosic ethanol production technology, could revolutionize the field of bioenergy, obviate the issue of food vs. fuel, improve the energy balance of U.S. ethanol production, and displace a much more significant percentage of oil consumption. While corn-based ethanol provides 26 percent more energy than is required for its production, cellulosic provides 80 percent more energy. Furthermore, cellulosic ethanol reduces GHG emissions 80 percent to 100 percent, while conventional ethanol is between ten percent to twenty percent below gasoline. Cellulosic technology is proven and in use, but reducing the costs through process innovation is estimated to be 5 to 10 years away. The U.S. government has offered just $385 million in government subsidies to bring cellulosic ethanol to the market.[50] A much greater commitment is necessary.

In addition, innovation to integrate biorefineries to utilize all waste products not only improves efficiency, but also has the potential to displace both oil imports and related petrochemicals with biochemicals.

Hydrogen
The eventual conversion to hydrogen power has become the "holy grail" of alternative energy technological progress for decades. General Motors (GM), which has been working on hydrogen engines since the 1960s, estimates it has spent $1 billion on developing this technology, but it remains economically unviable.[51] Hydrogen cars cost around $1 million each to build, and just around 60 to 80 hydrogen buses and 200 cars are on the road worldwide.[52] Yet the rationale behind converting to hydrogen is compelling; hydrogen is abundant, and its separation by a fuel cell produces water and energy, but no tail pipe

emissions. The catch is that hydrogen is essentially a medium for storing energy, so hydrogen fuel cells will only be as clean as their source of power, be it a coal-fired power plant or renewables like biomass. This choice is not a reason to dismiss hydrogen's potential, as critics suggest, but should guide our progress and investment in this technology.

INFRASTRUCTURE

There will be infrastructure requirements associated with changing our energy matrix, some greater than others, but all with a government role. This should be considered an initiative akin to the development of railroads in the 19th century and our highway system in the middle of last century.[53] For biofuels today, there is a major need for investment in distributive capacity, making available E85 or true flex-fuel options at service stations throughout the country to allow consumers to exercise the choice their flex-fuel vehicles offer them. The oil majors together have approximately 55,000 owned or branded stations. These companies would need to retrofit pumps for E85 or true flex options at 50 percent of their stations to reach 25 percent of the U.S. market, with an estimated cost of $12 million to $24 million.[54]

Developing the infrastructure to support a genuine shift away from fossil fuels to hydrogen technology will require major government support because the infrastructure needed to accommodate the widespread rollout of hydrogen powered vehicles will require huge changes in the U.S. fuel distribution infrastructure.[55] Transport of hydrogen is a high cost proposition, with pipelines estimated to cost more than $1 million per mile, and trucking even more expensive. A University of California-Davis study found that station costs range from $500 thousand to $5 million, based on size, which has an inverse relationship to fuel cost.[56] Other studies have shown that, should the private sector bare the entire burden of developing this infrastructure, it would take many years to break even.[57]

Of Leadership and Sacrifice: Is the Battlefield the "Easy" Option?

After a while the options and the numbers begin to boggle the mind. How do you add up the savings that a comprehensive policy of conservation, diversification, and innovation might bring? Is it reasonable to assume that we can reduce dependence on foreign oil by 50 percent over the course of the next 15 years? Based on turning to just some of the above, clearly we can. Is more possible? Again, based on what we could do, were our visions, leadership by politicians, and national political will to align properly, more may well be possible. After all, someday, sometime in this century, the dominance of oil as an energy source likely will come to an end, much as has occurred in past energy eras.

As of now, we are clearly seeing a sea change in discussions about such policies. Beyond the impact of the "perfect storm" noted earlier, concerns about growing demand for energy worldwide and limited petroleum supplies have produced study after study suggesting that the current climate of high-energy prices, reliance on unstable or problematic suppliers, apprehensions about the economic consequences of resource competition, and growing concerns about threats to the global climate will only continue. However, even with these factors in place, changing America's energy culture will be an uphill struggle.

First, the American political system is an ideal environment in which established, monied corporate interests, seeking to forestall change in order to maximize returns on already-made investments, can exert pressure in ways that advocates for new industries cannot. In 2004, oil and gas companies alone spent $25.6 million in campaign support, with 80 percent going to Republicans and 20 percent to Democrats. In the same cycle, alternative energy interests spent just over $155 thousand. While in 2006, the ratio changed to $19 million for big energy and $300 thousand for alternative energy, it demonstrates that the playing field is still not level in a Washington environment in which cash is still king.[58] Furthermore, big energy has big allies such as those in the auto sector, who resist key changes fiercely and seek special advantages for investments of the type that are most important to them.

Furthermore, as noted above, there is no way to make the changes most important to America's energy mix and usage without both political courage and public sacrifice. The 2008 election is likely to see more discussion of these issues than any since the gas crises of the 1970s. Nevertheless, the tough measures — like a gas tax, high CAFE standards, major efforts at conservation, or standing up to special interests — have been avoided to date. Indeed, even within a Democratic Party establishment more inclined to embrace such changes, leaders have, in putting together the current Senate energy package, bowed to the influence of auto-producing states to keep CAFE improvements modest, and a real gas or British Thermal Unit (BTU) tax is considered radioactive even as bipartisan expert groups, such as a recent discussion convened at the Carnegie Endowment, conclude nothing could be more central to an effective policy.

Part of it is how these issues are framed. To the extent that they are lumped in with relatively "softer" or more "long-term" concerns like those associated with the environment, it will be very difficult to get many political leaders to call for measures that will clearly cost the consumer and require a change of habits. This is yet another reason that it is so important to view these issues through the lens of national security. Only when issues of the utmost national urgency arise are political leaders and the public at large willing to accept more dramatic steps and to actually change their behaviors substantially.

In this respect, the facts help make the case. American troops are fighting in the Middle East today because there is oil in that region and we want to make sure that its flow is not inhibited. Concerns about the terrorist threat are clearly overstated, and rhetoric about extending democracy clearly lies somewhere between window-dressing and the triumph of hope over experience. The cost of the intervention in Iraq is likely to pass half a trillion dollars. Had that cost been associated with our real reasons for being in the region, it could have produced a useful national debate: "If our goal is energy security and we are willing to spend hundreds of billions to get it, what is the best way to allocate those resources?" The fact that our current strategy is unlikely to bear fruit and may actually have made the region less stable and thus had a negative impact on our core goal would clearly have a decisive impact on such a discussion. Nevertheless, the alternative approach advocated here offers multiple benefits beyond simply not being the misguided strategy we have followed so far. In purely foreign policy terms, it takes a lever away from potential enemies, increases our self-reliance, stimulates the economic well-springs of our strength, reduces the risks to our economy and our troops, and allows us to deploy some portion of our military assets more effectively where they are needed the most.

As it is, we face years more of involvement in the Middle East at a high cost. We also confront potentially significant costs associated with resource competition and instability in other regions that are increasingly important to our petroleum supplies including Africa, Central Asia, Russia, and Venezuela. With that unsettling reality in mind, one of the most important lessons of Iraq consists of demanding that debate about future commitments of military, political, and financial resources begin with a rigorous, objective search to identify our real underlying national interests. From there we must ensure we do not choose courses of action that are arrived at by force of habit or limited by the narrow institutional perspectives of the experts involved. Finally, we must ask ourselves why it is that American political leaders feel it is easier to sell a war to the American people than it is to sell national sacrifice and discipline? Why is it easier to sell potentially stirring short-term gains than it is to sell the methodical, long-term approaches that real problems require? If politicians continue to think battlefield losses are easier to sell than gasoline taxes and a commitment to conservation, that is precisely the outcome we will have. The first step is in recognizing that the two are related and that we have to better understand the relationship between them. The next step will be to see who is willing to accurately frame these choices for an American public that thus far has been making them inadvertently and with devastating consequences.

■ ■ ■ ───

David Rothkopf is a visiting scholar at the Carnegie Endowment for International Peace, where he has written *Running the World: The Inside Story of the National Security Council and the Architects of American Power* and the upcoming *Superclass: The Global Power Elite and the World They are Making* and where he chairs the Carnegie Economic Strategy Roundtable. In addition, he is also President and CEO of Garten Rothkopf, an international advisory firm specializing in transformational global trends, notably those associated with energy, security, and emerging markets. Previously, Mr. Rothkopf was Founder, Chairman and CEO of Intellibridge, a firm offering open-source intelligence and advisory services on international issues, after serving for two years as managing director of Kissinger Associates. Mr. Rothkopf served as Deputy Under Secretary of Commerce for International Trade Policy in the Clinton Administration. Prior to his government service, he founded and served as Chairman and CEO of International Media Partners, where he was editor and publisher of *CEO* magazine and *Emerging Markets* newspapers, as well as Chairman of the CEO Institute. Mr. Rothkopf currently serves as Chairman of the National Strategic Investment Dialogue and as a member of the advisory boards of the U.S. Institute of Peace, the Center for Global Development, and the Johns Hopkins/Bloomberg School of Public Health. He is the author of many articles on international themes for publications including *The New York Times, Washington Post, Financial Times, Foreign Affairs*, and others. Mr. Rothkopf attended Columbia University, as an undergraduate and as a graduate, and currently serves the university as an Adjunct Professor of International Affairs.

[1] United States, "Major Foreign Holders of Treasury Securities," Chart, Treasury International Capital System, *United States Department of the Treasury*, 13 Jul. 2007 <http://www.treas.gov/tic/mfh.txt>.

[2] "Global Trends in Sustainable Energy Investment 2007," United Nations Environment Program and New Energy Finance Ltd. 2007.

[3] United States, "U.S. Imports by Country of Origin," Chart, Energy Information Administration, *United States Department of Energy*, 19 April 2007, 13 Jul. 2007, <http://tonto.eia.doe.gov/dnav/pet/pet_move_impcus_a2_nus_ep00_im0_mbblpd_a.htm>.

[4] International Energy Agency, Oil Market Report (Paris: IEA, 12 Jun. 2007).

[5] "States Still 'Leading the Way' With Energy-Saving Appliance Standards: New Report Details 15 New Efficiency Standards for Common Products," ACEEE News Release, *American Council for an Energy-Efficient Economy*, 15 Mar. 2006, 13 Jul. 2007 <http://www.aceee.org/press/a062pr.htm>.

[6] Amory Lovins, "Winning the Oil Endgame: Innovation for Profits, Jobs, and Security," <http://www.ethanol-gec.org/information/briefing/5.pdf>.

[7] "Creating Jobs, Saving Energy, and Protecting the Environment: An Analysis of the Potential Benefits of Investing in Efficient Cars and Trucks – A 2007 Update," Union of Concerned Scientists 2007, <http://www.ucsusa.org/assets/documents/clean_vehicles/ucs-fuel-economy-and-jobs-2007-final.pdf>.

[8] United States Department of Energy, "Department of Energy Submits $23.6 Billion Spending Plan to Congress for FY'07" 16 March 2007, <http://www.energy.gov/news/4884.htm>.

[9] "A Strategic Approach to Energy," *Defense Technology International*, May/June 2006, <http://www.oft.osd.mil/energy/docs/A%20Strategic%20Approach%20To%20Energy-Pudas.pdf>.

[10] "Honeywell Wins U.S. Military Biofuels Contract," AutoBlogGreen, 2 July 2007.

[11] Sara Parker, "U.S. Retailers Save with Solar PV & Energy Efficiency," Renewable Energy Access, 29 June 2007, <http://www.renewableenergyaccess.com/rea/news/story?id=49104>.

[12] Wal-Mart Stores, accessed 13 July 2007, <http://www.walmartstores.com/GlobalWMStoresWeb/navigate.do?catg=645>.

[13] "Hybrid Cars Low Impact on Oil Imports," <http://blogs.business2.com/greenwombat/2007/06/report-hybrid-c.html>.

[14] *Ibid.*

[15] United States. Congressional Research Service, Energy Tax Policy: History and Current Issues, Washington: GPO, 2006.

[16] United States. Congressional Research Service, Energy Tax Policy: History and Current Issues, Washington: GPO, 2006.

[17] Yergin, Daniel, "Ensuring Energy Security," Foreign Affairs, Vol. 85, Number 2, March/April 2006.

[18] United States Department of Energy, "Indicators of Energy Intensity in the United States," <http://intensityindicators.pnl.gov/total_highlights.stm>.

[19] Bang, Guri, et al. "The United States and International Climate Cooperation," Energy Policy, Ed. 35, 2007: pp. 1282 – 1291.

[20] Bang, Guri, et al. "The United States and International Climate Cooperation," Energy Policy, Ed. 35, 2007: pp. 1282 – 1291.

[21] United States, "The Economic Costs of Fuel Economy Standards Versus a Gasoline Tax," Congressional Budget Office, Dec. 2003, 13 Jul. 2007, <http://www.cbo.gov/ftpdoc.cfm?index=4917&type=0&sequence=1>.

[22] Carbaugh, Robert and Charles Wassell Jr., "Reducing American Dependence on Oil," *Challenge*, Vol. 49, No. 6, November/December 2006, pp. 55 – 77.

[23] Sandalow, David, "Ending Oil Dependence," Brookings Institution, 22 January 2007.

[24] Vencat, Emily Flynn, "The Carbon Folly," *Newsweek International*, 12 March 2007.

[25] *Ibid.*

[26] "Doffing the Cap," *The Economist*, 14 June 2007.

[27] United States. Department of Energy, Energy Market and Economic Impacts of a Proposal to Reduce Greenhouse Gas Intensity with a Cap and Trade System, Washington: GPO, 2007

[28] United States Department of Energy, "Carbon Sequestration R&D Overview," July 16, 2007: <http://www.fossil.energy.gov/programs/sequestration/overview.html>.

[29] Carbaugh, Robert and Charles Wassell Jr., "Reducing American Dependence on Oil," *Challenge*, Vol. 49, No. 6, November/December 2006, pp. 55 – 77.

[30] Sandalow, David, "Ending Oil Dependence," Brookings Institution, 22 January 2007.

[31] Teixeira, Ruy, "What the Public Really Wants of Energy and the Environment," Center for American Progress, 2 March 2007.

[32] Huber, Peter, "Follow the Money," Op-Ed, *Forbes*, Vol. 179, Issue 7: pp. 105.

[33] Lavelle, Marianne, "Lots of Heat, Little Light," *U.S. News & World Report*, 25 June 2007.

[34] Bang, Guri, et al. "The United States and International Climate Cooperation." Energy Policy. Ed. 35, 2007: pp. 1282 – 1291.

[35] <http://www.nei.org/documents/New_Nuclear_Plant_Status.pdf>.

[36] <http://www.nei.org/documents/New_Nuclear_Plant_Financing.pdf>.

[37] Jon Gertner, "Atomic Balm?" *The New York Times*, 16 July 2006.

[38] "The Drive for Low Emissions," *The Economist*, 31 May 2007.

[39] Sandalow, David, "Ending Oil Dependence," Brookings Institution, 22 January 2007.

[40] Sandalow, David, "Ending Oil Dependence," Brookings Institution, 22 January 2007.

[41] "The Drive for Low Emissions," *The Economist*, 31 May 2007.

[42] "A Good Gas Idea," Editorial, *Wall Street Journal*, ed. 9 May 2006.

[43] United States, "International Energy Outlook 2007," *Energy Information Administration* (Washington: Department of Energy, 2007), 62.

[44] "Wind Energy Fact Sheet: Wind Energy: The Fuel of the Future Is Ready Today," *American Wind Energy Association*, 16 Jul. 2007 <http://www.awea.org/pubs/factsheets/wetoday.pdf>.

[45] "Renewable Energy Tax Credit Extended Again, but Risk of Boom-Bust Cycle in Wind Industry Continues," Citizens and Scientists for Environmental Solutions, *Union of Concerned Scientists*, 14 Feb. 2007, 16 Jul. 2007 <http://www.ucsusa.org/clean_energy/clean_energy_policies/production-tax-credit-for-renewable-energy.html>.

[46] "Fast Solar Energy Facts," *Solar Buzz*, 16 Jul. 2007, <http://www.solarbuzz.com/FastFactsIndustry.htm>.

[47] P. Denholm, "The Technical Potential of Solar Water Heating to Reduce Fossil Fuel Use and Greenhouse Gas Emissions in the United States," United States, *National Renewable Energy Laboratory*, Mar. 2007, 16 Jul. 2007 <http://www.nrel.gov/docs/fy07osti/41157.pdf>.

[48] Sandalow, David, "Ending Oil Dependence," Brookings Institution, 22 January 2007.

[49] <http://www.autobloggreen.com/2006/12/12/alt-car-expo-ex-cia-head-james-woolsey-says-saudi-arabia-can-t/>.

[50] "The Drive for Low Emissions," *The Economist*, 31 May 2007.

[51] "The Drive for Low Emissions," *The Economist*, 31 May 2007.

[52] "The Drive for Low Emissions," *The Economist*, 31 May 2007.

[53] Elhefnawy, Nader, "Toward a Long-Range Energy Security Policy," Parameters, Spring 2006: pp. 101 – 114.

[54] Sandalow, David, "Ending Oil Dependence," Brookings Institution, 22 January 2007.

[55] Sandalow, David, "Ending Oil Dependence," Brookings Institution, 22 January 2007.

[56] J. Weinert, T. Lipman, "An Assessment of the Near-Term Costs of Hydrogen Refueling Stations and Station Components," *Institute of Transportation Studies* (Davis: University of California Davis, 2006).

[57] U.S. Department of Energy, "Fuel Choice for Fuel Cell Vehicles: Hydrogen Infrastructure Costs," September 2005: <http://www.hydrogen.energy.gov/pdfs/progress05/iii_7_lasher.pdf>.

[58] *Election Overview*, Opensecrets.org. 15 July 2007, <http://www.opensecrets.org/industries/indus.asp?cycle=2006&ind=E1500>.

"But one thing has remained constant throughout the ages: since man first learned to harness the power of fire, the success in acquiring a reliable supply of fuel and means to convert it to energy has been central to our survivability, physical convenience, and economic well-being."

— STEVE BIEGUN

◼ The Global AMERICAN Politics of Energy

Steve Biegun
Vice President, International Governmental Affairs
Ford Motor Company

Wood, Fire, and Smoke

By the time this chapter is discussed on day five of our Aspen meetings, several days of stimulating conversation and timely interventions will have surely covered everything there is to cover on any dimension of energy policy. And, in the finest tradition of the Aspen Strategy Group, by the final day of the meetings there is likely even an emerging bipartisan consensus on the key domestic and national security interests at stake, as well as the preferred actions to resolve those challenges. Of course, also in the finest tradition of Aspen, this consensus is unlikely to serve to limit conversation, for as the late Senator Richard Russell once famously observed at a Senate hearing: "Everything that can be said on this topic has been said, but not everyone has yet had a chance to say it." Nonetheless, for the sake of moving the conversation to a subject that may have not been exhaustively discussed — the politics of energy — this chapter will take certain conclusions either on faith or as scientific certainties.

First, as an economic and national security imperative, the United States must address an increasingly unstable dependence on imported energy, especially oil, that is particularly vulnerable due to the regions of the world from which it originates. Second, due to the growing concentration of carbon in the atmosphere, significant changes are happening in the earth's climate that are altering weather patterns, putting economic pressure on geographically unfortunate populations, and creating a substantial burden of relieving victims of weather calamities. Third, policies and practices, particularly in the major industrialized economies — are not keeping pace with the urgent nature of these problems. It is this last point, the challenge of building a durable political consensus for action, which will be discussed below.

Addressing the need for energy, whether assuring an adequate supply or access to the physical processes of converting fuel to energy, is a challenge that mankind has grappled with since the beginning of time. When man first discovered and tamed fire — the release of the potential energy in wood through the rapid oxidation of fire — it was undoubtedly an epochal event. For primitive man, to have fire was to have light and heat — advantages that expanded mankind's horizon infinitely. Fire served as a tool, a weapon, and a convenience. Cold climates were now inhabitable. Nighttime could now be as productive as day time. While primitive man was slightly burdened by the need to collect the fuel for his fire, and perhaps to address the venting of smoke from his cave or hut, the net gains in convenience, quality of life, and even survivability were incomparable to these complications.

Reduced to its simplest form, our debates over energy policy are still about wood, fire, and smoke. Of course, in today's world we produce energy from many sources other than wood. Likewise, the process to convert fuels into energy involves many options beyond a simple fire. And as for smoke, proper venting from inside to outside has become infinitely more important as we find that "outside" is actually the atmosphere, and the very climate, in which we live. But one thing has remained constant throughout the ages: since man first learned to harness the power of fire, the success in acquiring a reliable supply of fuel and means to convert it to energy has been central to our survivability, physical convenience, and economic well-being.

This year, energy policy is a major topic of debate in the halls of American government. In his January 2007 State of the Union address, the amount of President Bush's remarks that were devoted to energy policy was second in length only to those on Iraq and terrorism. Both the House of Representatives and the Senate will devote a minimum of several weeks this year to hearings, debate, and legislating on new energy policies. Climbing gasoline prices have alarmed consumers and stories about energy supply, gas prices, and climate change routinely top the news and the popular culture. Companies each day seem driven to one-up each other in demonstrating that their products and corporate cultures are greener than the competition. In short, it seems as if bold action is certain. But is it?

The Political Players

While episodic attention has been given to energy policy by the American political class over the past few decades, the current debate on energy policy in the United States is perhaps different. In a new phenomenon, this debate has effectively unified distant parts of the political spectrum — that is, those concerned with the climate and environmental impact of greenhouse gases and those who are concerned about the national security implications of American energy dependence, especially dependence on politically unstable or undesirable oil-producing regimes in places like Venezuela, Nigeria, Russia, and the Middle East.

Something more than a marriage of convenience (and something less than a coalition), this larger group of politicians and policymakers has served to push the energy policy debate to the top of the U.S. legislative and political agenda. However, their shared concern for where energy is acquired, how energy is used, and the consequence of that for the national interest has at the same time served to mask deep-seated philosophical differences over what is to be done. Solutions like increasing nuclear energy divides greens from hawks. Conversely, within the goal of reducing foreign dependence, there is a tension between those wanting increased domestic exploration of fossil fuels versus increased efficiency and a reduction in demand. Also, as poll after poll suggests that energy (and climate change) issues are a relatively low area of concern for voters, generating a broad public consensus for action, particularly one that imposes a burden on consumers, will be difficult.

To understand the political equation on energy, it is worthwhile to start with trying to understand the actors. At some risk of oversimplification (and with great liberties taken with generalizations), the two sometimes cooperating factions that *support* significant revisions in U.S. energy policy can be labeled as the greens and the hawks. In addition to overcoming their own contradictions between the imperatives of reducing dependence on foreign oil and reducing CO_2 emissions to help with global warming, the greens and hawks must also convince or force the public and industry to accept the expense of change necessary to address energy needs. The challenge faced by the greens and the hawks is both aided and complicated by the wealth of opinion makers, agitators, and non-governmental organizations on both extremes of the debate that generate an ongoing commentary on how insufficient or excessive any proposed solution may be.

The *greens* tend to reside in the Democrat Party. They include environmentalists, multilateralists, pacifists, anti-sprawl advocates, religious leaders, and critics of unbridled capitalism. They are deeply troubled by climate change. They generally support expanded use of renewable energy, especially wind, solar, and geothermal sources, and they sometimes support biofuels (depending on whether they come from a farm state). They do not like expanding the exploitation of energy resources at home or abroad, especially not in off-shore coastal areas or in the Alaska National Wildlife Refuge (ANWR). They tend to be critical of oil-rich, undemocratic regimes upon which the United States is dependent for much of its oil. They usually support government imposed energy efficiency requirements (unless they come from a heavy manufacturing state) and they would not rule out taxes and tax redistribution policies. They hate nuclear energy.

The *hawks* tend to reside in the Republican Party. They include conservationists, unilateralists, neo-conservatives, fiscal conservatives, free traders, and a range of corporate interests. They support expanded exploration and development of coal and especially oil, internationally and domestically, including in ANWR and in coastal, off-shore areas. They support the development of nuclear energy (in other peoples' backyards) but oppose earmarks to research curtailing bovine flatulence. They were opposed to the Chinese takeover of Unocal. They hate being dependent upon oil-rich, undemocratic regimes for oil.

Industry is in effect the economy and it straddles the line on energy and climate. In general, industry wants to be seen as green. They join expert groups and coalitions active on energy and climate issues as a competitive imperative. Green business goals are seen as a market opportunity. Non-renewable energy producers support exploration at home and abroad, and they like prices that are high (but not too high). They feel the imperative to, at a minimum, research renewables. They fear price volatility and they hate taxes and price controls. Renewable energy producers support carbon mitigation and energy diversification. They fear that a world without mandates or government subsidies will put them out of business. In regard to biofuels, they hate free trade. Manufacturers support government incentives and rewards (grants or tax rebates) for using renewable fuels and developing energy-efficient products. They like when they have a product that consumers prefer for its energy efficiency — especially when it sells well. They hate regulatory mandates.

The *public* are both the consumer and the voter. They do not like paying more for gasoline or electricity, but they may on occasion purchase a more expensive version of a consumer product premised on a payback over time from lower energy usage costs. They sense that the climate around them is changing — hotter summers and less snow in the winter — though polls show that a majority does not necessarily agree that climate change is man-made. They are exposed to a steady drumbeat of opinion on energy and climate issues in the news and the popular culture. They want the government to do something about energy prices and they would prefer it was not too hot outside nor too wet. They enjoy their conveniences like mobility, a second refrigerator in the basement, and air conditioning. They want the freedom to drive what and where they want in their own vehicle, to live in any size house (or houses), and to fly anywhere they want — and do so in their own plane, if they are so privileged. They generally do not like to pay more for anything that they do and they want no diminishment in conveniences.

The Political Paradigm

The political equation surrounding energy is extraordinarily complex — involving the greens, hawks, industry, and the public in ways that frequently put the interests of each directly at odds with one another. There are the political interests of producers and processors of the raw materials — oil, natural gas, uranium, hydrogen, coal, corn and other bio-fuel sources — and geographical interests related to fossil fuel deposits, hydropower sources, optimal wind, sun or geothermal locations, and agricultural (biofuel) regions. There are the trans-shippers of energy — pipelines, ships, tankers, power grids — and then there are the distributors who deliver energy in a usable form to consumers — gas stations, electric power companies, gas companies, etc. Add to this the fact that energy travels from its raw form to its end use, often times passing through different owners on its way to market. There are the political interests of consumers of energy — individuals, corporations, and even national economies — and, if that is not enough, there is a geopolitical dimension to contend with on energy.

Juxtaposed against the complex interests involved in the energy and climate policy debates are three basic avenues of approach: market solutions, structured market solutions, and heavy regulation. Not surprisingly, these approaches represent deeply held political and philosophical differences as to the role and responsibilities of government, the private sector, and individuals. Any significant steps that are taken on energy and climate policy must find a way to bridge at least part of this divide.

Market solutions primarily depend upon the development of less expensive or less polluting fuels and products that appeal to consumers. Here the market alone rewards innovation and consumers freely choose to bestow their business — perhaps motivated by more than economics (e.g., social conscience). To shape and educate the views of the consumer in the market, the government can require initiatives like energy consumption and environmental performance labeling (e.g., miles per gallon and annual energy usage for appliances). Consumer preferences are further impacted by dramatic increases in energy prices and increasing public consensus or popular culture messages around the notions of an energy crisis and global warming. In the market, companies driven by the imperative of consumer demand efficiently and profitably develop innovative, new products and technologies such as hybrid vehicles, carbon sinks, and alternative fuels to reduce energy usage and its consequences.

Market solutions would win support from the greens, the hawks, the public, and industry. However, because many consumers may need or prefer less energy-efficient choices on the market, greens in particular would consider the effect of the market alone to be too slow and too small to make the necessary impact — particularly in regard to climate change. Also, economic efficiency does not mean that an equal effort is made across the economy or that the burden is felt by all individuals. The market would instead pluck the low hanging fruit or find the specific customers that have the most opportunity to choose, or the least opportunity to avoid, added cost for energy efficiency.

The second avenue is the *structured market*. This could include fees or taxes on the consumption of energy and emissions of greenhouse gases in order to create a greater market imperative for efficiency. In its purest form, this would include an economy-wide carbon cap and trade system in which carbon allotments are freely bought and sold between carbon emitters. The goal of such a system would be to produce the fastest and most substantial reduction of carbon emissions (and consequent efficiency) by giving a value to carbon and then unleashing market forces. The structured market could also include tax incentives and rebates for consumers as well as incentives and mandates for industry. Consumers could receive tax refunds for installing solar panels on their roof or buying a hybrid vehicle. On the other hand, they can be required to pay higher fees for higher energy use, such as a heavy vehicle fee. Industries could be supported by government mandates such as the requirement for renewable energy resources to constitute a percentage of electrical power transmission or vehicle fuels. Likewise, the manufacturers of energy efficient products can be recipients of federal research and development assistance, and tax breaks toward the goal of jump-starting the market or expediting introduction of new technologies within a market system.

The greens are not universally hostile to cap and trade although they (like many others) doubt whether it could be protected from cheating. Moreover, greens are loathe to allow a market system that, while making substantial reductions in carbon emissions, could in theory allow a specific industry (e.g., the auto industry) to actually thrive while making no improvement in energy efficiency by cheaply paying instead to reduce carbon at a more heavily polluting industry (e.g., coal burning power plants). Greens also do not oppose consumer or manufacturer incentives, although the shaping of federal incentives to support politically influential industries or sectors of the economy can diminish green support. The hawks do not like taxes though some find a cap and trade system appealing because it employs market logic.

The pressure for improvements in a structured market pits various sectors of the economy against each other over who will be at the table, and who will be on the menu. Many in industry say that there must be a comprehensive solution, which is code for saying that my industry should not bear the entire burden or that someone else's should bear a bigger part of the cost. Among industry, fossil energy producers do not like cap and trade systems or taxes as they simply add to cost of energy — although many renewables would be able to operate more profitably outside a carbon market. The renewable energy industry fully supports mandates, incentives, and market protection to stay in business. Manufacturers like the general principle of an economy-wide cap and trade system, and they like incentives and tax breaks to subsidize the expense of developing energy-saving technologies.

The public does not want to pay higher taxes on top of already higher fuel prices. While any structured market solution will add cost to consumers, they may most readily accept a cap and trade system as it would disguise cost and distribute it economy-wide and thus be more acceptable.

Heavy regulation would have the government take the lead on the challenges of energy efficiency and greenhouse gas emissions. Energy efficiency mandates have been and would continue to be given to manufacturers of consumer products such as home appliances or vehicles. Manufacturers are given a performance target and required by law either to meet the target or in some cases pay a non-compliance fine. Similar mandates are applied for emissions from smokestacks and tailpipes. Regulatory reach can also affect other forms of travel — short-hop airlines are a current target of interest in Europe. In short, the goal of regulatory action is to gain efficiency at the source of the energy using product, require the private sector to make the business case and develop the solution, and expose the consumer to the consequences in terms of restricted choices or higher costs (though these are often less noticeable than say, a direct tax would be).

Greens like heavy regulation. There is a finality and enforceability to regulatory action that, at least in theory, guarantees results where market forces may not.

Hawks are surprisingly open to heavy regulation provided that the regulation directly decreases energy dependence. The public will complain about heavy regulation to the extent that their appliances perform poorly, their home lighting is less effective, or, in some cases, they have to choose less powerful or smaller vehicles. But mandates generally do not add to prices for consumers in a manner that they feel significantly, so the complaints are generally manageable. Industry, again, is divided. Energy providers generally support heavy regulation as the burden falls upon the manufacturers and consumers of energy. Manufacturers oppose most such regulations because they tend to shift the cost of energy efficiency onto them.

The challenge for policymakers seeking to enact new measures on energy will be to mobilize a substantial majority of the affected interests on a solution or combination of solutions. This will undoubtedly require compromising some core principles among greens, hawks, industry, and the public. For example, can the greens accept additional fossil fuel exploration or even nuclear energy? Can the hawks accept an energy tax? Will the public accept a diminution in convenience and choice or an increase in cost to meet the energy challenge? Will industry seek business opportunities in meeting the challenge of increased regulation and higher costs, or will they use their political influence to fight it? These are the very questions at the top of the Congress' agenda today.

What Is to Be Done?

At the beginning of this chapter, it was suggested that certain conclusions should be taken either on faith or as scientific certainties: that the United States must take action to address an increasingly unstable dependence on imported oil; and, that due to the growing concentration of carbon in the atmosphere, significant changes are happening in the earth's atmosphere. If these assertions are in fact true, as I expect is nearly a consensus among Aspen participants after five days of discussion, the consequences for the nation and the imperative for our political leaders are urgent.

So much has been written and said on the prescriptions for U.S. energy policy that it is difficult to say anything that is new on the subject. Many excellent resources are available that consider the range of policy options. One that is particularly worthwhile is the 2004 National Commission on Energy Policy report entitled, "Ending the Energy Stalemate; a Bipartisan Strategy to Meet America's Energy Challenges." In that report, members of the commission recommend a broad set of policies that include enhancing oil security, reducing risks from climate change, increasing energy efficiency, ensuring affordable and reliable energy supplies, strengthening essential energy systems, and developing energy technologies for the future.

All of these recommendations represent a bipartisan consensus among a highly qualified and politically balanced set of commissioners. Yet, three years after these findings were published, few if any have been implemented. Not for the first time in the annals of political debate in Washington, D.C., just because all of the solutions are on the table does not mean individuals will act upon them. That challenge of building a workable consensus to convert ideas into action is, in effect, the politics of energy.

Against the backdrop of political players, interests, and influences involved in the energy debate, it is perhaps explicable that a workable consensus has yet to be found on energy and climate change policies. So, what would be the compromise? Where is the overlap of the competing agendas and interests? Is doing nothing an option? Is incremental change the only real option? Are political leaders up to the task and are industry and the public ready to bear the burden of energy policy changes? President Kennedy once said that, "The American, by nature, is optimistic. He is experimental, an inventor and a builder who builds best when called upon to build greatly." Is it possible that policy makers have failed to address our energy challenges not because they have asked too much, but rather that they have asked too little?

■ ■ ■ ───

Stephen Biegun is a corporate officer and Vice President of International Governmental Affairs for Ford Motor Company. Prior to joining Ford, Mr. Biegun served as National Security Advisor to Senate Majority Leader Bill Frist. From 2001 to 2003, Mr. Biegun served in The White House as Executive Secretary of the National Security Council, working as a Deputy to National Security Advisor Condoleezza Rice, and performing the functions of chief operating officer for the National Security Council. Prior to joining The White House staff, Mr. Biegun served for 13 years as Foreign Policy Advisor to members of both the House of Representatives and the United States Senate. From 1992 to 1994, Mr. Biegun served as Resident Director in the Russian Federation for the International Republican Institute, a democracy-building organization established under the National Endowment for Democracy. Mr. Biegun graduated from the University of Michigan, where he majored in political science and the Russian language. He is a member of the Aspen Strategy Group.

"For the past 30 years, the energy security strategy of the United States has revolved around the issue of access to oil. This model, clearly, is failing. The next administration must instead implement a strategy that is oriented toward the goal of climate security."

— JOHN PODESTA, PETER OGDEN

■ A Blueprint for Energy Security

John Podesta
President and CEO
Center for American Progress

Peter Ogden
Senior National Security Analyst
Center for American Progress

We are now in an era of energy insecurity. It is an era defined by high and volatile oil prices, deepening dependence on fossil fuels, global climate change, and an eroding international nuclear non-proliferation regime.[1] Whether we are at the end of this era or only the beginning will be determined by the steps that the United States takes — or fails to take — in the near future.

Policymakers in the United States have intermittently sought to address our country's fundamental energy insecurity, with success in some areas (e.g., the formation of the International Energy Agency) and far less in others (e.g., nuclear waste disposal). The scale and urgency of today's challenge, however, requires much more aggressive, sustained, and comprehensive energy measures than in the past. But this is not to say that energy security is beyond our reach. Rather, by implementing a multifaceted strategy, we will be able to:

- Combat climate change.
- Reduce America's oil dependence without jeopardizing economic growth.
- Eliminate key proliferation threats posed by nuclear energy technologies.
- Protect and modernize the global energy infrastructure.
- Strengthen our energy relationship with China, India, and other developing countries.[2]

America's Energy Security Challenge

The U.S. Energy Information Administration (EIA) anticipates the following energy growth rates for the United States and the world given current consumption rates:

ENERGY PROJECTIONS: UNITED STATES AND THE **WORLD**

2003 quantity/2030 quantity

	% Growth Rate United States		% Growth Rate World	
Total Energy (Quadrillion BTUs)	98.1/166.2	(1.3%)	420.7/721.6	(2.0%)
Oil (Million barrels/day)	20.1/27.6	(1.2%)	80.1/118	(1.4%)
Natural Gas (Trillion cu feet)	22.3/26.9	(0.7%)	95.5/182	(2.4%)
Electricity (Billion kWe-h)	3669/5619	(1.6%)	14,781/30,116	(2.6%)
Nuclear electricity (Billion kWe-h)	764/871	(0.5%)	2,523/3,299	(1.0%)
Coal (Million short tons)	1095/1704	(1.9%)	5250/10581	(2.5%)
CO$_2$ Emissions (10^6 metric tons)	5,796/8,115	(1.3%)	25,028/43,676	(2.1%)
GDP per capita (Dollars)	35,467/63,148	(2.9%)	8,048/17,107	(2.8%)
Energy per capita (10^6 BTU)	337/454	(1.1%)	66.7/88.0	(1.0%)

Source: EIA International Energy Outlook 2006 — reference case projection

The risks of this energy future are four-fold:

I   *The Impacts of Climate Change Will Intensify.* The effects of climate change in the next few decades will be far greater than what we have experienced to date. It is now simply too late for the United States to mitigate the impacts entirely. As a result, we are locked into a future of climate-induced security challenges stemming from food and water shortages, natural disasters, and disease outbreaks. There will be widespread instability and conflict, including (but not limited to) massive human migration throughout Africa and South Asia, fierce water competition in the Middle East, devastating hurricanes and wildfires in the United States, and deadly disease epidemics in Latin America. Policymakers can (and must) attempt to cushion the impact, cope with the inevitable geopolitical turmoil, and shift the world's pattern of energy consumption so that yet even more severe climate change does not occur.

If policymakers fail in this last task and worldwide carbon emissions reach or exceed the level projected by the EIA (whose projections have been low in the past), we will be running the additional risk of pushing the earth beyond that unknown temperature threshold at which positive feedback loops could be triggered (e.g., the release of carbon dioxide and methane from thawing permafrost). Such feedback loops would accelerate the rate of environmental change while magnifying and multiplying its impacts. The consequences would be truly catastrophic.

In addition to these national security and foreign policy implications, climate change will have significant economic consequences as well. The United States will be burdened with rising health costs associated with more frequent heatwaves, a deterioration of air quality, and an increase in water-borne diseases. Furthermore, natural disasters already cost the United States billions of dollars annually, and this figure is certain to grow as the number of major storms and wildfires increases. As Berkshire Hathaway Chairman Warren Buffet wrote in his annual letter to shareholders in 2006:

> Were the terrible hurricane seasons of 2004 – 05 aberrations? Or were they our planet's first warning that the climate of the 21st century will differ materially from what we've seen in the past? If the answer to the second question is yes, 2006 will soon be perceived as a misleading period of calm preceding a series of devastating storms. These could rock the insurance industry. It's naïve to think of Katrina as anything close to a worst-case event.[3]

Most fundamentally, however, the entire global economy could be jeopardized. The Stern Review of the Economics of Climate Change, authored by former Chief Economist of the World Bank Nicholas Stern, put it this way: "Our actions over the coming few decades could create risks of major disruption to economic and social activity … on a scale similar to those associated with the great wars and economic depression of the first half of the 20th century." Thus, while it is certain that developing countries will suffer the most because of their lack of capacity to cope with the effects of climate change, it is developed countries that will incur the greatest financial cost because of their exposure to the global economy. As the superpower of the global economy, the United States stands to lose the most of all.

II *U.S. Oil Dependence Will Deepen.* Even as oil becomes an increasingly poor fuel choice for a country seeking a stable, secure, and affordable supply of energy, demand for oil in the United States is projected to grow by one-third by 2030.

As a result, America will become progressively more vulnerable to high oil prices and market fluctuations. This is particularly dangerous because in the years to come we can expect greater upward pressure on oil prices and persistent market volatility due to a number of factors, including instability in many oil-exporting countries, terrorist or insurgent attacks on oil facilities (successful or not), ever-increasing state control over oil production in countries such as Russia and Venezuela, surging demand in the developing world (notably China and India), and supply manipulation by OPEC.

At the same time, conventional domestic oil production will steadily decline, forcing the United States to import a growing percentage of its oil. This dependence on foreign oil will continue to undermine our foreign policy and national security objectives by, among other things, limiting our diplomatic range of action in oil-producing regions and empowering oil-rich states and their customers (such as China) to pursue agendas and form political relationships that are not aligned with U.S. interests.

We also will face new challenges from a number of non-state actors who have recognized that attacking the international energy infrastructure is a highly effective means of fomenting instability and of driving up world energy prices. In Nigeria, for instance, the Movement for the Emancipation of the Niger Delta has carried out a successful campaign of armed attacks, sabotage, and kidnappings that has forced a shutdown of 25 percent of the country's oil output. Given that Nigeria is the world's eighth largest (and Africa's single largest) oil exporter, this instability is having an impact on the price of oil and could have significant political implications throughout the region.

Furthermore, in a videotape circulated in December of 2005, deputy Al Qaeda leader Ayman al-Zawahiri identified the global energy infrastructure as a critical target for his followers as part of their ongoing quest to bankrupt America and the West. Within two months, suicide bombers attacked the Abqaiq oil processing facility in Saudi Arabia, where two-thirds of the country's output — some 6.8 million barrels per day — is refined. The attackers failed to disrupt oil production at the facility, but they were nevertheless successful at increasing the risk premium for each barrel of oil on the world market, thereby costing the American people many millions of dollars.[4]

III *The Threat of Nuclear Proliferation Will Increase.* The EIA's *International Energy Outlook 2007* forecasts an expansion of nuclear power generation in every region of the world except Organisation for Economic Co-Operation and Development (OECD) Europe through 2030. The growth will be particularly rapid in non-OECD Asia: nuclear power generation is projected to grow 7.7 percent annually in China and 9.1 percent annually in India.

A rapid expansion of nuclear power presents a serious risk of proliferation as well as of nuclear accidents. The development of nuclear power capabilities and the associated facilities for the manufacture and production of nuclear fuels threatens to bring many more countries to the brink of nuclear weapon status. The risk of commercial fuel cycle technology being transferred to a country that is interested in developing a clandestine nuclear weapons program also increases.

Approximately a dozen countries in the Middle East and North Africa have recently sought International Atomic Energy Agency (IAEA) assistance in developing nuclear energy programs. Political insecurity coupled with the increased availability of nuclear fuel cycle technology may lead these countries over time to pursue nuclear weapons programs as well.

Moreover, if global carbon reduction policies are indeed adopted in this time frame, nuclear energy will become more cost-competitive with fossil fuels. This could provide added political justification for countries to develop domestic commercial nuclear power programs that might lead to new weapons programs or rekindle interest in weapons programs that had been abandoned.

Despite these risks, however, nuclear power will continue to play an integral role in the energy strategies of many countries that are seeking to stabilize the cost of electricity generation or reduce their carbon emissions, making it all the more imperative that the international community redouble its nonproliferation efforts.

IV *An Empowered Russia.* In the coming decades, energy will play an increasingly important role in defining the political relationship between the United States and Russia. No country in the world stands to benefit more in the short term than Russia from the growing strategic significance of natural gas and the environmental impacts of climate change. Russia holds by far the world's largest proven natural gas reserves (almost twice those of Iran, the country with the second largest proven reserves), and it currently supplies Europe with two-thirds of its imported natural gas. A warmer climate will help to reduce Russia's domestic demand for energy (freeing up more for export) and, in the longer term, could also open up ice-locked northern shipping routes to allow for the year-round export of liquefied natural gas (LNG) and oil.

Of chief concern, however, is Russia's willingness to use its energy assets — assets which are steadily being brought under state control — as a political tool to coerce its customers, particularly nascent democracies in Central and Eastern Europe.[5] In January 2006, for instance, it dramatically increased the price of natural gas in the run-up to the Ukrainian parliamentary elections. Ukraine refused to pay the new rates, which led to a supply reduction that left it, as well as several EU countries that are supplied through its territory via pipeline, short of natural gas in the middle of winter.[6] This tension will be exacerbated (and become a more direct challenge to the national security of the United States) if NATO expands to include the Ukraine, Georgia, or other countries that are embroiled in ongoing energy conflicts with Russia.

Russia's energy relationship with China, meanwhile, will deepen as it becomes a major supplier of energy to East Asia. This could lead to a closer alignment of Chinese and Russian interests on a range of issues. For instance, their joint leadership in the Shanghai Cooperation Organization (SCO), a regional group that includes Kazakhstan, Kyrgyzstan, Tajikistan, and Uzbekistan, could enable them to exert significant influence over this critical region's energy supplies and pipelines, as well as its overall political and strategic relationship with the West. At their July 2005 summit, for instance, SCO members issued a declaration calling for the closure of U.S. military bases in the region, and before the end of the month, the United States had been formally evicted from its base in Uzbekistan.[7]

Toward a New National Energy Security Strategy

For the past 30 years, the energy security strategy of the United States has revolved around the issue of access to oil. This model, clearly, is failing. The next administration must instead implement a strategy that is oriented toward the goal of climate security. This does *not* mean that our country's other energy security objectives are less critical, but rather that by adopting this new paradigm the United States will be able to address the full range of today's energy threats — from oil dependence to nuclear waste to catastrophic global warming.

Consequently, the next energy security strategy must drive the transformation of the U.S. economy from its current high-carbon, high-emissions economic model toward a low-carbon, low-emissions future.[8] It should do so by supporting an effective environmental regulatory framework and an aggressive energy Research, Development and Demonstration (RD&D) program, both of which will accelerate the development and widespread deployment of much needed new energy technologies and alternative fuels (e.g., carbon capture and sequestration for coal-fired power plants and cellulosic ethanol or other advanced biofuels for the transportation sector). Ultimately, it is only by pursuing this economic transformation that the United States will develop the policies, the energy technologies, and the political credibility that it needs to meet its national and international energy security challenges.

Challenges of this magnitude, however, require the next president to make energy security among his or her top three priorities and to create the necessary structures within the White House to manage a complex interagency process involving cross-cutting commitments, public-private partnerships, and the broadest possible range of policy instruments. Only then will the United States be able to implement a new energy security strategy that can achieve its five core objectives:

I *Confront the threat posed by climate change.* The United States cannot solve the climate crisis alone, and the international community cannot solve the climate crisis without the United States. At present, however, our country lacks the credibility to lead on this issue. To move forward, the United States must:

- Set a goal of reducing carbon emissions by 80 percent below its 1990 level by 2050, with enforceable interim reduction goals along the way.

- Develop a national greenhouse gas emissions cap-and-trade system that includes the most successful elements of those developed by the Northeastern states and the European Union, and which can be effectively merged into an international trading regime post-2012.

- Re-engage in international climate change negotiations and provide the leadership needed to reach a global, binding climate agreement. This requires, first of all, that the United States restore its credibility on the issue. Rapidly emerging countries such as China simply will never be persuaded to curb their own carbon emissions until the United States has demonstrated a serious commitment to reducing its own.

- Establish a national Renewable Electricity Standard mandating that 25 percent of domestic electricity be produced from renewable sources by 2025.[9]

- Require that all new coal plants built in the United States be subject to the terms of any future national carbon cap-and-trade system. This provision, which must apply to both pulverized coal plants and integrated gasification combined cycle (IGCC) plants, would prevent companies from rushing to construct new plants in an effort to remain exempt from forthcoming carbon cap-and-trade regulations.

- Complete carbon dioxide capture and sequestration demonstration projects at scale to establish the costs, benefits, and large-scale feasibility of this coal technology.

- Assist developing countries in their efforts to build efficient and environmentally sustainable domestic energy infrastructures and to cope with the impact of climate change. Two-thirds of the growth in energy demand over the next 25 years will come from developing countries, many of which are only beginning to establish their energy infrastructure. With guidance and development assistance from the United States, the World Bank, and others, they can avoid the trap of oil dependence, make better use of renewable fuels and clean forms of energy, and cope more effectively with the impacts of climate change.

- Continue research into the development of safe, cost-effective nuclear power that addresses the problems currently posed by: the threat of proliferation; the management of nuclear wastes; the perceived safety, environmental, and health risk; and the high relative costs of production.

II *Reduce dependence on foreign oil without jeopardizing economic growth.* This can be achieved by increasing the fuel efficiency of our vehicle fleet, promoting the use of biofuels and other low carbon fuel alternatives, maximizing the domestic production of fossil fuels while complying with rigorous environmental standards, curtailing oil demand, and investing in energy RD&D. The United States should:

- Set a goal of producing at least 25 percent of the liquid fuel consumed in the United States from renewable sources by 2025. An aggressive strategy to replace oil with low carbon alternative fuels, however, cannot rely solely on corn-based ethanol. The federal government and industry must boost their investments in the research, development, and widespread deployment of low carbon fuel alternatives such as cellulosic ethanol and biodiesel. Cellulosic ethanol, for instance, has the potential to become the most cost-effective liquid fuel source for the United States, particularly in a carbon-constrained economy where the market will put a premium on cleaner-burning low carbon fuels.

- Establish a counter-cyclical tax on liquid fuels for cars, trucks, and airplanes that is triggered when the price of oil falls below a certain level and with all of its revenue dedicated for alternative energy RD&D and the Low Income Home Energy Assistance Program (LIHEAP). Establishing a reasonable liquid fuel price base would encourage the production and purchase of fuel efficient vehicles; spur investment in new energy technologies by insulating investors from market fluctuations; and generate revenue for alternative energy RD&D and LIHEAP.

- Create additional incentives and mandates to improve energy efficiency and reduce overall demand for transportation fuel. Notably, the U.S. Senate has recently passed an energy bill that increases fleet-wide CAFE standards to 35 mpg by 2020, the first such increase in more than two decades. A similar effort should be made to use natural gas more efficiently by boosting standards and incentives for industrial energy efficiency and cogeneration capacity (i.e., the ability to produce heat and power simultaneously).

- While moving existing technologies to market as quickly as possible, continue research into the deployment of plug-in hybrid vehicles and the commercialization of lightweight materials, advanced internal combustion engines, and hydrogen fuel cells.[10]

III *Eliminate key proliferation threats posed by nuclear energy technologies.* The existing non-proliferation regime and its safeguards must be updated and expanded in order to cope with growing nuclear energy production around the world. In order to address the threat of proliferation, the United States must lead efforts to:

- Close the fuel cycle loophole of the Nuclear Non-Proliferation Treaty (NPT), which allows NPT signatories to acquire facilities that can be used to produce weapons-usable fissile materials under the guise of a peaceful nuclear research or energy program. To this end, the United States should help to build an international system in which select countries with full fuel cycle capacity commit to providing, removing, and storing nuclear fuel for any country that forswears all national enrichment and reprocessing programs and submits to international safeguards.

• Increase and strengthen inspections of suspected illegal nuclear facilities by expanding the responsibilities and authority of the IAEA.

• Reduce the threat of nuclear terrorism by expanding and accelerating Cooperative Threat Reduction Programs. For more than a decade, these programs have helped to secure or destroy hundreds of tons of vulnerable weapons-grade materials across the former Soviet Union. These programs have also improved the security of Russia's nuclear weapons and provided alternative employment and training to thousands of former weapons scientists. In recent years, however, progress on securing vulnerable materials has been inadequate.

• Accelerate efforts to "clean out" weapons-usable highly enriched uranium from nuclear research reactors worldwide.

• Reject any proposal to change the United States' longstanding policy of not reprocessing spent fuel from commercial nuclear reactors, and oppose all initiatives to separate plutonium from other nations' used fuel and develop reactors dependent on reprocessed plutonium. Reprocessing has numerous environmental, health, and proliferation risks and offers no benefits in terms of nuclear waste disposal. The United States must instead pursue an interim storage policy at reactor and federal sites that provides the country with time to arrive at a safe and environmentally sound geologic disposal option.

IV *Protect and modernize the global energy infrastructure and its distribution channels.* In an increasingly global energy market, a disruption at a single strategic point in the distribution system can have dramatic economic consequences around the world. The United States should work to defend the unrestricted flow of oil and gas supplies, strengthen and diversify the distribution networks for oil, gas, and electricity (e.g., the network of pipelines, transmission lines, and terminals), and maintain a strong emergency response system to cope with — and deter — disruptions and embargoes. To achieve these goals, the United States must:

- Strengthen national regulations for security at nuclear power reactors and other nuclear facilities where theft or sabotage poses a catastrophic threat.

- Implement the top priority recommendations of the National Strategy to Secure Cyberspace, including efforts to secure computer networks at nuclear power plants and power companies.

- Develop a "smart grid" electrical system. While markets reward efficiency, improved security requires sufficient redundancy to minimize the impact of energy disruptions, whether caused by natural or manmade events. A "smarter" electrical grid would help to prevent a reoccurrence of the cascading system failure that affected the northeastern United States and Canada in August 2003. It would also encourage the development of new markets for distributed generation of domestic renewable energy.

- Develop geographically diverse strategic gasoline and jet fuel reserves within the United States, as well as maintain the existing strategic petroleum reserve. Geographical diversity could be achieved by setting minimum inventory requirements for domestic oil refineries. In addition, the procedures for releasing oil and gas from these stockpiles must be made more transparent so as to reduce market speculation and price volatility.

- Promote new transit routes and pipelines that can reduce pressure on vulnerable choke points (e.g., the Strait of Hormuz and Strait of Malacca) or bypass Russia and the Middle East (as does the Baku-Tbilisi-Ceyhan pipeline).

- Provide military training and technological assistance to the Malaysian and Singaporean forces that are responsible for securing the Strait of Malacca, as well as promote cooperative regional security measures in the Bosphorus and at other key transit points worldwide.

- Promote the development of a global liquefied natural gas market. This will make natural gas into a more fungible commodity, thereby reducing the likelihood of targeted embargoes and helping to bring the world's vast untapped natural gas resources to market. This issue is particularly pressing for the United States' European allies, many of whom are becoming increasingly dependent on natural gas from Russia and Algeria.

V *Strengthen our energy relationship with China, India, and other developing countries.* The United States must work to bolster its energy relationship with potential partners in the developing world, particularly with rapidly emerging China and India. Not only is this a prerequisite for the formation of an effective international carbon cap-and-trade system, but it will create other opportunities for strategic cooperation and promote an efficient and open global energy marketplace. To this end, the United States must:

- Establish a formalized partnership between the International Energy Agency (IEA) and both China and India. Founded in the wake of the 1973–1974 oil crisis, the IEA has become an important forum for international cooperation on energy security issues. It facilitates information sharing on energy markets and technologies, and its oil stockpile requirement ensures that oil-importing member countries build and maintain strategic reserves. It is also a useful forum for coordinating emergency responses (e.g., the drawdown of strategic oil reserves or the rerouting of shipments). Establishing a formalized partnership with India and China would enhance the IEA's planning, information sharing, and emergency response mechanisms, and it would expedite the development of strategic petroleum reserves and the implementation of more rigid carbon control policies in these countries.

- Create an "E-8" international forum. Modeled on the G-8, the E-8 should be comprised of the world's major carbon-emitting nations and have an annual summit devoted exclusively to international ecological and resource issues.[11]

- Utilize appropriate mechanisms to develop new rules and regulations for international energy transactions and acquisitions. The China National Offshore Oil Company's failed bid for Unocal, for instance, was not the last time that America's energy companies or assets will attract the interest of foreign investors, and it is important to establish clear guidelines for when such transactions will be allowed. The United States must be careful in the future not to increase China's mistrust of the global energy market — a mistrust that drives China's aggressive pursuit of long-term government-to-government energy deals that include significant non-market elements (e.g., building airports, offering credit, and tying foreign assistance to energy investment).

- Protect global sea lanes in order to ensure the safe movement of oil and LNG shipments around the world. Significantly, China will seek to become involved in securing global sea lanes (particularly the routes linking Northeast and Southeast Asia) when it develops a blue water navy in the next few decades. The United States and Chinese navies must develop a system and set of policies to coordinate their movements if they are to avoid potentially dangerous miscommunication or interference with one another.

- Develop and enforce new legislation and investment guidelines that bolster international anti-corruption efforts, such as the U.N. Convention Against Corruption and the OECD Anti-Bribery Convention. Corruption plagues oil- and gas-rich countries around the world, and it poses an ongoing threat to regional stability. The United States should lead efforts to compel OECD banks to disclose all deposits made by foreign leaders that are derived from the sale of oil and natural gas. Such measures would also be useful in tracking terrorist financial networks.

- Promote the export of U.S. clean energy technologies and services to China, India, and other developing countries (using, for example, expanded Export-Import financing and financial assistance), and provide loan guarantees and other incentives for the construction of new coal-fired plants with carbon capture and storage capability.

■ ■ ■

John Podesta is President and CEO of the Center for American Progress and Visiting Professor of Law at the Georgetown University Law Center. Mr. Podesta served as Chief of Staff to President William J. Clinton from October 1998 until January 2001. As Chief of Staff, he served on the President's Cabinet and as a principal on the National Security Council. From 1997 to 1998 he served as both Assistant to the President and Deputy Chief of Staff. Earlier he was Assistant to the President, Staff Secretary and a senior policy advisor on government information, privacy, telecommunications security, and regulatory policy. Mr. Podesta previously held a number of positions on Capitol Hill, including Counselor to Democratic Leader Senator Thomas A. Daschle; Chief Counsel for the Senate Agriculture Committee; Chief minority Counsel for the Senate Judiciary Subcommittees on Patents, Copyrights, and Trademarks; Security and Terrorism; and Regulatory Reform; and Counsel on the Majority Staff of the Senate Judiciary Committee. He is a graduate of Georgetown University Law Center and Knox College.

Peter Ogden is the Senior Policy Analyst for National Security and International Policy at the Center for American Progress. He works on energy security, military manpower, nuclear nonproliferation, and other related U.S. foreign policy issues. Mr. Ogden's writings have been published in a number of major journals and newspapers, including *Foreign Affairs* (November 2006), *The New York Times*, *The Washington Post*, *The American Interest*, *The Philadelphia Inquirer*, *Army Times*, and *The Baltimore Sun*. He served on the task force for *Energy Security in the 21st Century: A New National Strategy* (National Security Task Force on Energy, CAP 2006), and co-edited *Resources for Global Growth: Agriculture, Energy, and Trade* (CAP 2005). He received a master's degree from Princeton University and graduated summa cum laude from Amherst College.

[1] For a discussion of the impact of price volatility on the American consumer, see Amanda Logan and Christian Weller, "Pain in the Gas," Center for American Progress, May 2007.

[2] For more information, see "Energy Security in the 21st Century," a report by the National Security Task Force on Energy. Many elements of this strategy were developed and endorsed by the task force, in which the authors participated.

[3] *Available at* <http://www.berkshirehathaway.com/letters/2006ltr.pdf>.

[4] It is quite possible that Al Qaeda raised additional revenue for its cause in the process, as some of the money that the United States spends on oil finds its way into the hands of terrorists or is used to promote anti-American ideologies. However, it would be an exaggeration to say that terrorist organizations — which have relatively small operating costs and numerous illicit funding streams — would be financially crippled if the United States were simply to reduce its oil consumption. The National Commission on Terrorist Attacks Upon the United States determined that the attacks on 9/11 cost between $400,000 and $500,000 to carry out, in addition to the cost of training the hijackers in Afghanistan. For an explanation of how a risk premium functions in the oil market and its relevance to U.S. national security, see: <http://www.newyorker.com/talk/financial/2007/02/19/070219ta_talk_surowiecki>.

[5] This concern would be compounded if a natural gas cartel were to develop out of the Gas Exporting Countries Forum, in which Russia plays a role analogous to that played by Saudi Arabia within OPEC.

[6] The crisis was resolved shortly thereafter when President Viktor Yushchenko arranged a controversial new deal involving a mysterious energy company (RosUkrEnergo) with strong ties to Moscow (see Steven Lee Myers and Andrew E. Kramer, "Gas Deal Roils Ukraine," *New York Times*, March 3, 2006). The political ramifications of this episode have been severe for Yushchenko. Support for Viktor Yanukovych's pro-Moscow Party of the Regions jumped from 17.5 percent in November 2005 to 27.4 percent after the energy crisis, and Yanukovych's party finished well ahead of Yushchenko's in the subsequent parliamentary elections.

[7] For a fuller discussion of this and other elements of China's energy strategy, see John Podesta, John Deutch and Peter Ogden, "China's Energy Challenge," *China's March on the 21st Century* (Aspen Strategy Group, 2007).

[8] This challenge is deeply rooted in the transportation and electricity generation sectors, which are oil and coal intensive. Oil constitutes some 90 percent of transportation fuel, while coal powers approximately 50 percent of U.S. electricity generation. Taken together, the use of these two fuels accounts for more than 80 percent of all U.S. carbon emissions.

[9] In the near term, setting a Renewable Electricity Standard (as well as other such targets) can create important incentives for the production of cleaner fuels and the development of new energy technologies, but once a robust national cap-and-trade system is in place these targets should be gradually phased out.

[10] There has been a great deal of debate lately about the various costs and benefits of using liquefied coal as a substitute for oil. While liquefied coal has the virtue of being produced domestically, it is important that the United States develop liquid fuel substitutes that also contribute to the goal of reducing carbon emissions. Recent studies suggest that the United States has more promising options in this regard than liquefied coal.

[11] In addition, the Six-Party framework being used currently to address North Korea's nuclear weapons program should be preserved as a forum for resolving a narrower set of energy security issues in East Asia. For more information on the potential role of the E8, see: Todd Stern and William Antholis, "Action Memorandum: Creating the E8," *The American Interest*, January 2007.

"It takes time to persuade men to do even what is for their own good."

— THOMAS JEFFERSON

Concluding Observations

Kurt M. Campbell
Director, Aspen Strategy Group

Jonathon Price
Associate Director, Aspen Strategy Group

T he Aspen Strategy Group has a long history of examining the issues that are at the heart of U.S. national security and foreign policy challenges. Previous sessions of our group have explored the dangers of nuclear proliferation, examined China's rise to prominence in the 21st century, and analyzed the contours and complexities of the jihadist threat. However, increasingly, energy policy lies at the crossroads of every major challenge confronting the United States. The prospects for greater instability across the Middle East, rising anti-American sentiments and harsh rhetoric emanating from Iran and Venezuela, the ongoing conflict in Iraq, the rise of China and India, and even the future prospects for Russia's growing power, all relate to and intersect with America's quest for energy security. These complexities leave the United States dangerously vulnerable to supply shocks, bellicose dictators of energy-rich nations, the virtually insatiable demands of growing economies, and fragile relationships in the Middle East. As a consequence, the Aspen Strategy Group tackled the topic, *The Global Politics of Energy*, during our 2007 summer session.

The preceding chapters underscore the critical conundrums and the myriad perspectives that illuminate this debate. Together, these chapters represent a clarion·call by respected experts, policymakers, and academics on the urgent need for a more comprehensive and open debate on the elements necessary to achieve greater energy security for the United States in the 21st century. To this end, the chapters in this volume, and the ASG sessions themselves, helped clarify several key observations about the substance of the current debate. Here below are some key takeaways and observations from our proceedings and the preceding chapters.

Energy Security is Difficult to Define and Even Harder to Achieve

While the terminology "energy security" is attractive, it is an elusive and nuanced expression and one that has been badly misused in the sometimes distorted and often misunderstood national debate on energy policy. Energy experts cannot agree on the components, politicians argue for an unattainable energy independence, and nations interpret its meaning differently depending on the resources they have at hand and larger societal needs based on rising consumption. Moreover, numerous forces beyond a state's control make it difficult to obtain energy security. For instance, geopolitical considerations force the United States to be concerned with areas outside its borders. Emerging energy-empowered states such as Iran and Venezuela have publicly stated their intent to challenge America's global influence and have threatened to curb their energy exports. In Eurasia, Russia, with its petro-superpower status, is aggressively coupling its vast and diverse energy resources with a more assertive and, at times, aggressive foreign policy. Meanwhile, neighboring states clash over borders rich in energy resources while terrorists take aim at oil installations and facilities, all with the potential to disrupt supply, create market uncertainty, and inflict massive, indirect, economic damage on the United States and its allies. Together, these external factors necessarily complicate any clear definition of energy security and provide headaches for national leaders seeking greater stability and predictability when it comes to energy policy.

Achieving energy security in the United States first requires an agreement on the core challenges and a national conversation on the priorities for addressing such challenges. As an essential first step in this exercise, analysts should strive to identify and alleviate profound areas of energy insecurity where the United States maintains the ability to achieve results through unilateral or independent actions. This can take the form of strengthening energy supply infrastructure, looking beyond traditional fossil fuels, searching for greater areas of conservation, and admitting the potentially destabilizing impacts of climate change. Acknowledging America's vulnerability in a newly globalized energy arena, and actively addressing areas of profound energy insecurity, are necessary first steps for the nation in assessing this complex energy terrain.

☐ The Global Market Impact on U.S. Energy Security

With threats of energy shortages or disruptions to supply clearly visible on the horizon, the globalized energy market has been divided into nations primarily labeled as energy producers on the one hand or consumers on the other. In the United States, much has been made of the growing dependence on foreign oil, and there are temptations to identify dependence on fossil fuels as the major cause of American energy insecurity. It is undeniable that America's domestic oil production capabilities are surpassed by its demand; thereby forcing the United States to increasingly depend on foreign sources of oil, and it is also true that the U.S. has not made substantial progress in ensuring a greater diversity of supply from renewable and non-renewable sources. Nevertheless, although reducing its dependency on oil might provide a buffer from disruption or chaos in foreign supply countries, the globalization of energy markets will likely continue to ensnare the United States in the complex global political realities surrounding energy. Energy shortages can still reverberate profoundly and dangerously through the global economy. Moreover, whereas energy crises of the past have normally centered on supply constraints, the energy picture of today involves a dramatic increase in demand from China, India, and elsewhere. These rising centers of power, and their need for fuel to assist in their ascendancy, complicate the global energy picture and have ushered in the prospect of an international marketplace contemplating future scarcities.

Even if the United States could import its energy needs solely from stable political allies—and this is far from the current realities of the global political scene—a crisis elsewhere in the globe would spike the price of oil and send reverberating shock waves around the globe and would affect even those countries relatively buffered from sharp supply disruptions. Should the United States halt oil imports from nations it deems unfriendly or unstable, other nations will eagerly step in to fill the void and their tanks. In this respect, petroleum is a fungible global commodity on one level but also one where national concessions are also at a premium. Energy security can no longer be assured simply by changing the supplier. A more comprehensive approach that mixes new supply options and conservation practices is essential. Seeking to move beyond fossil fuels is but one part of a larger solution toward a new "energy security." Many other issues lie at the heart of this challenge and will require a larger strategy to address. This complex mix of technology, incentives, public policy, and global politics makes energy policy one of the most complicated areas of national endeavor, and one that the U.S. must address more urgently and fundamentally than ever before.

III A Flawed Definition of Energy Security Does not Equal a Missing American Strategy

The difficulty in characterizing energy security, with the rapidly changing terms of the debate, highlights the noticeable absence of a comprehensive energy strategy in the United States. And this absence is a reoccurring feature in American domestic politics. In recent years, our national leaders have been content either to publicly call for OPEC to further open the taps of supply or to call for new drilling rights in various wilderness areas in Alaska or elsewhere in the continental U.S. Although all the major candidates running for President have publicly presented their platforms to address energy concerns confronting the nation, as of April 2008, these have been long on vision and short on specifics. Truly, the United States has never had a comprehensive energy security strategy that takes into account all the interrelated challenges that are connected to national energy options. In this regard, the next President of the United States is presented with a historic opportunity and monumental challenge. Increasing fossil fuel dependence, the supply risks posed by continued reliance on unstable states, the dire repercussions of global climate change, and the skyrocketing prices at the gas pump should embolden the next administration and provide the necessary political context to create an environment conducive to the development of a detailed and actionable comprehensive energy strategy.

Such a strategy will allow for agreement on the terms for the approach and ensure that energy security is placed at the top of the next administration's agenda. Though the enunciation of a strategy alone will not solve the problem, it will provide a new frame of reference that can draw together incentives, ingenuity, and government capacity to deal with the energy challenges of the 21st century.

IV Government's Role: From Vision to Implementation

In our ASG discussions, debate swirled over the appropriate role for government in meeting these challenges. Historically, the U.S. government has had great difficulty in picking winners in the energy sphere due to high costs, imperfect technologies, indecisiveness over incentive structures, interest group impacts, and larger competing political interests. Congress in particular has exposed the great difficulties in achieving bipartisan political consensus on an issue that exemplifies diverse ideologies — evident in the numerous versions of the recently passed 2007 energy bill. In certain cases, individual states, weary of waiting for federal action, have seized control and now chart their own courses on energy related matters. Some states, such as California, whose bold attempt to set tougher vehicle emissions standards than the federal government has caused considerable controversy, are clearly moving towards new green technologies and have put in place policies of their own without national directives and sometimes over the objections of the federal government. Yet, many other states, industries, and powerful actors remain heavily reliant on traditional forms of energy—twenty-seven states produce coal and forty-seven use it for electric power generation. While these traditional sources of power potentially cause enormous environmental damage, oil and coal are both relatively plentiful and reliable, cost effective, and often central to a state's economy. Bearing in mind that any energy strategy must be broadly inclusive, outreach on future legislation will need to include lawmakers and stakeholders from these key states and industries, many of which hold strikingly different views on the components of energy security and the relative environmental costs. The next administration must elevate the debate above partisan tones, and initiate a larger conversation among critical stakeholders—producers, consumers, and activists alike—on the nature of the stakes involved.

Despite the federal government's mixed record of accomplishment on energy, there has been progress in the quest to achieve some stability and security in our energy calculations. Imperatives continue to drive the United States towards renewable sources of energy. In nearly every corporate sector, striking advances have been made over the last decade. New technologies and unusual partnerships have made "going green" a trendy new component of any company's vocabulary. However, these steps, while inspiring, are still quite modest. Rather than leaving choices on conservation and efficiency solely in the hands of the private sector, the government's role in building and implementing an energy security strategy will need to be prominent, consistent, and sustained, requiring a complex coordination across agencies, departments, and the executive and legislative branches. The harbinger of, and engine for, major long-term change still rests with the federal government.

V A Global Burden and Effort

To meet the challenge of assuring some order of stability and confidence in future energy policy, achieving energy security must be seen as a transnational pursuit and opportunity rather than a unilateral challenge. While specific solutions might vary according to interest groups, there has been surprising agreement on the urgency of the challenge of energy security between groups historically hostile towards one another. In the United States, the emerging recognition that a continued reliance on fossil fuels and the consequences of climate change are national security issues has brought together a bipartisan chorus of national security proponents and environmental advocates—hawks and tree huggers—that believe the current course of energy-use trends and environmental consequences are unsustainable.

On a global level, the work of a few multilateral institutions such as the United Nations is visible in the energy equation through the International Atomic Energy Agency (IAEA), the Intergovernmental Panel on Climate Change (IPCC), and the United Nations Environment Programme (UNEP). The IMF and World Bank have their own part to play in this effort by directing investments in alternative energy sources, and in providing funds to aid developing countries increase energy efficiency. But there was a profound recognition of the general inadequacy of existing international institutions to address the issues of energy security and indeed climate change. On this score, ASG members discussed the creation of an E8, modeled after the G8 summits, to bring together world leaders to highlight successes, identify challenges, and encourage further global cooperation in the overall energy arena.

In the coming years, the forging of new global alliances will be necessary to address the most critical aspects of the energy challenge, from diversification of supply to dealing with climate change. A few key developing nations provide a special opportunity in this respect. China, often cited as a threat to America's energy security, has periodically shown a propensity to join with other states to address larger transnational challenges when properly persuaded. We have seen such cooperation in the field of combating terrorism and dealing with disease and piracy as well. To this end, the United States should make it a priority to actively seek cooperation with global partners, such as India and China, and identify areas for joint endeavors, in energy related fields. Increasingly, these states must be drawn into an international dialogue about the larger challenges confronting the global community with respect to all aspects of energy policy, from innovation, carbon sequestration, and conservation, to diversification of supply.

VI Challenge Breeds Opportunities

While the twin threats of energy security and climate change are important global challenges for the United States, they also present an opportunity to restore U.S. leadership in the world. Over the last decade, the world has seen the image of America portrayed as unwilling or unable to bring energy policy and climate issues to the forefront. A major commitment by the next American President to make energy security a priority and earnestly tackle climate change would help reconnect the U.S. with key allies in Europe and elsewhere who may have been alienated by other American policies in the international arena.

Timing remains a key factor in restoring America's standing. In Australia, elections ushered in a new Prime Minister who made it a priority to ratify Kyoto within 90 days of taking office. A similar move by a new U.S. administration on a climate related theme — such as taking a progressive position in advance of the upcoming UN talks in Copenhagen on a successor to Kyoto — would help signal a new direction in the American worldview. With America's global standing at near historic lows, the opportunity to take a dramatic and new approach on global climate change, acknowledge its legacy share of the accumulated burden of prior emissions, both past and present, and move decisively to adopt a plan for reducing emissions would result in major strides in rebuilding frayed ties on a global scale. Once a first step has been taken, opportunities abound for renewed global engagement, including cooperation on innovative technologies and the prospects for new steps in public-private partnerships. Although such small steps might be decried as not going far enough, every gesture of progress lays the groundwork for future and promising areas of long-term collaboration.

VII. The Role of Crisis

The chapters herein have put forth a number of future energy-related challenges that are possible, and perhaps even likely to occur in the near term. However, many of the participants in Aspen expressed pessimism that the American public would be ready for a national carbon tax or other measures that might appear punitive. Though the tide is certainly turning towards green technologies, alternative energy sources, and even acceptance on the realities of climate change, the necessary political action may take time and a comprehensive engagement to public education. In that gulf between dawning recognition and fundamental action, energy-related crises which are probably inevitable and predictable will occur. A disruption in global oil supply, continued dramatic changes in the climate, or price spikes could all have the potential impact of exposing the fundamental vulnerability of our overall energy system. By doing so, our energy vulnerabilities could be transformed into a full-blown crisis affecting virtually every aspect of American life.

Although fraught with dangers, a prolonged and severe energy crisis will greatly impact the national debate over policy. In American politics, such sustained periods of crisis have often served as a catalyst for abrupt change. While a crisis can create the political imperative for action, it can also produce a knee-jerk reaction that is often neither thoughtful nor coordinated — two important qualities for addressing this challenge. It is imperative that the conversation between scientists and politicians, academics and policymakers be allowed and encouraged so action is taken before a crisis arrives and forces their hand. From day one, a new President must work with Congress on a longer-term effort to raise public consciousness on energy-related matters and possible solutions rather than waiting for a crisis to set the agenda.

Conclusion

In the field of energy supply and demand, fortunes can change quickly. Russia, in the years after the Soviet Union dissolved, was on the verge of bankruptcy. Today, it is enjoying newfound wealth and clout on the world stage. China was an afterthought on the global energy scene a decade ago, today Beijing is a major player with enormous and growing demand for all sources of energy to power its 21st century dynamic economy. Ten years ago, agreements between Iran and Venezuela would not have raised much concern. Today, both have leaders who take pride in vocalizing contempt for America, and use their resources strategically as a means to gain friends and isolate political enemies. Africa received scant attention at the strategic level for years, but growing demand for new sources and supplies of petroleum and natural gas have led to a new scramble among external powers for positions of influence in a variety of African capitals. Energy — and increasingly the intersection of energy and climate change — is becoming the driving force of global politics.

This is the new international template for the Global Politics of Energy. Only a thin, but potentially explosive, line delineates the newly powerful states that possess the energy commodities the world demands and those nations that remain critically dependent on foreign energy sources for its economic well-being and livelihood. Without a robust and sustained national strategy by a new administration to assess and counter these underlying risks, the United States remains alarmingly vulnerable to remaining in the second category, with the potential for major disruptions to American power and position in the world. To pull back from this red line, the United States must realistically analyze its vulnerabilities and address them, while harnessing America's past history of technological ingenuity, and unite others in this national and global effort.

Moreover, all of this focus on energy potentially pales with the significance of global climate change. If left unattended, the impact of climate change may well trigger dramatic changes on the planet by exacerbating existing conflicts or creating new tensions over scarce resources, producing a wave of climate refugees fleeing droughts or other harsh weather conditions, and an increased proliferation of disease. Depending on the severity of global climate change, governments and their populations might also need to prepare for much harsher consequences. Despite the advanced infrastructure and preparedness, the immunity of industrialized nations, including the United States, from such severe climate change impacts is a myth. On both energy security and climate change, the time for action is now.

The observations above, and the chapters in this book, do not present a single worldview or solution to the challenges ahead, but are rather a rich tapestry of perspectives for advancing the debate on energy and climate forward. No single solution will prove to be a cure-all, but rather these strategies and the ideas represented in this book must be put into practice in tandem. In the long term, as funding and research for alternatives rise, new opportunities and ideas will be presented that can dramatically alter the current course. By looking forward now and planning for these challenges, there is hope the United States can avert disaster, isolate its vulnerabilities, ensure its own security, and restore its global position and standing by opening up a new chapter of international cooperation on achieving energy security. America's place in the global politics of energy is not on the periphery of the debate where it has been for the last several decades — but rather at the center, rising to this century's greatest challenge.